AF323708

Picked-By-You Guides®
Top Rated Outdoor Series

Top Rated™
Big Game Hunting
in North America

by Maurizio Valerio

PICKED-BY-YOU GUIDES®
Top Rated Outdoor Series
Copies of this book can be ordered from:
Picked-By-You
PO Box 718
Baker City, OR 97814
Phone: (800) 279-0479 • Fax: (541) 523-5028
www.topguides.com • e-mail: maurice@topguides.com

Artwork by Steamroller Studios, Cover Art by Fifth Street Design
Maps by Map Art, Cartesia Software
Cover thumbnail photos by Jerald D. Stansel, Fairbanks, Ak.
Printed in Korea

Publisher's Cataloging-in-Publication
(Provided by Quality Books, Inc.)

Valerio, Maurice.
    Top rated big game hunting : in North America / by Maurizio
Valerio. -- Rev. ed.
    p. cm. -- (Top rated outdoor series)
    Includes indexes.
    Preassigned LCCN: 98-67991
    ISBN: 1-889807-11-7

    1. Big game hunting--North America--Directories.
    2. Hunting guides--North America--Directories. 3. Hunting
    lodges--North America--Directories.   I. Title.

SK12. V35 1999   799.2'6'0257
                                           QBI98-1373

Dedication

To Allison, Marco and Nini

Acknowledgment

My sincere, deepest, and loving gratitude to my wife, my friend and my treasurer, Allison. My thanks to Grace Martin for her very patient and knowledgeable work, Maria Isabel Gonzales de Araisa for her sweet and relentless help, Julia Moist for her "comments", Lynn and Shelby for their wonderful dinners, Tony for his technical support, Marco and Nini for their understanding and for the time that we did not have to play together.

About the Author

Maurizio (Maurice) Valerio received a Doctoral degree Summa cum Laude in Natural Science, majoring in Animal Behaviour, from the University of Parma (Italy) in 1981, and a Master of Arts degree in Zoology from the University of California, Berkeley in 1984.

He is a rancher, a writer and a devoted outdoorsman who decided to live with the wild animals that he cherishes so much in the Wallowa Mountains of Northeast Oregon. He has hunted the Old and the New World for more than 25 years. His dedication to preserve our Hunting Heritage is second only to his love for his family and his hunting hat.

Maurice is a Life Member of RMEF, NRA, MCA and Member of MDF, SCI, FNAWS.

Table of Contents

Introduction

Years of hunting in the United States and different parts of the world, have prompted me to look for an objective way to wisely choose reputable *hunting outfitters.* I have been lucky several times booking hunts with outfitters that have later become real friends. But this was not always true and, on a few occasions, I, along with many of you, had awful experiences.

The intent of this publication is to provide the hunter with an easy to read and objective reference source that lists only the guides and outfitters that have been overwhelmingly endorsed by their past clients.

There are many great guides and outfitters out there that deserve full recognition for putting their experience, knowledge, long hours, and a big heart, into this difficult job. With this book we want to reward those deserving professionals.

We asked the people that hunted with a particular guide and outfitter, in the recent past, to rate their services, knowledge and professionalism. Only the ones that received A- to A+ scores from their clients are listed in these pages. Please note that the guides and outfitters featured in this book have not paid (nor will they pay), one single penny to Picked-by-You Guides® or the author. They have earned a spot in the book thanks to **their hard work and dedication to their clients.**

We want to thank all the guides and outfitters that have participated in our endeavor, whether they qualified or not. The fact alone that they accepted to be rated by their past clients is a clear indication of how much they care.

We also want to thank all those hunters that have taken the time to complete the questionnaires and share their hunting memories with us. Some of the comments sent to us were hilarious, some truly touching.

We were immensely pleased by the reaction of the hunting community at large. The idea of "Picked-by-You Guides®" was supported from the beginning by serious professionals and hunters alike. We listened to their suggestions, their comments, their criticisms and we are now happy to share this information.

May your powder stay dry, may your arrow fly straight, and may the sounds of the mountains, the hills and the forest fill your dreams. Until next time.

Maurice Valerio
A hunter

The Picked-By-You Guides® Idea

Mission Statement

The intent of this publication is to provide the outdoor enthusiast and his/her family with an objective and easy-to-read reference source that would list only those businesses and outdoor professionals who have **agreed to be rated** and have been overwhelmingly endorsed by their past clients.

There are many great outdoor professionals (Guides, Captains, Ranches, Lodges, Outfitters) who deserve full recognition for putting their experience, knowledge, long hours, and big heart, into this difficult job. With this book we want to reward those deserving professionals while providing an invaluable tool to the general public.

Picked-By-You Guides® are the only consumer guides to outdoor activities.

In this respect it would be useful to share the philosophy of our Company succinctly illustrated by our Mission Statement:

"To encourage and promote the highest professional and ethical standards among those individuals, Companies, Groups or Organizations who provide services to the Outdoor Community.

To communicate and share the findings and values of our research and surveys to the public and other key groups.

To preserve everyone's individual right of a respectful, knowledgeable and diversified use of our Outdoor Resources".

Our business niche is well defined and our job is simply to listen carefully.

THEY 'the experts' Vs. WE 'the People'

Picked-By-You books were researched and compiled by **asking people such as yourself**, who rafted, fished, hunted or rode a horse on a pack trip with a particular outdoor professional or business, to rate their services, knowledge, skills and performance.

Only the ones who received A- to A+ scores from their clients are found listed in these pages.

The market is flooded with various publications written by 'experts' claiming to be the ultimate source of information for your vacation. We read books with titles such as " The Greatest River Guides", "The Complete Guide to the Greatest Fishing Lodges" etc.

We do not claim to be experts in any given field, but we rather pass to history as good....listeners. In the preparation of the Questionnaires we listened first to the outdoor professionals' point of view and then to the comments and opinions of thousands of outdoor enthusiasts. We then organized the findings of our research and surveys in this and other publications of this series.

Thus we will not attempt to tell how to fish, how to paddle or what to bring on your trip. We are leaving this to the outdoor professionals featured in this book, for they have proven to be outstanding in providing much valuable information before, during and after your trip.

True [paid] advertising: an oxymoron

Chili with beans is considered a redundant statement for the overwhelming majority of cooks but it is an insulting oxymoron for any native Texan.

In the same way while 'true paid advertising' is a correct statement for some, it is a clear contradiction in terms for us and certainly many of you. A classic oxymoron.

This is why we do not accept commissions, donations, invitations, or, as many publishers cleverly express it, "...extra fees to help defray the cost of publication". Many articles are written every month in numerous specialized magazines in which the authors tour the country from lodge to lodge and camp to camp sponsored, invited, or otherwise compensated in many different shapes or forms.

It is indeed a form of direct advertising and, although this type of writing usually conveys a good amount of general information, in most cases it lacks the impartiality so valuable when it comes time to make the final selection for your vacation or outdoor adventure.

Without belittling the invaluable job of the professional writers and their integrity, we decided to approach the task of **researching information and sharing it with the public** with a different angle and from an opposite direction.

Money?.. No thanks!

We are firmly **committed to preserve the impartiality** and the novelty of the Picked-By-You idea.

For this reason we want to reassure the reader that the outdoor professionals and businesses featured in this book have not paid (nor will they pay), any remuneration to Picked-by-You Guides® or the author in the form of money, invitations or any other considerations.

They have earned a valued page in this book solely as the result of *their hard work and dedication to their clients.*

"A spot in this book cannot be purchased: it must be earned"

Size of a business in not a function of its performance

Since the embryonic stage of the Picked-By-You idea, during the compilation of the first Picked-By-You book, we faced a puzzling dilemma.

Should we establish a minimum number of clients under which a business or outdoor professional will not be allowed to participate in our evaluating process?

This would be a 'safe' decision when it comes the time to elaborate the responses of the questionnaires. But we quickly learned that many outdoor professionals limit, by choice, the total number of clients and, by philosophy of life, contain and control the size of their business. They do not want to grow too big and sacrifice the personal touches or the freshness of their services. In their words "we don't want to take the chance to get burned out by people." They do not consider their activity just a job, but rather a way of living.

"WHY, NO MAM, WE NEVER HAVE HAD ANY OF THOSE SASQUATCH SIGHTINGS IN THESE PARTS."

But if this approach greatly limits the number of clients accepted every year we must say that these outdoor professionals are the ones who often receive outstanding ratings and truly touching comments from their past clients.

Some businesses have provided us with a list of clients of 40,000, some with 25 . In this book **you will find both the large and the small.**

From a statistical point, it is obvious that a fly fishing guide who submitted a list of 32 clients, by virtue of the sample size of the individuals surveyed, will implicitly have a lower level of accuracy if compared to a business for which we surveyed 300 guests. (Please refer to the Rating and Data

Elaboration Sections for details on how we established the rules for qualification and thus operated our selection).

We do not believe that the size of business is a function of its good performance and we feel strongly that those dedicated professionals who choose to remain small deserve an equal chance to be included.

We tip our hats

We want to recognize all the Guides, Captains, Ranches, Lodges and Outfitters who have participated in our endeavor, whether they qualified or not. The fact alone that they accepted to be rated by their past clients is a clear indication of how much they care, and how willing they are to make changes.

We also want to credit all those outdoor enthusiasts who have taken the time to complete the questionnaires and share their memories and impressions with us and thus with you. Some of the comments sent to us were hilarious, some were truly touching.

We were immensely pleased by the reaction of the outdoor community at large. The idea of "Picked-by-You Guides®" was supported from the beginning by serious professionals and outdoor enthusiasts alike. We listened to their suggestions, their comments, their criticisms and we are now happy to share this information with you.

Questionnaires

"Our books will be only as good as the questions we ask."

We posted this phrase in the office as a reminder of the importance of the 'tool' of this trade. The questions.

Specific Questionnaires were tailored to each one of the different activities surveyed for this series of books. While a few of the general questions remained the same throughout, many were specific to particular activities. The final objective of the questionnaire was to probe the many different facets of that diversified field known as the outdoors.

The first important factor we had to consider in the preparation of the Questionnaires was the total number of questions to be asked. Research shows an *inversely proportionate relation* between the total number of questions and the percentage of the response: the higher the number of questions, the lower the level of response. Thus we had to balance an acceptable return rate with a meaningful significance. We settled for a compromise and we decided to keep 20 as the maximum number.

The first and the final versions of the Questionnaires on which we based our surveys turned out to be very different. We asked all the businesses and outdoor professionals we contacted for suggestions and criticisms. They helped us a great deal: we weighed their different points of view and we incorporated all their suggestions into the final versions.

We initially considered using a phone survey, but we quickly agreed with the businesses and outdoor professional that we all are already bothered by too many solicitation calls when we are trying to have a quiet dinner at home. We do not want you to add Picked-By-You to the list of companies that you do not want to talk to, nor we want you to add our 800 number to your caller ID black list.

In using the mail we knew that we were going to have a slightly lower percentage of questionnaires answered, but this method is, in our opinion, a more respectful one.

We also encouraged the public to participate in the designing of the questionnaire by posting on our Web at www.topguides.com the opportunity to submit a question and ...."Win a book". Many sent their suggestions and , if they were chosen to be used in one of our questionnaires, they were given the book of their choice.

Please send us your question and/or your suggestions for our future surveys at:

PICKED-BY-YOU Guides®, P.O. Box 718, Baker City, OR 97814

Rating (there is more than one way to skin the cat)

We considered many different ways to score the questionnaires, keeping in mind at all times our task:

translate an opinion into a numerical value

Some of the approaches considered were simple *averages* [arithmetical means], others were sophisticated statistical tests. In the end we opted for simplicity, sacrificing to the God of statistical significance. WARNING: if $p \leq 0.001$ has any meaning in your life stop reading right here: you will be disappointed with the rest.

For the rest of us, we also made extensive use in our computation of the *median*, a statistic of location, which divides the frequency distribution of a set of data into two halves. A quick example, with our imaginary Happy Goose Outfitter, will illustrate how in many instances the *median* value, being the center observation, helps describing the distribution, which is the truly weak point of the *average*:

Average salary at Happy Goose Outfitters $ 21,571

Median salary at Happy Goose Outfitters $ 11,000

5,000	10,000	10,000	11,000	12,000	15,000	98,000
Wrangler	Guide	Guide	Senior Guide	Asst.Cook	Cook	Boss

Do not ask the boss : "What's the average salary?"

These are the values assigned to **Questions 1-13**:

    5 points   OUTSTANDING

    4 points   EXCELLENT

    3 points   GOOD

    2 points   ACCEPTABLE

    1 points   POOR

    0 points   UNACCEPTABLE

Questions 14 - 16 = 5 points

Questions 19 - 20 = 10 points

Question 17 relates to the weather conditions and Question 18 to the pressure from other hunters in the area.

    Good=0   Fair=3   Poor=5

The intention here was to reward the outdoor professional who had to work in adverse weather conditions.

The individual scores of each Questionnaire were expressed as a percentage to avoid the total score from being drastically affected by one question left unanswered or marked "not applicable." All the scores received for each individual outdoor professional and business were thus added and computed.

The 90 points were considered our cutoff point. Note how the outfitters must receive a combination of Excellent with only a few Good marks (or better) in order to qualify.

Maximum score   **130 points** (only obtainable with non-kill bonus points)
                      125 points (with animal killed)

Minimum score **0 points**

Cutoff point   **90 points** (obtainable with a solid "excellent")

A+ **score >= 110 points** (obtainable with Q.4-Q.13 = **outstanding**)

A   **score >= 96 points** (Q.4 - Q.13 = **excellent**)

A- **score >= 90 points** (combination of **excellent** and **good**)

B+ **score >= 86 points**

B   **score >= 82 points** (Q.4- Q.13 = **good**)

Only the Outfitters, Captains, Lodges, Guides who received an A- to A+ score did qualify and they are featured in this book.

We also decided not to report in the book pages the final scores with which the businesses and the outdoor professionals ultimately qualified. In a way we thought that this could be distractive.

In the end, we must admit, it was tough to leave out some outfitters who scored very close to the cutoff mark.

It would be presumptuous to think that our scoring system will please everybody, but we want to assure the reader that we tested different computations of the data. We feel the system that we have chosen respects the overall opinion of the guest/client and maintains a more than acceptable level of accuracy.

We know that …. "You can change without improving, but you cannot improve without changing."

The Power of Graphs (how to lie by telling the scientific truth)

The following examples illustrate the sensational (and unethical) way with which the 'scientific' computation of data can be distorted to suit one's needs or goals.

The *Herald* presents a feature article on the drastic increase of total tonnage of honey stolen by bears (mostly Poohs) in a given area during 1997.

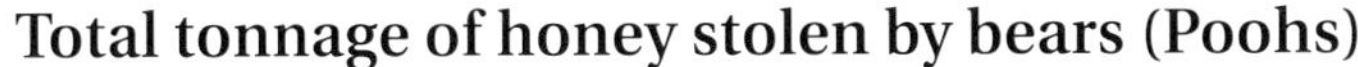

Total tonnage of honey stolen by bears (Poohs)

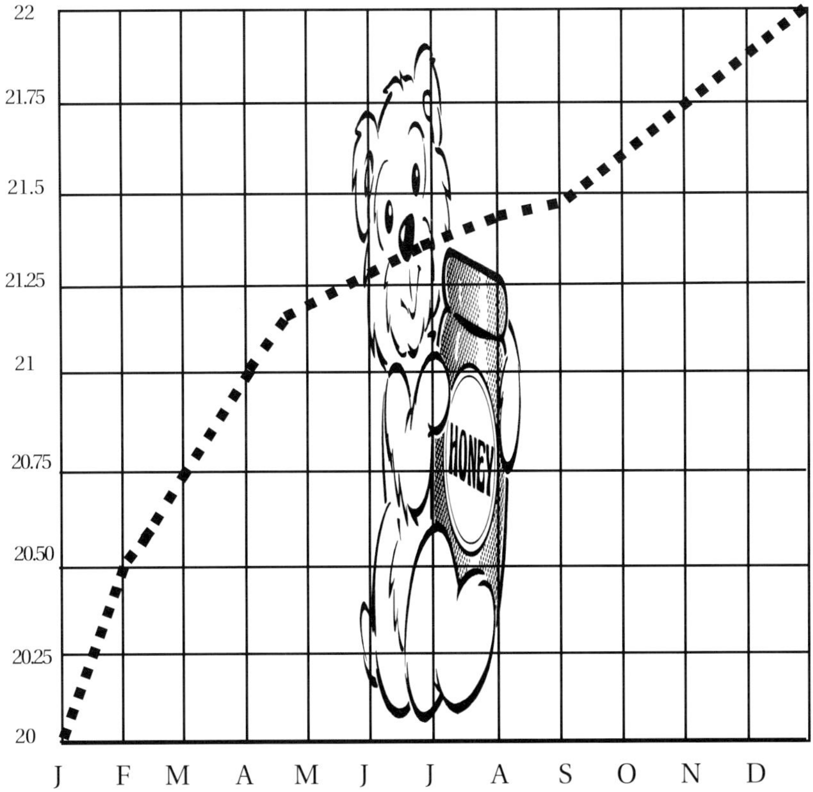

It is clear how a journalist, researcher or author must ultimately choose one type of graph. But the question here is whether or not he/she is trying to make "his/her point" by choosing one type versus the other, rather than simply communicate some findings.

Please note that the bears, in our example, are shameless, and remain such in both instances, for they truly love honey!

Graphs were not used in these our books. We are just too worried not to use the correct ones.

The Book Making Process

Research

We **researched** the name and address of every business and outdoor professional **in the United States and** in all the **provinces of Canada** (see list in the Appendix). Some states do not require guides and outfitters or businesses providing outdoor services to be registered, and in these instances the information must be obtained from many different sources [Outfitter's Associations, Marine Fisheries, Dept. of Tourism, Dept. Environmental Conservation, Dept. of Natural Resources, Dept. of Fish and Game, US Coast Guard, Chamber of Commerce, etc.].

In the end the database on which we based this series of Picked-By-You Guides® amounted to more than 23,000 names of Outfitters, Guides, Ranches, Captains etc. Our research continues and this number is increasing every day. The Appendix in the back of this book is only a partial list and refers specifically to Top Rated Big Game Hunting.

Participation

We **invited** businesses and outdoor professionals, with a letter and a brochure explaining the Picked-By-You concept, to join our endeavor by simply sending us a <u>**complete list of their clients**</u> of the past two years. With the "Confidentiality Statement" we reassured them that the list was going to be kept **absolutely confidential** and to be *used one time only* for the specific purpose of evaluating their operation. Then it would be destroyed.

We truly oppose this "black market" of names so abused by the mail marketing business. If you are ever contacted by Picked-By-You you may rest assured that your name, referred to us by your outdoor professional, will never be sold, traded or otherwise used a second time by us for marketing purposes.

Questionnaires

We then **sent a questionnaire** to **every single client on each list** (to a maximum of 300 randomly picked for those who submitted large lists with priority given to overnight or multiple day trips), asking them to rate the

services, the **knowledge** and **performance** of the business or outdoor professional by completing our comprehensive questionnaire (see pages 180-181). The businesses and outdoor professionals found in these pages may or may not be the ones who invest large sums of money to advertise in magazines, or to participate at the annual conventions of different clubs and foundations. However, they are clearly the ones, according to our survey, that put customer satisfaction and true dedication to their clients first and foremost.

Data Elaboration

A **numerical value was assigned to each question**. All the **scores were computed**. Both the **average** and the **median** were calculated and considered for eligibility. Please note that the total score was computed as a percentile value.

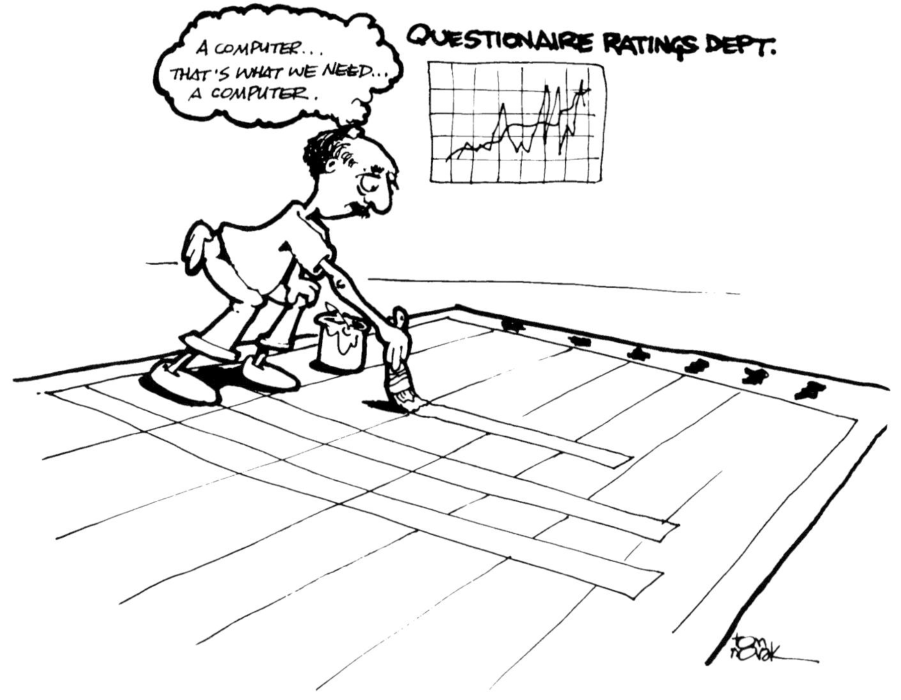

This allows some flexibility where one question was left unanswered or was answered with a N/A. Furthermore, we decided not to consider the high and the low score to ensure a more evenly distributed representation and to reduce the influence which an extreme judgement could have either way (especially with the small sample sizes).

We also set a **minimum number of questionnaires** which needed to be answered to allow a business or an outdoor professional to qualify. Such number was set as a function of the total number of clients in the list: the smaller the list of clients, the higher was the percentage of responses needed for qualification.

In some cases the outfitter's average score came within 1 points of the A-cutoff mark. In these instances, we considered both the median and the average were considered as well as the guests' comments and the total number of times that this particular business was recommended by the clients by answering with a 'yes' question 19 and 20.

Sharing the results

Picked-By-You will share the results of this survey with the businesses and the outdoor professionals. This will be done at no cost to them whether or not they qualified for publication. All questionnaires received will, in fact, be returned along with a summary result to the business, keeping the confidentiality of the client's name when this was requested. This will prove an invaluable tool to help improving those areas that have received some criticisms.

The intention of this series of books is to research the opinions and the comments of outdoor enthusiasts, and to share the results of our research with the public and other key groups.

One outfitter wrote us about our Picked-by-You Guides® series, "I feel your idea is an exciting and unique concept. Hopefully our past clientele will rate us with enough points to 'earn' a spot in your publication. If not, could we please get a copy of our points/questionnaires to see where we need to improve. Sincerely…"

This outfitter failed to qualify by just a few points, but such willingness to improve leaves us no doubt that his/her name will be one of those featured in our second edition. In the end it was not easy to exclude some of them from publication, but we are certain that, with the feedback provided by this survey, they will be able to improve those areas that need extra attention.

We made a real effort to keep a position of absolute impartiality in this process and, in this respect, we would like to repeat that the outfitters have not paid, nor they will pay, one single penny to Picked-By-You Guides® or the Author to be included in this book.

The research continues.

Animal Icon Legend

White Tail Deer
(Odocoileus virginianus)

Mule Deer
(Odocoileus hemionus)

Black Tail Deer
(Odocoileus hemionus columbianus)

Sitka Deer
(Odocoileus hemionus)

Coues' Deer
(Odocoileus virginianus couesi)

Antelope
(Antilocapra americana)

Moose
(Alces alces)

Elk
(Cervus elaphus canadensis)

Bighorn Sheep
(Ovis canadensis canadensis)

Stone's Sheep
(Ovis dalli stonei)

Desert Bighorn Sheep
(Ovis canadensis nelsoni)

Dall's Sheep
(Ovis dalli dalli)

Animal Icon Legend

Mountain Goat
(Oreamnos americanus)

Caribou
(Rangifer sp.)

Black Bear
(Ursus arctos)

Brown Bear
*(Ursus middendorfii)**

Grizzly Bear
*(Ursus horribilis)**

Polar Bear
(Thalarctos maritimus)

Wolf
(Canis lupus)

Wolverine
(Gulo luscus)

Cougar
(Felis concolor)

Bobcat
(Lynx rufus)

Coyote
(canis latrans)

Javelina
(Pecari angulatus)

Bison
(Bison bison)

Wild Boar
(Sus scrofa)

*Modern taxonomists recognize both Grizzly and Brown Bear as 1 specie, *Ursus arctos.*

Weapons and Transportation

Rifle

Bow

Muzzleloader

Handgun

Bush plane

Snowmobile

Drift Boat

Horse/Pack String

Canoe

Raft

Motor Boat/
Jet Boat

Motor Yacht/
Cabin Cruiser

Weapons and Transportation

Back Packer

ATV

4 x 4 Vehicle

Accommodations and Special Services

Wall Tent Camp

Motel

Spike Tent Camp

Drop Camp

Cabin/Lodge

Families

Women Only Camp

Trailer Camp

Handicapped

Index of Outfitters by State/Province

Distribution of Outfitters

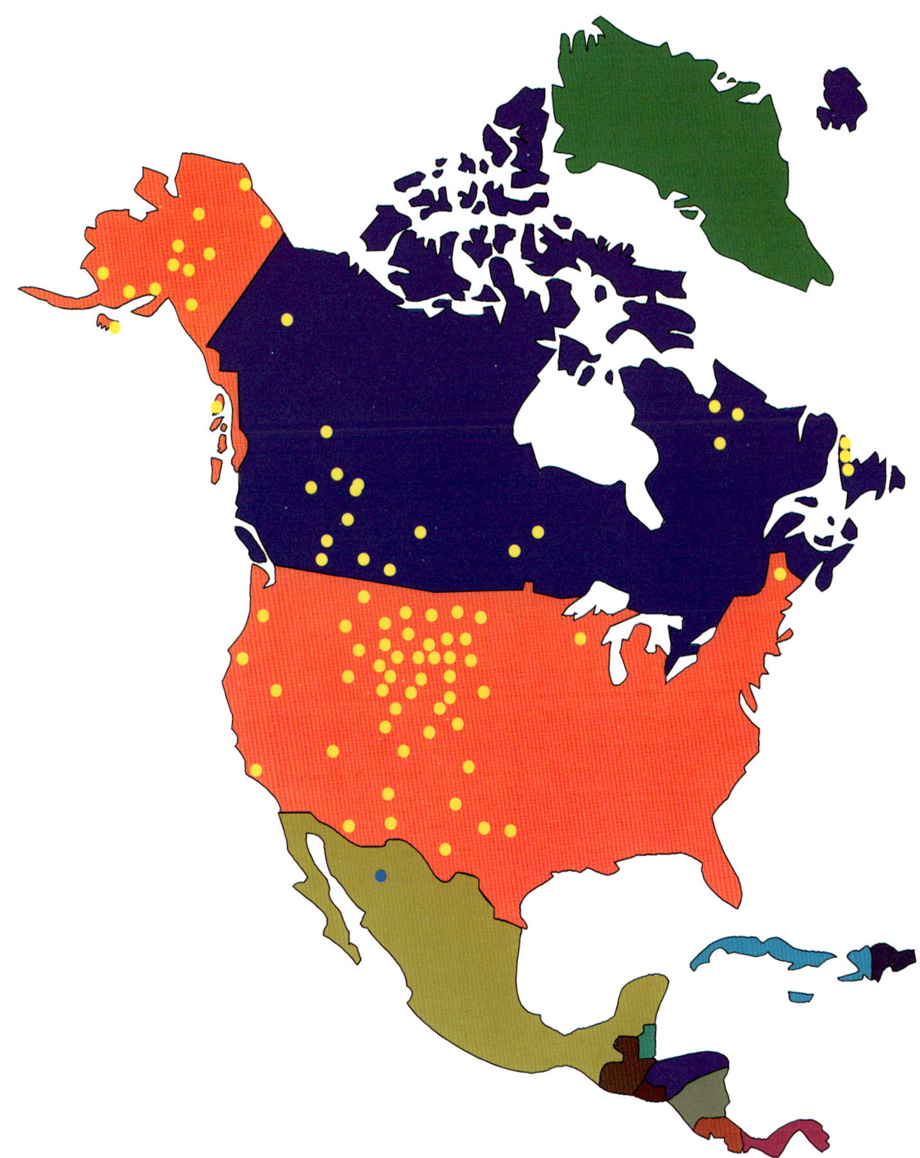

Please note:

Comments: These were actual "quotes" extracted from the Questionnaires returned by the Outfitter's clients.

Alaska

Outdoor Professionals

1. Adams Alaskan Safaris
2. Afognak Wilderness Lodge
3. Alaska Wilderness Ventures
4. Bill Slemp's Wild Alaska
5. Bristol Bay Outfitters
6. Brooks Range Adventures
7. Denali Wilderness Outfitters, Inc.
8. Kichatna Guide Service
9. Lake Country Lodge, Inc.
10. Sheep River Hunting Camp
11. T.C. Lewis Lodge

Useful information for the state of

Alaska

State and Federal Agencies

Alaska Dept. of Fish & Game
PO Box 25556
Juneau, AK 99802-5526
phone: (907) 465-4100

Alaska Region Forest Service
709 West 9th Street
Box 21628
Juneau, AK 99802-1628
phone: (907) 586-8863
TTY: (907) 586-7816

Chugach National Forest
3301 C Street, Ste. 300
Anchorage, AK 99503-3998
phone: (907) 271-2500
TTY: (907) 271-2332

Tongass National Forest:
Chatham Area
204 Siginaka Way
Sitka, AK 99835
phone: (907) 747-6671
TTY: (907) 747-8840

Bureau of Land Management
Alaska State Office
222 W. 7th Avenue, #13
Anchorage, AK 99513-7599
phone: (907) 271-5960
or (907) 271- Plus Extension
fax: (907) 271-4596

National Parks

Denali National Park
phone: (907) 683-2294

Gates of the Arctic National Park
phone: (907) 456-0281

Glacier Bay National Park
phone: (907) 697-2230

Katmai National Park
phone: (907) 246-3305

Kenai Fjords National Park
phone: (907) 224-3175

Kobuk Valley National Park
phone: (907) 442-3890

Lake Clark National Park
phone: (907) 271-3751

Wrangell-St. Elias National Park
phone: (909) 822-5235

Associations, Publications, etc.

Alaska Professional Hunters Assoc.
PO Box 91932
Anchorage, AK 99509-1932
phone: (907) 522-3221

License and Report Requirements

• State requires licensing of Outdoor Professionals.

• State requires a "Hunt Record" for big game.

• State to implement a "logbook" program for charter vessel/guided catches of King
Salmon in Southeast Alaska by the 1998 season.

Adams Alaskan Safaris

Dale Adams

P.O. Box 6021 • Sitka, AK 99835
phone: (907) 747-6108

Hunt brown bear and black bear in southeast Alaska with Adams Alaskan Safaris aboard the motor vessel, "Celtic Aire."

This boat hunt is a unique experience. A mobile base camp allows you to move to a new area frequently. You will travel the Inside Passage in search of salmon-fed brown bear and some of the largest black bear in the world. Deep fjords and secluded bays offer a taste of fresh seafood, including crabs, clams and shrimp.

Dale Adams offers a fair chase hunt in this beautiful setting — the famous A.B.C. Islands of southeast Alaska.

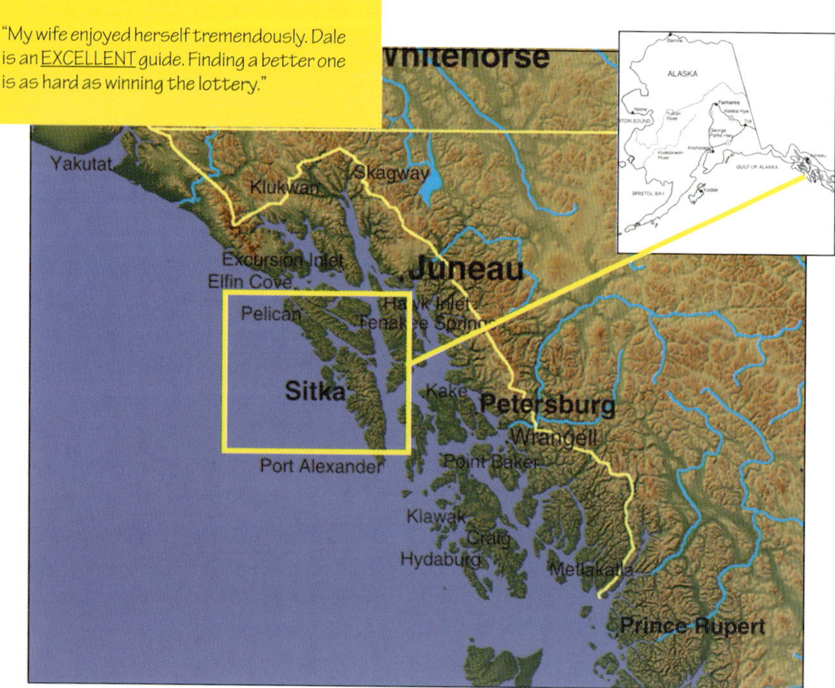

Afognak Wilderness Lodge

Roy and Shannon Randall
Seal Bay, AK 99697
phone: (907) 486-6442 • fax: (907) 486-2217

Retreat to the classy, rustic elegance of Afognak Wilderness Lodge within the Kodiak Island archipelago. Hunters have enjoyed a high rate of success for all species over the past 23 years.

Experienced hunters/guides Roy and Josh Randall are responsible for many happy departing hunters.

Hunt from comfortable, fast cabincruisers by day, eat hearty and sleep deep at night in your own spacious log guest cabin. Very comfortable for lady hunters and non-hunters.

Many repeat and referred guests worldwide.

Floatplane access from Kodiak.

"They are very knowledgeable about the fish and wildlife resources of Afognak Island and provide the best opportunities in this area for a successful hunt."

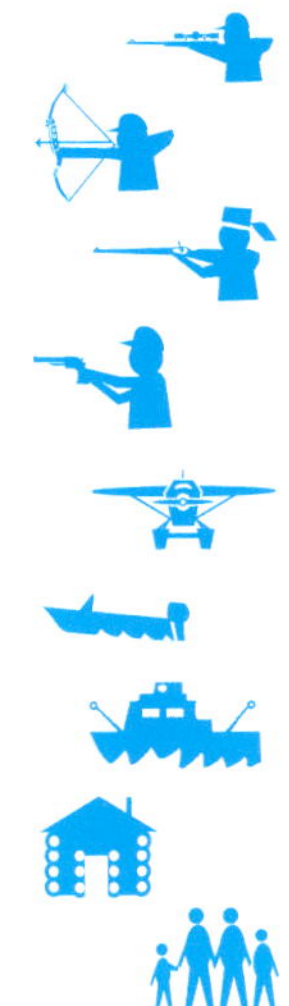

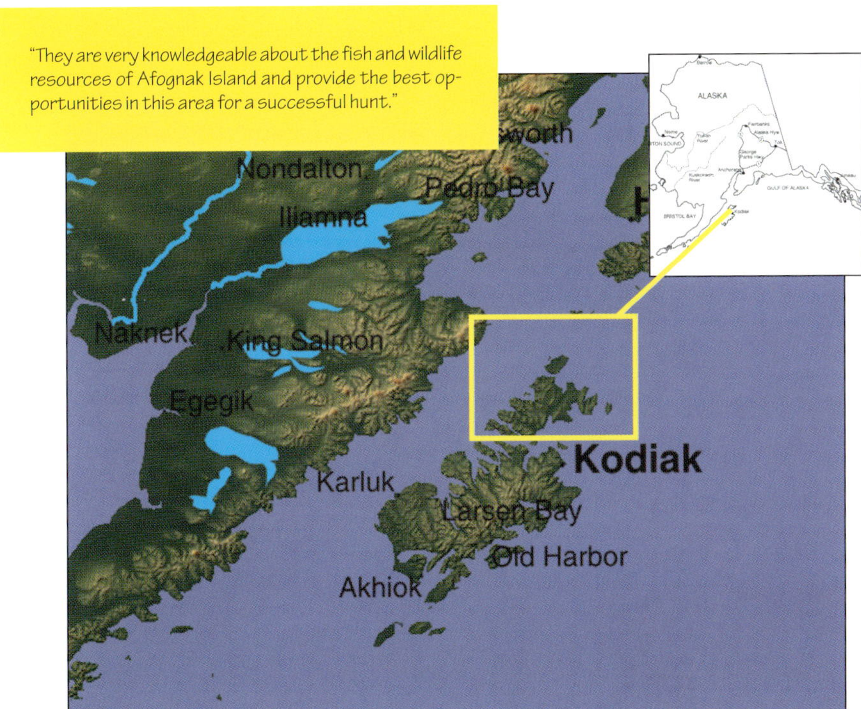

Alaska Wilderness Ventures

Len Mackler
411 Rhonda Street • Fairbanks, AK 99712
phone: (907) 488-3259

Len has guiding rights covering more than 8,000 square miles, including exclusive rights to one-sixth of the Alaska Arctic National Wildlife Refuge, the largest great wilderness in America.

This is the best Dall's sheep area in the Brooks Range. Len has very high success, yet runs strictly fair chase hunts. More than 50% of his hunters are repeat clients or friends of previous clients. He hunts an excellent population of dall sheep, mountain grizzly, caribou, wolf and wolverine, all in the same area. Float hunts with excellent fishing also available.

Len is a detail-oriented planner and logistician with impeccable equipment and very loyal, experienced, longtime guides. Video available.

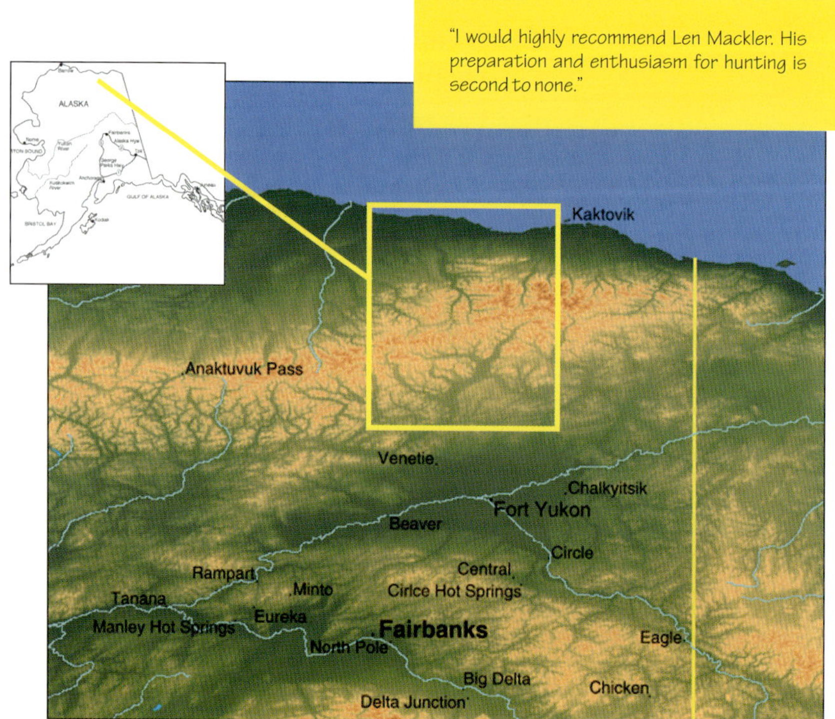

Bill Slemp's Wild Alaska

Bill Slemp

P.O. Box 963 • Soldotna, AK 99669
phone: (907) 262-7409 • fax: (907) 262-2463

Bill Slemp has been hunting Alaska for more than 25 years. The hunt area is accessible only by aircraft.

All hunts are conducted from tent camps, because regulations do not permit structures in the hunt area. We hunt from a main base camp consisting of large, heated weatherport tents.

Aircraft is used to transport our hunters to spike camps where we hunt on foot.

Our hunts are conducted in Units 17 and 19. All hunts are guided one-to-one to obtain the highest possible success.

> "This outfitter was the best he could possibly be and did everything he could do for me and my Dad."

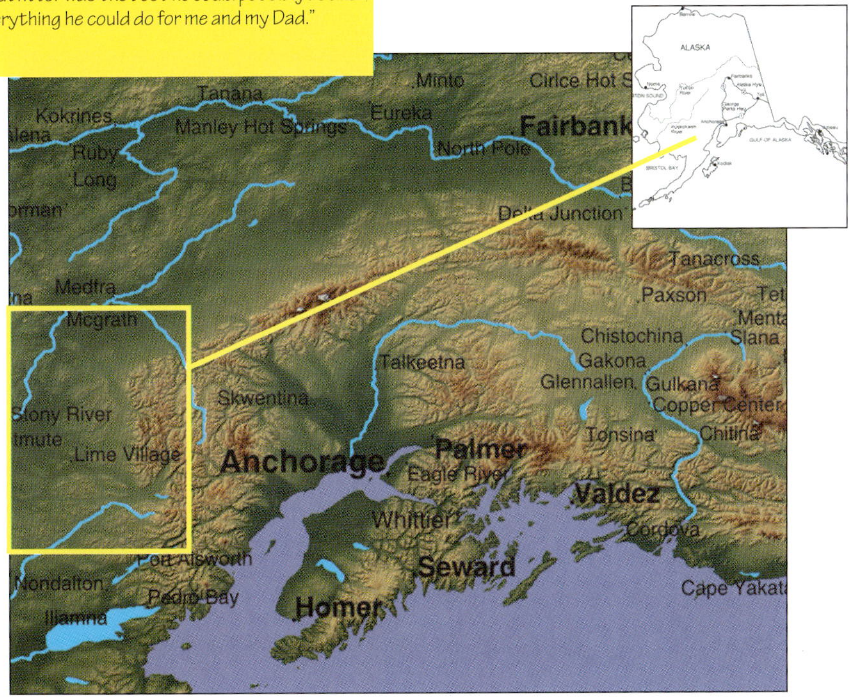

Bristol Bay Outfitters

John Peterson

3450 Stanford Dr. • Anchorage, AK 99508
phone: (907) 278-0994

Bristol Bay Outfitters offers experienced, dependable guide service and excellent big game hunting opportunities in some of Alaska's most scenic and pristine wilderness. Comfortable tent camps, all meals and equipment such as rafts, motorboats, and bush planes are provided.

Access to hunting camps is by small aircraft, utilizing either tundra tires, skis or floats depending on the season and area.

My clients have enjoyed consistent success in taking good trophies of their desired species in a fair chase and sportsmanlike manner. From our camps near the salmon-choked streams and lakes of Bristol Bay, to the high arctic sheep valleys of the Brooks Range, my assistants and I work hard to ensure a memorable and rewarding experience.

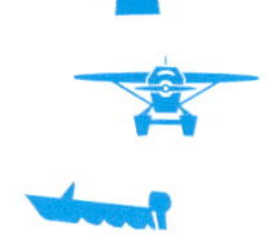

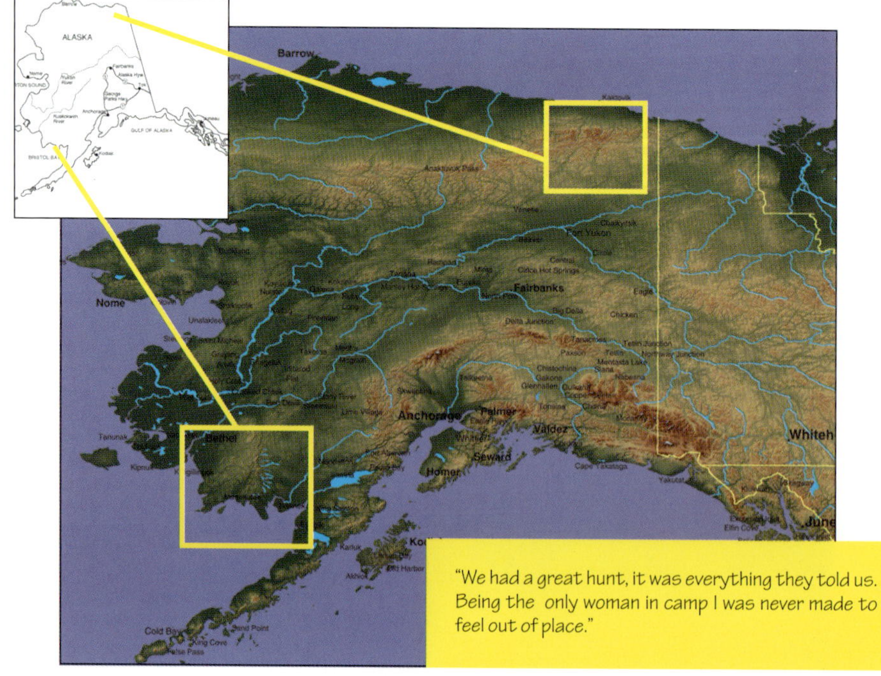

Brooks Range Adventures

Art Andreis, Master Guide

P.O. Box 55818 • North Pole, AK 99705
phone: (907) 488-2352

Master guide Art Andreis has hunted Alaska since 1969, guiding in Units 8,9,12,20,25,26 and 27.

Hunting brown bear on the Alaska Peninsula and Kodiak, Dall's rams, grizzly, moose, caribou and wolf in the interior.

Art's guides are experienced, licensed professionals, are current in first aid/CPR, prepared for emergencies, and trained in firearms safety.

Art offers dedication and experience and insists on the integrity and maximum effort on your behalf to ensure success. Art arranges your bush flying and purchases licenses and tags in advance.

"I intend for you to be successful."

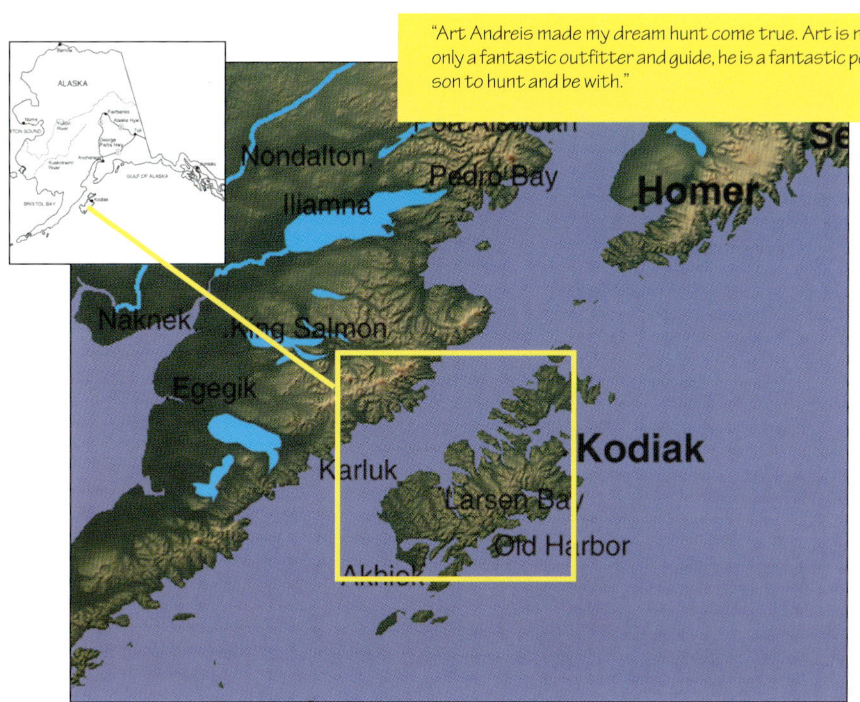

Denali Wilderness Outfitters, Inc.

Kirk Martakis
P.O. Box 127 • Cantwell, AK 99729
phone: (800) 367-8173 • phone/fax: (907) 768-2620

Fair chase hunting for Alaska's big game while on horseback is not only more enjoyable, but more rewarding with higher success and nicer trophies.

I take a lot of pride in my outfit, and offer only the highest quality hunts in excellent areas. Hunting big game is not only my profession; it's my life. I maintain high mobility and flexibility in my hunting organization to take you to the right place at the right time. We hunt the interior and the coast with most hunts conducted on horseback, though boats, snowmobiles and aircraft are also used.

I take great pride in extending a personal invitation for you to join us on one of the finest Alaskan hunts available.

Kichatna Guide Service

Master Guide Harold "Zeke" Schetzle

P.O. Box 670790 • Chugiak, AK 99567
business phone/fax: (907) 694-2200 • residence: (907) 696-3256

Kichatna Guide Service was established in 1974. Master guide Harold "Zeke" Scheztle, author of two hunting books, "Alaska Safari" and "Alaska Wilderness Hunter," has been actively guiding throughout Alaska for the past 25 years.

Alaska big game hunting is the experience of a lifetime and Kichatna Guide Service endeavors to provide a true wilderness hunt that emphasizes fair chase. "Zeke" offers backpack Dall's sheep hunts (wolf, caribou, grizzly options) in the Artic National Wildlife Refuge (Northern Brooks Range), combination hunts for moose, caribou, black bear and brown /grizzly bear in Alaska Range (hunts from cabins as well as spike tents) and hunts Kodiak brown bear and Sitka blacktail deer (mountain goat if permit drawn) in the Kodiak National Wildlife Refuge on Kodiak Island. Depending on type of hunt, Kodiak hunts are based from wall tent camps. Single sideband radios are at all base camps for emergency purposes.

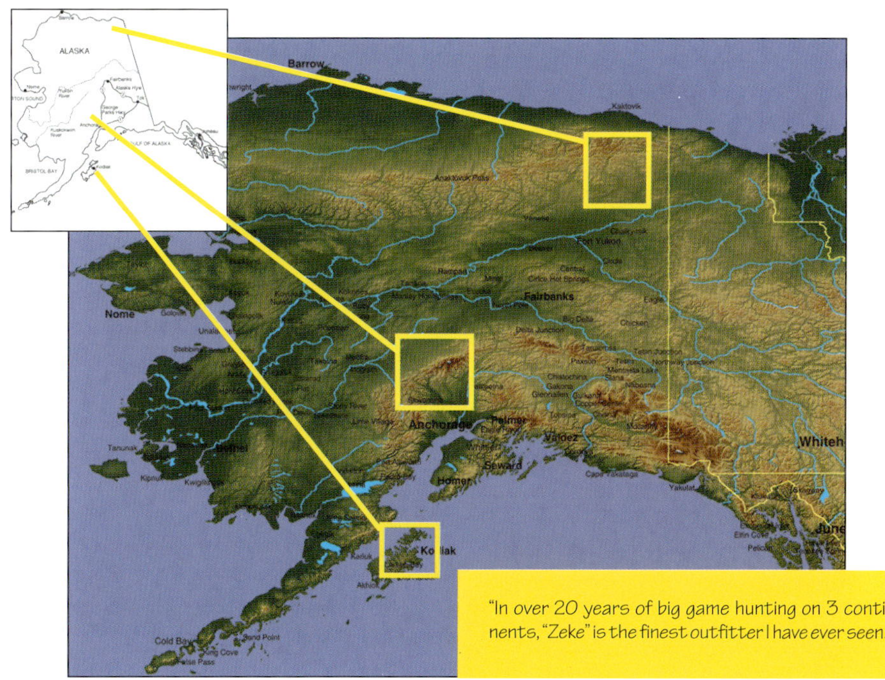

Lake Country Lodge, Inc.

John C. Davis

HC-2 Box 852 • Soldotna, AK 99669
phone: (907) 283-5821 • (907) 781-2245 • fax: (907) 283-9177

We offer hunting for brown/grizzly bear, caribou, moose and black bear in Alaska Lake, Clark and Mulchatna River areas.

Our trophy game populations are some of the very best in the entire state. We hunt out of our main lodge in tent camps, featuring spacious Cabela's six- and eight-man dome tents with vestibules. All of our camps and hunters are flown in with float- or wheel-equipped aircraft.

Registered guides are provided and packers if needed. Aircraft camp fly-overs and moves are provided daily or as needed.

Ask for free brochures with references and full information.

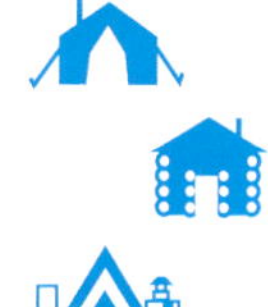

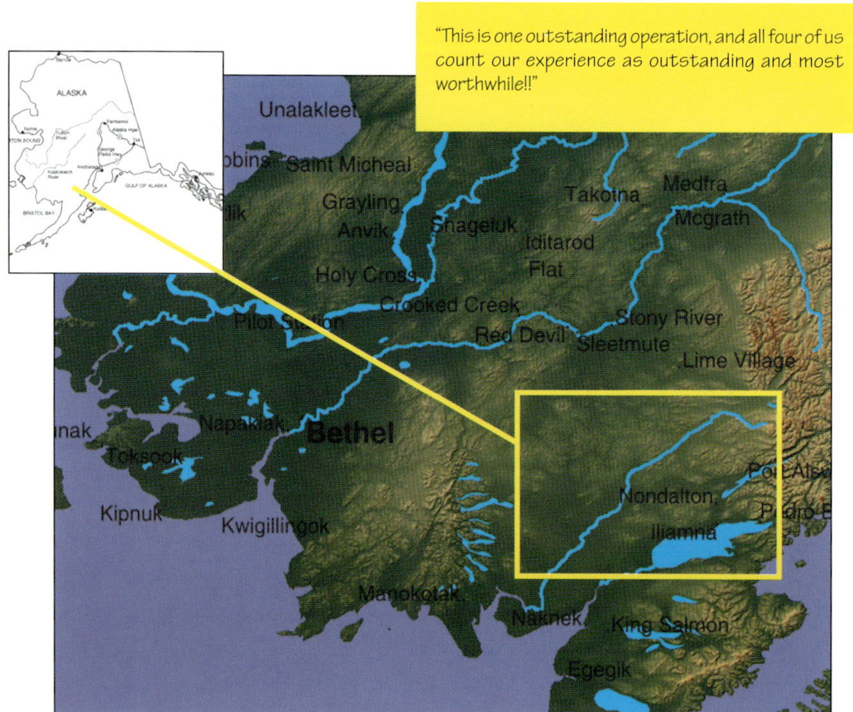

Sheep River Hunting Camp

Master Guide Ed and Deb Stevenson

P.O. Box 875149 • Wasilla, AK 99687
phone: (907) 745-0479

Sheep River Hunting Camp prides itself on providing old-fashion hunts in Alaska.

Professional guides with many years experience assure a quality trip to remote hunting and fishing areas that few people ever see.

The area we hunt provides Alaskan grizzly/brown bear, black bear, Dall's sheep and moose and the best rainbow and salmon fishing, depending on the season.

From the flight into camp to the days on the trail, SRHC provides its clients with the highest quality equipment, top guides, great food, and a hunting adventure surely not to be forgotten.

Good hunting!

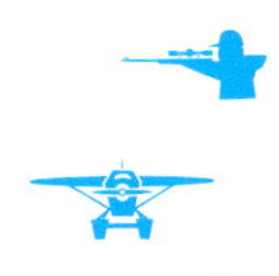

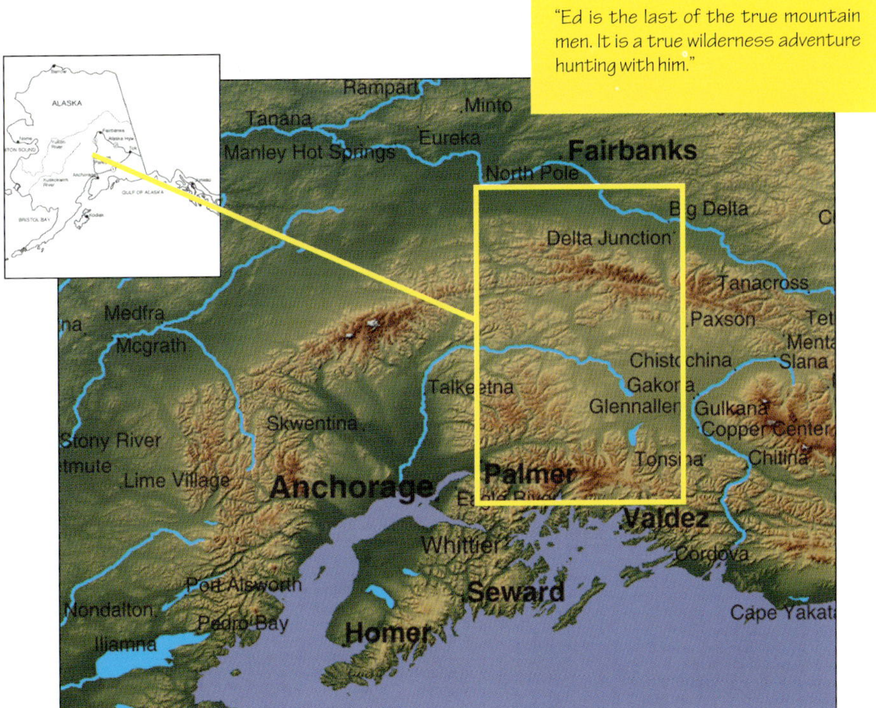

T.C. Lewis Lodge

Joe and Candice Caraway
Beluga River • Beluga, AK 99695
phone: (907) 583-2025

T.C. Lewis Lodge snuggles beside Cook Inlet. The guide area rises from sea level to the perpetual snow of the Alaska Range.

Joe Caraway has hunted Alaska for 23 years and guided for 11. His respect and reverence for the animals and the land leads him to hunt, trap, and fish year-round; he knows and lives with his work.

Candice's cooking and support keeps base camp humming. Guests are not just "hunters." They are encouraged to "homestead," to fish, pick agates or mushrooms; to live the life.

Their informal motto, "Just go for it," drives Joe, Candie, their daughters, Kaydee and Holly, to work hard to accommodate hunters before, during, and after the hunt.

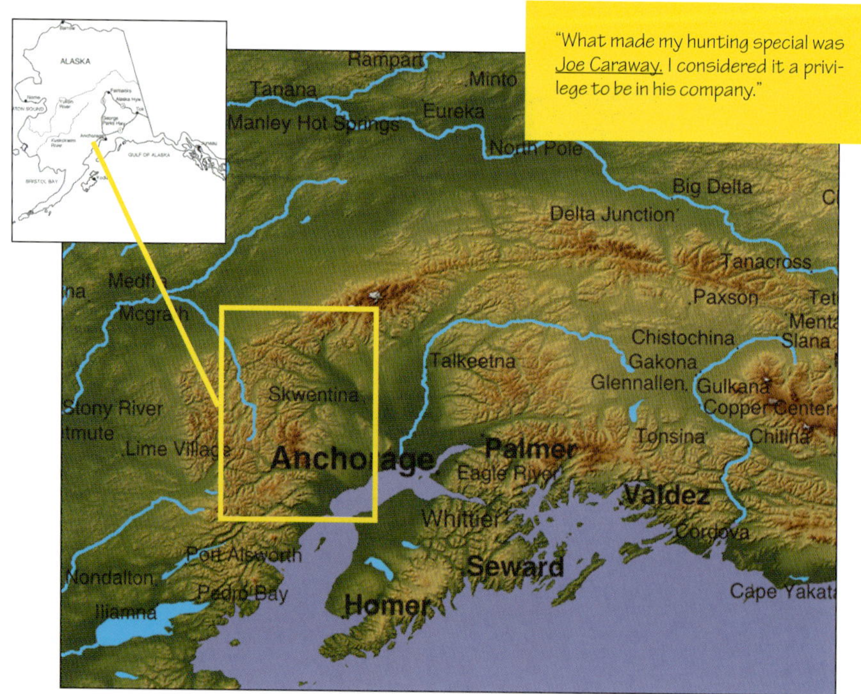

"What made my hunting special was <u>Joe Caraway.</u> I considered it a privilege to be in his company."

Arizona

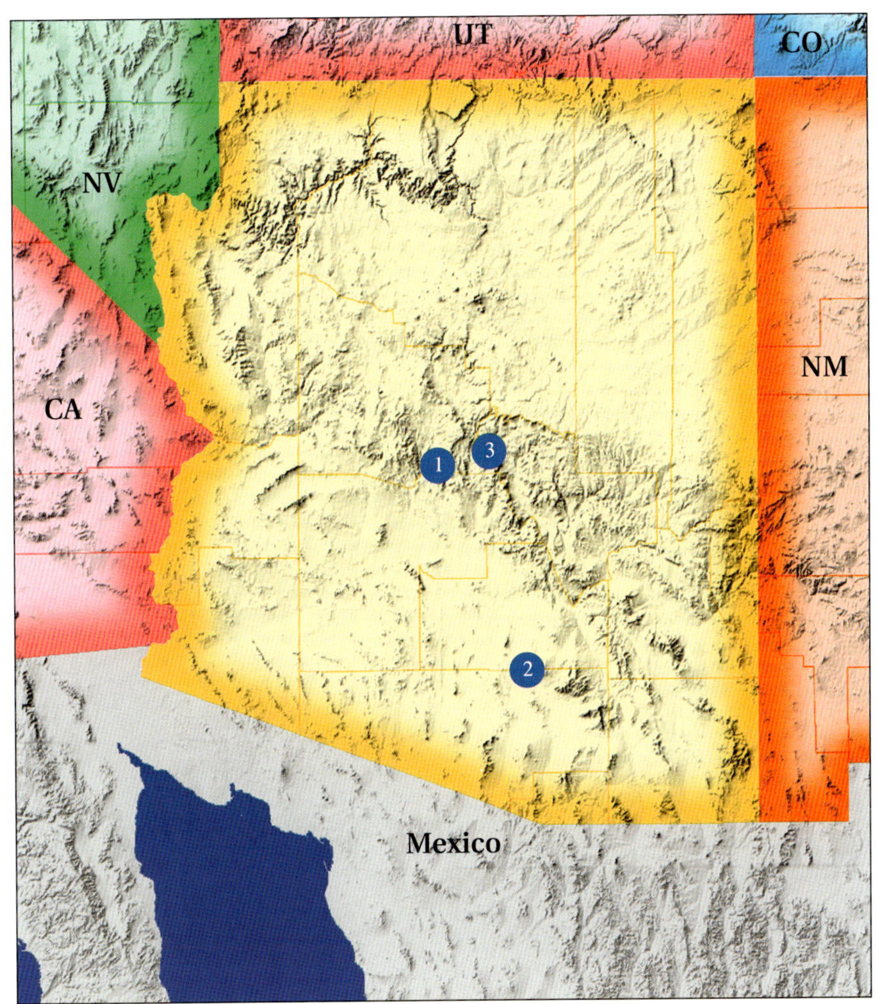

Outdoor Professionals

1. Ponderosa Outfitters and Guide Service
2. Pusch Ridge Outfitters
3. Timberline Outfitters

Useful information for the state of
Arizona

State and Federal Agencies

Arizona Game & Fish Dept.
2222 West Greenway Rd.
Phoenix, AZ 85023
phone: (602) 89-3210

Forest Service
Southwestern Region
Federal Building
517 Gold Avenue SW
Albuquerque, NM 87102
phone: (505) 842-3300

Apache-Sitgreaves National Forests
Federal Building
PO Box 640
Springerville, AZ 85938
phone: (520) 333-4301

Coconino National Forest
2323 East Greenlaw Lane
Flagstaff, AZ 86004
phone: (520) 527-3600

Coronado National Forest
300 West Congress Street
Tucson, AZ 85701
phone: (520) 670-4552

Kaibab National Forest
800 South Sixth Street
Williams, AZ 86046
phone: (520) 635-8200

Prescott National Forest
344 South Cortez Street
Prescott, AZ 86303
phone: (520) 771-4700

Tonto National Forest
2324 East McDowell Road
Phoenix, AZ 85010
phone: (602) 02-225-5200

Bureau of Land Management
Arizona State Office
222 North Central Avenue
P.O. Box 555
Phoenix, AZ 85004-2203
phone: (602) 417-9200
or (602) 417-plus ext.
fax: (602) 417-9556

Office Hours: 7:45 a.m. - 4:15 p.m.

National Parks

Grand Canyon National Park
phone: (602) 638-7701

Petrified Forest National Park
phone: (602) 524-6228

Associations, Publications, etc.

Safari Club International
4800 W. Gates Pass Road
Tucson, AZ 85745
phone: (602) 620-1220
fax: (520) 622-1205

License and Report Requirements
• State requires licensing of Outdoor Professionals.

• State requires an "End of Year Guides Report" for all big game and fishing.

• "Use permit" required for anyone using BLM, National Forest, Indian reservations,
and National Parks for rafting, back packing, big game, fishing, etc. Guides
required to file "End of Year Guides Report" for all activities on Federal Lands.

Ponderosa Outfitters and Guide Service

Ron and Sharon Eichelberger

8215 W. Patrick Lane • Peoria, AZ 85382

phone: (602) 566-3152

Ron and Sharon take great pride in providing clean, comfortable camps and quality tailored hunts with experienced guides. New Mexico elk hunt packages include private land permits, and the January "archery combo" javelina and Coues' deer in Arizona, has 100% drawing odds.

Their eight-year-old operation is organized and emphasizes the client's satisfaction, which has resulted in repeat business year after year. With more than 30 years experience in the Southwest, Ron is very knowledgeable of the hunting areas and offers assistance in the application process.

Ron and Sharon would be happy to tailor your next hunting adventure to the beautiful Southwest.

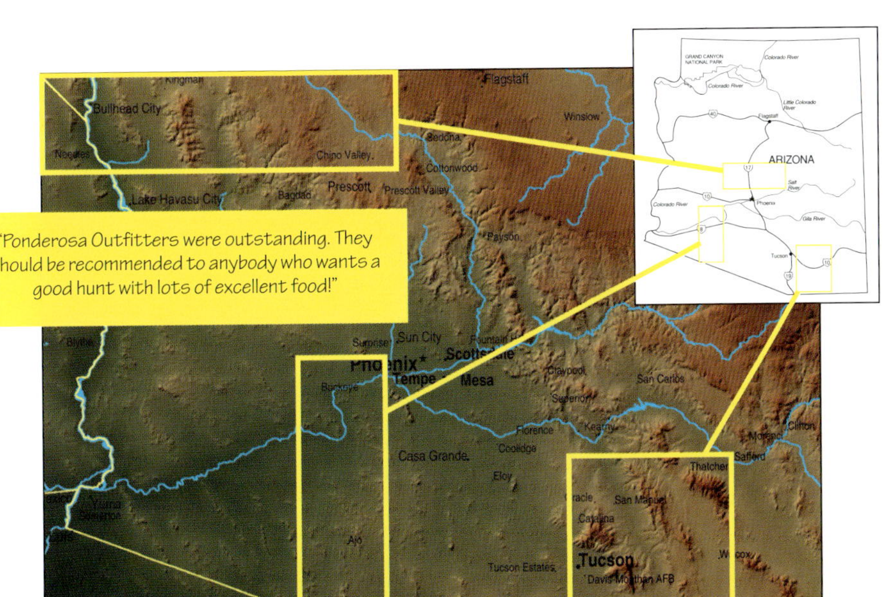

Pusch Ridge Outfitters

Kirk and Roxane Kelso

10260 N. Hardage Lane • Oro Valley, AZ 85737
phone: (520) 544-0954

Kirk Kelso of Pusch Ridge Outfitters is noted as one of the premier outfitters in the country for Coues' whitetail.

The hunt area has produced some of the top heads in Boone & Crockett, Safari Club International, Pope & Young and the Longhunter Record Books. Hunters take a number of bucks scoring 100-plus points every year, including a buck in 1995 that scored 121 points.

The Kelsos are noted for their successful antelope, elk, desert bighorn sheep, Rocky Mountain bighorn, desert mule deer and javelina hunts. Antelope and elk are hunted in Arizona and New Mexico with high-scoring trophies taken every year.

Their New Mexico antelope lease produced four B&C heads out of eight hunts in 1995.

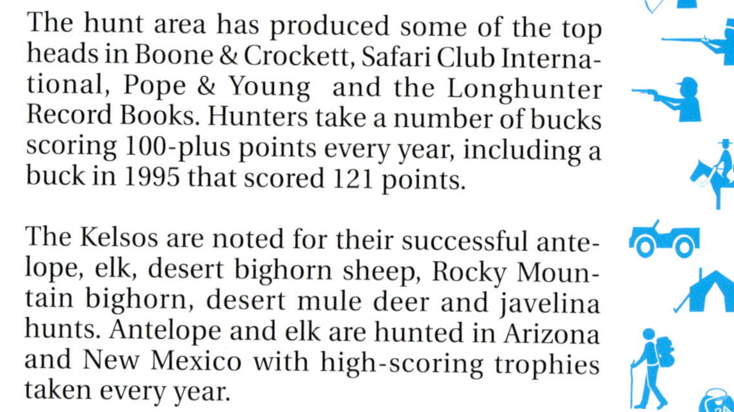

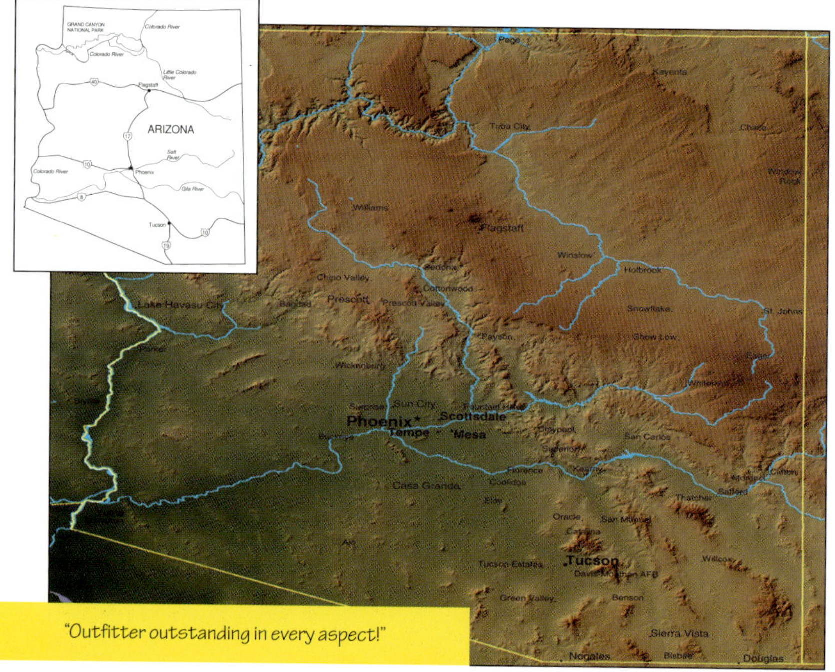

Timberline Outfitters

Perry and Brenda Hunsaker

19831 E. Warner Rd. • Higley, AZ 85236
phone: (505) 547-2413 • (602) 988-9654

All clients are guided one-on-one unless otherwise arranged. Our guides are seasoned hunters and know what it takes to get you on your trophy.

It's no secret that the areas we hunt are considered by most experts the best in North America. New Mexico and Arizona are the hot spots. If your dream is a trophy-class animal, you are in the right spot.

Our meals consist of roast beef and turkey with all the trimmings. You will not go hungry in this camp. Camps range from ranch headquarters with individually-heated rooms to comfortable tent camps.

We want your trip to be a success. You have my word we will do our best so that your stay will be a memorable and rewarding experience.

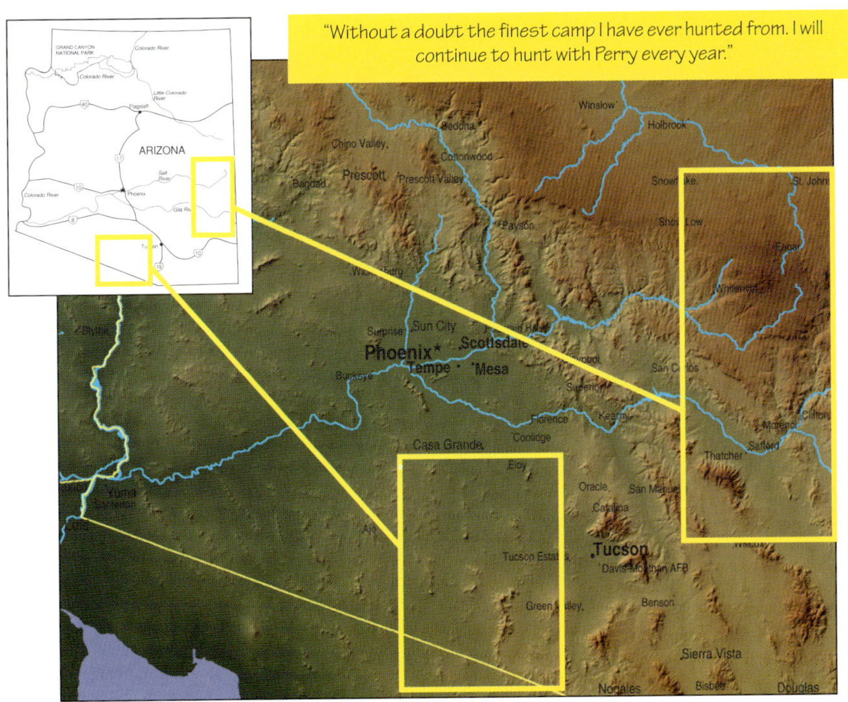

California

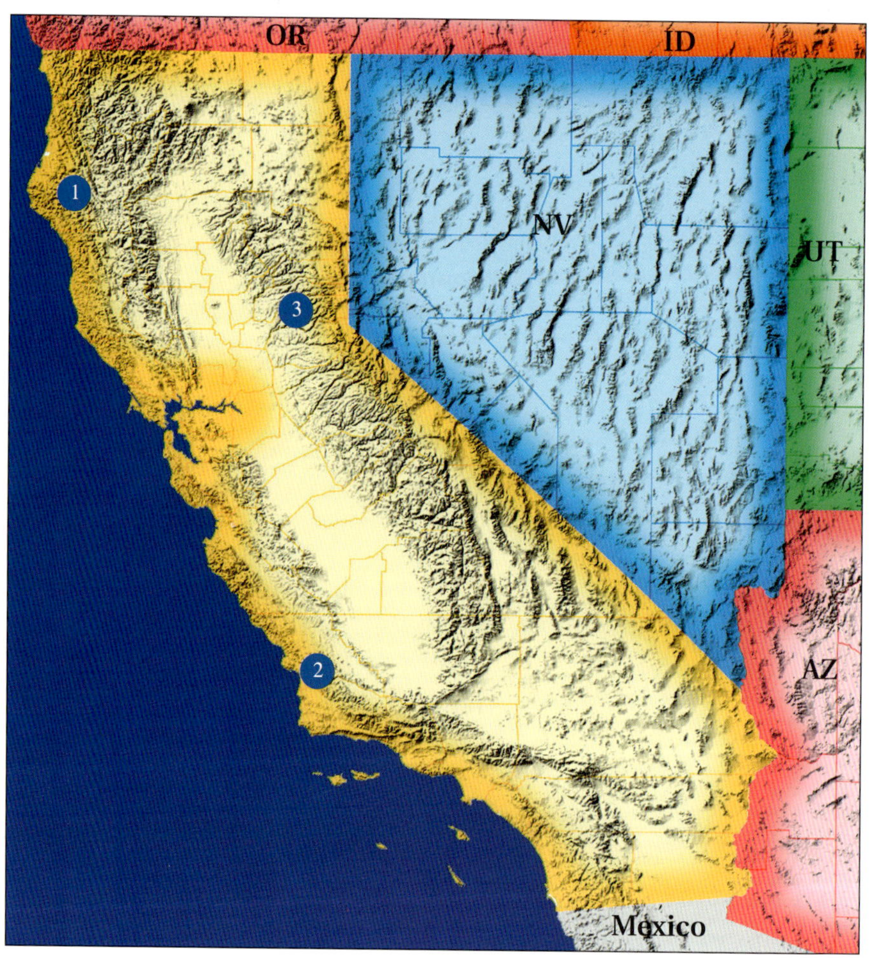

Outdoor Professionals

1. Arrow Five Outfitters
2. O' Rourke's Outdoor Adventures
3. River S Enterprises

Useful information for the state of
California

State and Federal Agencies

California Fish & Game Commission
License & Revenue Branch
1416 9th Street
Sacramento, CA 95814
phone: (916) 227-2244

Pacific Southwest
Forest Service Region
630 Sansome St.
San Francisco, CA 94111
phone: (415) 705-2874
TTY: (415) 705-1098

Inyo National Forest
phone: (619) 373-2400

Klamath National Forest
phone: (916) 842-6131

Lake Tahoe Basin
phone: (916) 573-2600

Lassen National Forest
phone: (916) 257-2151

Modoc National Forest
phone: (916) 233-5811

Sequoia National Forest
phone: (209) 784-1500

Shasta Trinity National Forest
phone: (916) 246-5222

Sierra National Forest
phone: (209) 97-0706

Stanislaus National Forest
phone: (209) 532-3671

Tahoe National Forest
phone: (916) 265-4531

Bureau of Land Management
California State Office
2135 Butano Drive
Sacramento, CA 95825
phone: (916) 978-4400
fax: (916) 978-4620
Office Hours: 7:30 - 4:00 p.m. (PST)

National Parks

Lassen Volcanic National Park
phone: (916) 595-4444

Redwood National Park
phone: (707) 464-6101

Sequoia & Kings Canyon National Parks
phone: (209) 565-3341

Yosemite National Park
phone: (209) 372-0200

Channel Islands National Park
phone: (805) 658-5700

Associations, Publications, etc.

National Field Archery Association
31407 Outer I-10
Redlands, CA 92373
phone: (909) 794-2133

License and Report Requirements

• State requires licensing of Outdoor Professionals.

• State requires the filing of a "Monthly Guide Log" for fishing and hunting.

• River Outfitters need a "Use Permit", required for BLM, National Forest, Indian
reservations, and National Parks.

Arrow Five Outfitters

Jim Schaafsma

Star Route 1, Box 64A • Zenia, CA 95595
phone/fax: (707) 923-9633

Arrow Five Outfitters has been owned and operated by Jim Schaafsma since 1981.

Our blacktail deer, black bear, boar and turkey hunts are in both Humboldt and Trinity counties, located in Northern California.

We have a 100% success on our rifle deer hunts in California and 98% success on archery.

Our hunts offer an excellent chance for record book SCI, Pope & Young, and Boone & Crockett. We also provide Roosevelt elk and blacktail hunts in Medford and Myrtle Creek, Oregon, and Coues' deer hunts in Sonora, Mexico.

All our hunts are one-to-one and fully-guided on private property.

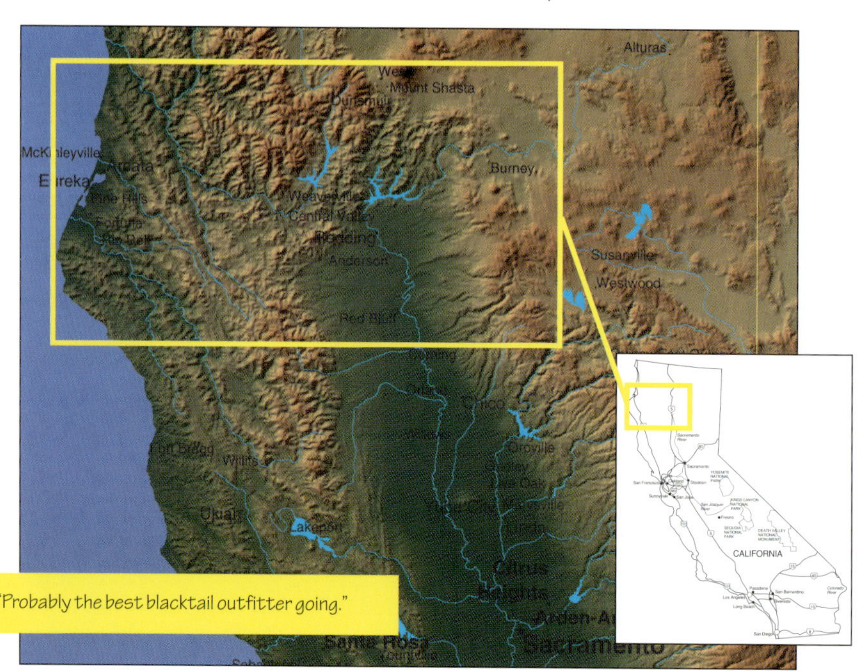

> *"Probably the best blacktail outfitter going."*

O'Rourke's Outdoor Adventures

Richard O'Rourke
P.O. Box 86 • LaPorte, CA 95981
phone: (916) 675-2729

We operate in the Plumas National Forest in Plumas County, California. Our black bear hunting is great.

We have 6,000 acres of private land, and our own hunting club.

Number of hunters is limited to ten members and two outside guests per weekend.

Snowmobiles are hot in the winter for varmints. Call us for more information.

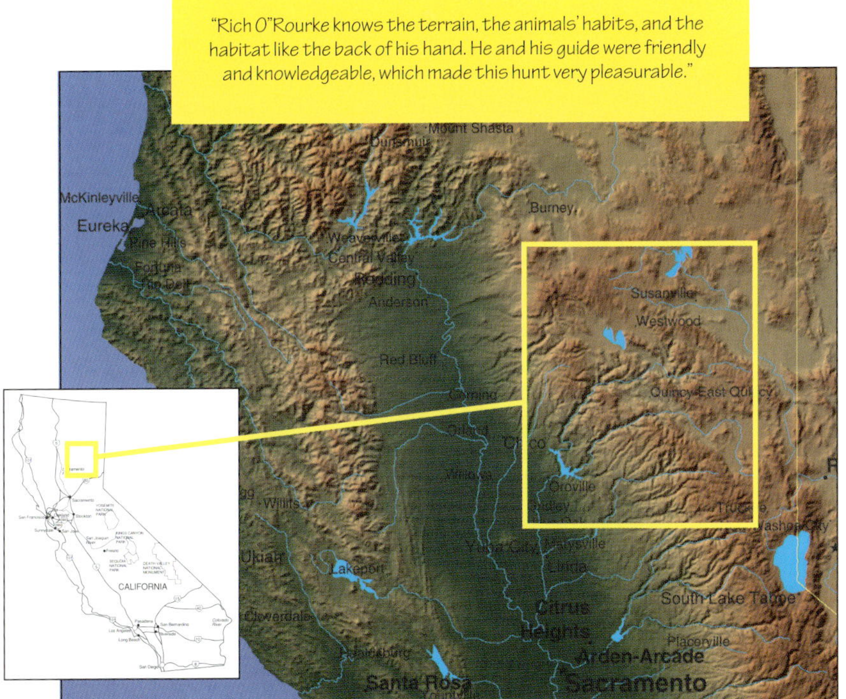

River S Enterprises

Mike and Debbie Schwiebert

P.O. Box 286 • Santa Margerita, CA 93453
phone: (805) 466-7741 • fax: (805) 466-9903
cellular: (805) 440-0109

All hunts are conducted on quality, well-managed private concessions in California and Wyoming under exclusive leases.

Meals are excellently prepared, nutritious and plentiful. Hunts are conducted with one guide for two hunters.

Guides are experienced professionals who are dedicated to the client's success. Mike and Debbie are dedicated to providing the finest quality outdoor experience possible. It is their policy to provide each client with a safe, successful and enjoyable outdoor experience.

They put forth 100% to meet these objectives. "Should a client feel that we have not fulfilled our efforts, we will refund 100% of the cost."

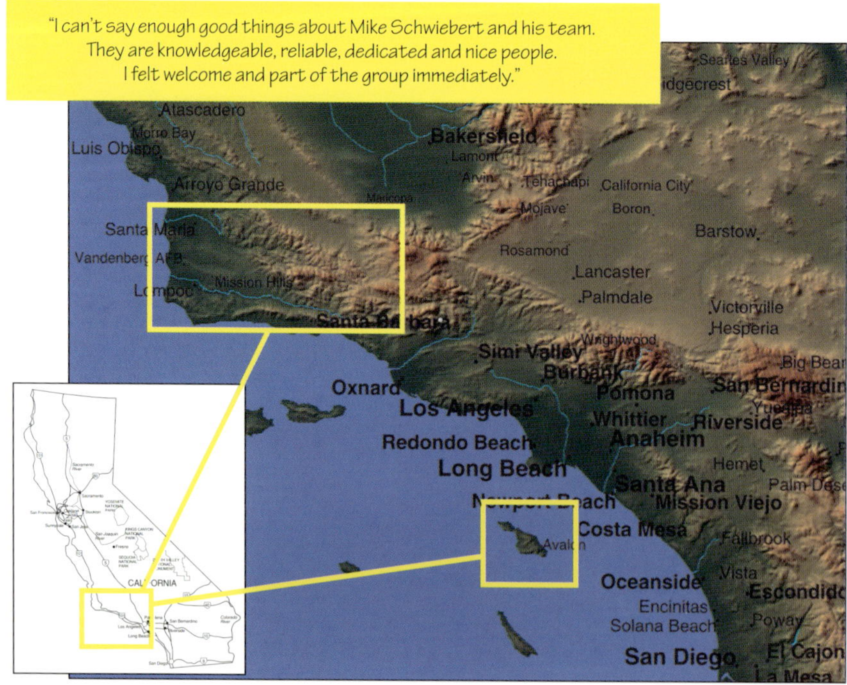

Colorado

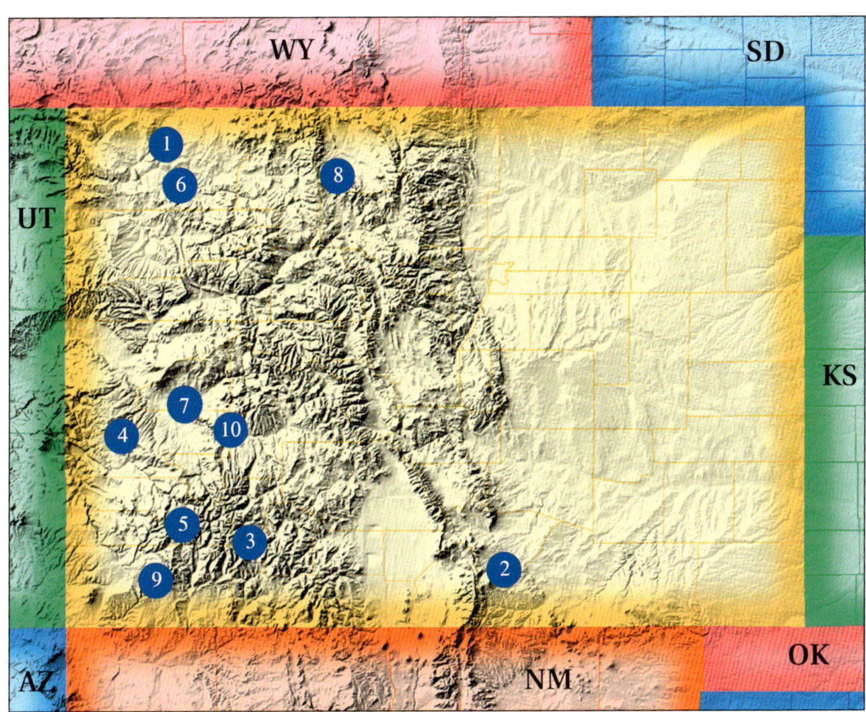

Outdoor Professionals

1. 4 + 2 T Ranch
2. Echo Canyon Guest Ranch & Outfitters
3. Frazier Outfitting
4. Garvey Brothers Outfitters
5. Lakeview Resort & Outfitters
6. Lone Tom Outfitting
7. Phil's Bowhunting Adventures
8. Samuelson Outfitters
9. San Juan Outfitting
10. Spadafora Ranch Lodge

Useful information for the state of
Colorado

State and Federal Agencies

Colorado Agencies of Outfitters Registry
1560 Broadway, Suite 1340
Denver, CO 80202
phone: (303) 894-7778

Colorado Dept. of Natural Resources
1313 Sherman, Room 718
Denver, CO 80203
phone: (303) 866-3311

Forest Service
Rocky Mountain Region
740 Simms Street
PO Box 25127
Lakewood, CO 80225
phone: (303) 275-5350
TTY: (303) 275-5367

Arapaho-Roosevelt National Forests
Pawnee National Grassland
phone: (970) 498-2770

Grand Mesa-Umcompahgre
Gunnison National Forests
phone: (970) 874-7641

Pike-San Isabel National Forests
Commanche & Cimarron National
Grasslands
phone: (719) 545-8737

San Juan-Rio Grande National Forest
phone: (719) 852-5941

White River National Forest
phone: (970) 945-2521

Bureau of Land Management
Colorado State Office
2850 Youngfield St.
Lakewood, Co. 80215-7093
phone: (303) 239-3600
fax: (303) 239-3933
Tdd: (303) 239-3635
Email: msowa@co.blm.gov

Office Hours: 7:45 a.m. - 4:15 p.m.

National Parks

Mesa Verde National Park, CO 81330
phone: (303) 529-4465

Rocky Mountain National Park
phone: (303) 586-2371

Associations, Publications, etc.

Colorado Outfitters Association
PO Box 1304
Parker, CO 80134
phone: (303) 841-7760

International Hunter Education Assoc
PO Box 347
Jamestown, CO 80455
phone: (303) 449-0631
fax: (303) 449-0576

Rocky Mountain Bighorn Society
PO Box 8320
Denver, CO 80201

License and Report Requirements

• State requires licensing of Outdoor Professionals.

• State requires an "Inter-Office Copy of Contract with Client" be submitted each time
  a client goes with an Outfitter. Colorado Agencies of Outfitters Registry sends this
  copy to client to fill out and return to their agency.

4 + 2 T Ranch

Craig T. Tomke
P.O. Box 896 • Hayden, CO 81639
phone/fax: (970) 276-4283 • cellular: (970) 846-3780
Lic. #868

Our main goal is that our guests are completely satisfied with every aspect of our operation. We enjoy an 80%-plus re-book from our guests and feel we our meeting our goals of "high quality" and "first-class" service. By hunting the largest elk herd in the world, we also provide some of the highest success on 4x4 or better bulls <u>any-where</u> !

We have always listed <u>everyone</u> who hunts with us as references every year.

If your goal is a first-class hunt in a tremendous game country — please contact us and we will help plan the hunt you will remember forever. We have been in business 11 years and hunt both private and public land.

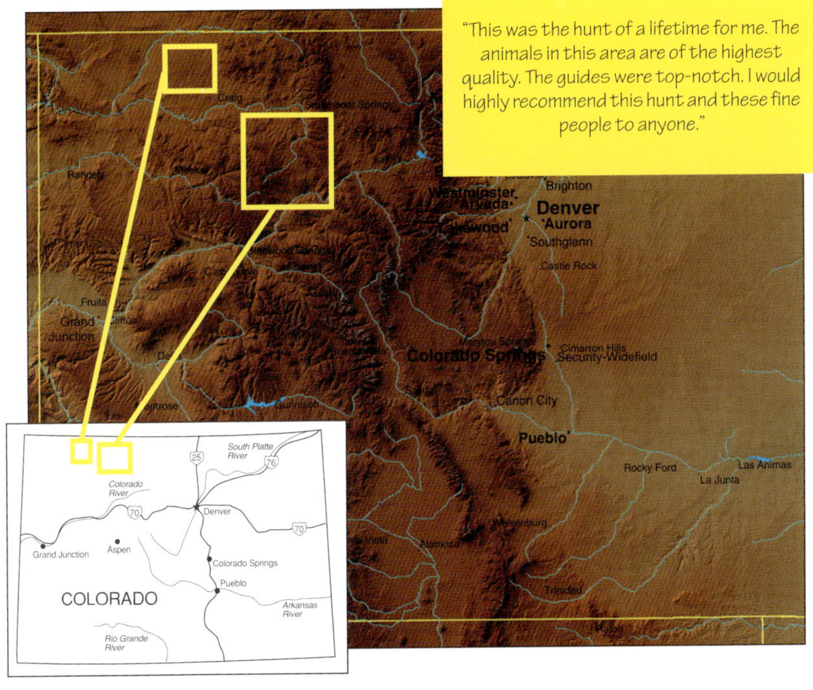

"This was the hunt of a lifetime for me. The animals in this area are of the highest quality. The guides were top-notch. I would highly recommend this hunt and these fine people to anyone."

Echo Canyon Guest Ranch & Outfitters

David Hampton

P.O. Box 328 • LaVeta, CO 81055

phone: (800) 341-6603 • (719) 742-5524 • Lic. #1143

Echo Canyon Outfitters provides first-class trophy-quality hunts on a private ranch in Unit 851 of Southern Colorado. Our hunters are guided one-on-one by experienced guides who are very knowledgeable of the terrain and wildlife. The hunts are extremely professional, offering quality accommodations, food, stock, and personnel.

We are active members of Rocky Mountain Elk Foundation as sponsors, donors and habitat partners. Our Long Canyon Ranch is strictly managed for wildlife habitat and trophy-class production under a conservation easement with RMEF. The outfit brings 11 years' of solid experience to our business. We annually re-book more than 75% of our clients two years in advance.

We specialize in trophy elk and mule deer, black bear, mountain lion and turkey.

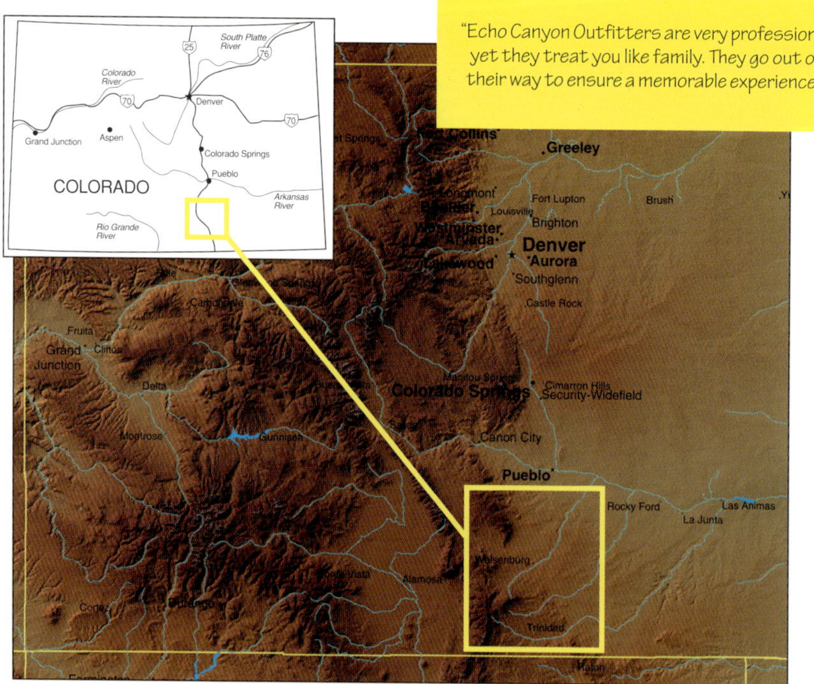

"Echo Canyon Outfitters are very professional yet they treat you like family. They go out of their way to ensure a memorable experience."

Frazier Outfitting

Sammy Frazier

HC 34, Box 81 • Rye, CO 81069

ph. (719) 676-2964 • Lic. #1738

Frazier Outfitting is located 40 miles southwest of Creede, Colorado, at the headwaters of the Rio Grande River. We operate in Unit 76, a limited draw area since 1986, where the bull cow ratio is 35 to 100.

We are a horseback operation offering muzzleloader, archery and rifle hunts. Hunting Unit 76 in the Rio Grande National Forest and Weminuche Wilderness at an alpine elevation of 10,000–13,000 feet, can be physically challenging for most individuals. In 1991, '94 and '95, our hunters received awards from the Colorado Outfitters Association for the "best elk taken." The majority of our hunters harvest quality bulls, taking 5x5 or better in all hunts.

We are a small business offering quality service and quality bulls.

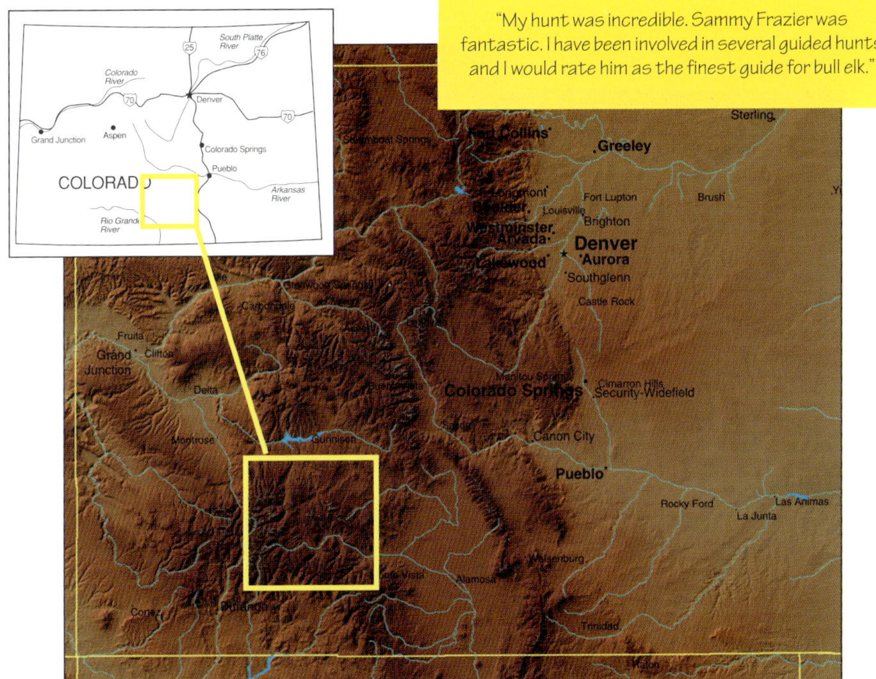

Garvey Brothers Outfitters

Stan Garvey
Box 555 • Nucla, CO 81424
phone: (970) 864-2243 • Lic. #606

Garvey Brothers Outfitters provides a full-service guided hunt. Giving you small camps, our motto is not the quantity of hunters but the quality of your hunt. Speaking of quality, the area we hunt (Unit 61) takes a minimum of three years for elk and two for deer in rifle season.

As this hunt has taken you years to plan, we would like to make it a hunt you have dreamed about.

Animals are spotted daily and the percentage of animals taken in the last three years is about 95%. We hunt both public and private lands.

Homemade food, fresh pies and bread baked daily make for a memorable hunt.

"This outfitter is a 'real' hunter. He knows the quarry, knows the area, and he has the ambition to go get them."

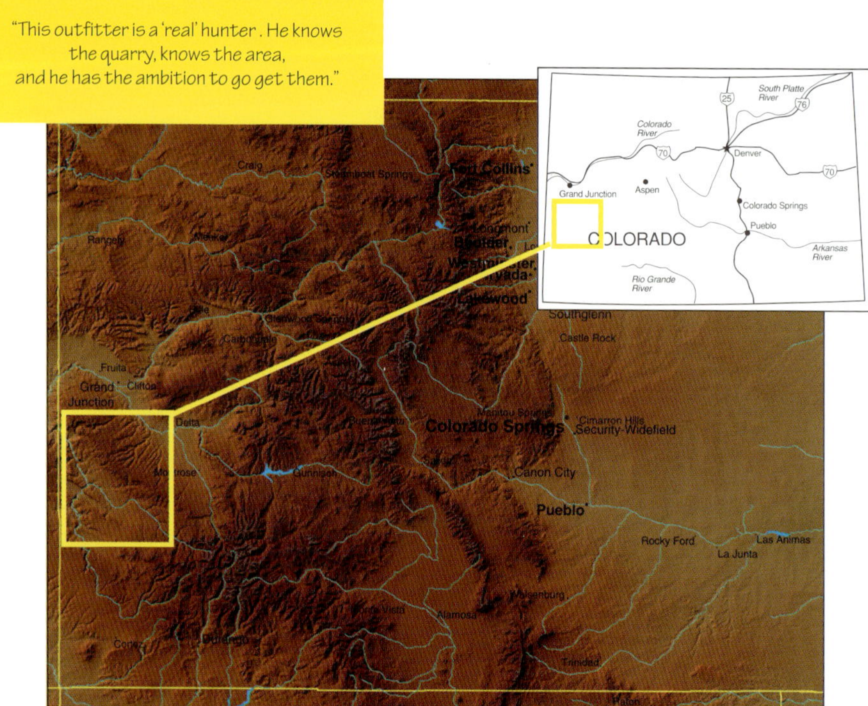

Lakeview Resort & Outfitters

Dan Murphy

P.O. Box 1000 • Lake City, CO 81235
phone: 800-456-0170 • (970) 944-2401 • fax:(970) 641-5952 • Lic. # 939

Our 36 years' of combined guide experience in the field provides a hunt that sells itself with limited hunters and a high number of trophy deer, new jeeps and fully-equipped camps.

Our wilderness area and horse camps are top quality.

Each archery, muzzleloader or rifle combo deer and elk hunt are limited to four-to-six hunters with three guided hunts per season.

These small camps allow time for personal treatment and room to move.

"We're in the business of making memories."

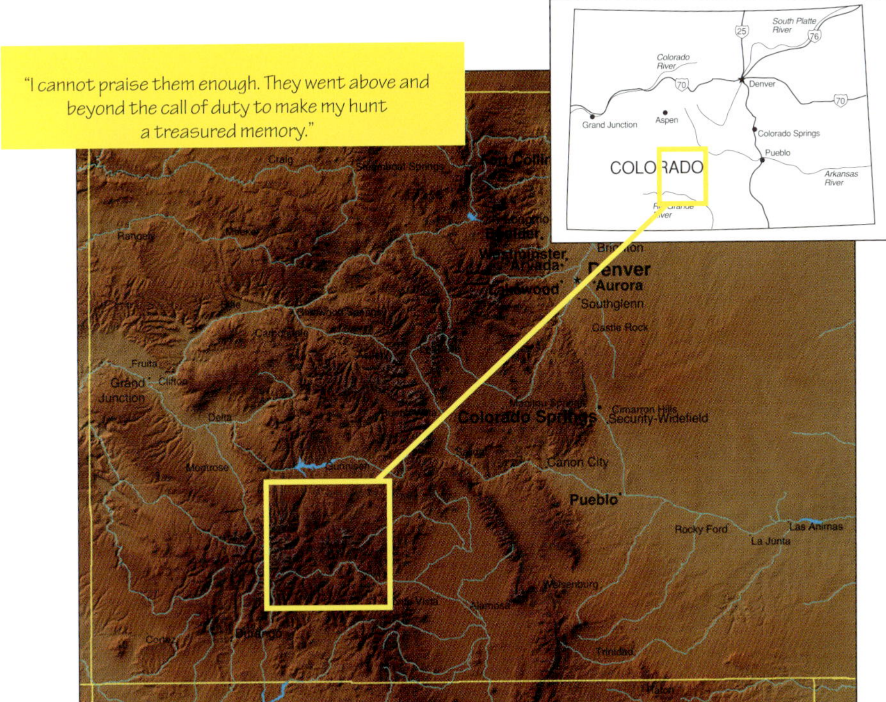

Lone Tom Outfitting

Paul Janke
12888 County Road 8 • Meeker, CO 81641
phone: (970) 878-5122 • Lic. #284

I offer fully-guided hunts or drop-camps for elk. They are all tent camps and pack-in horseback.

I hunt all archery, muzzleloader and rifle seasons. All camps are located in the Flattops Wilderness area.

Mountain Lion hunts are conducted from my lodge. I use 4-wheel drive and snowmobiles. Rooms and meals are included.

I have had 100% success for eight years.

Summer wilderness horseback trips are also available.

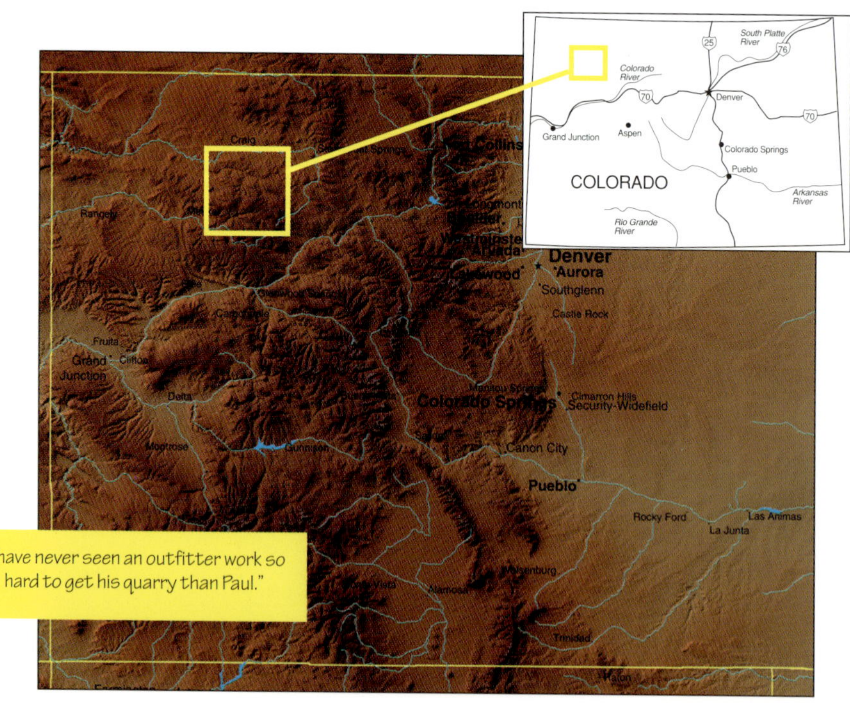

"I have never seen an outfitter work so hard to get his quarry than Paul."

Phil's Bowhunting Adventures

Phil Phillips
P.O. Box 786 • Montrose, CO 81402
phone/fax: (970) 249-8068 • Lic. #977

Here at Phil's Bowhunting Adventures, we specialize in archery antelope hunts. We hunt Northwest Colorado near Maybell on 40,000-plus deeded acres. We work under a Ranching for Wildlife Program, which guarantees hunters a tag without a draw. In the past six years we have 100% shooting opportunities and more than 90% success with 65% record book animals.

After eight years of trophy management our number of trophy animals just keeps getting better.

Well known, Chuck Adams has hunted with us the past six years and is booked through the year 2000. We have been in business 15 years. We also offer mule deer, elk and mountain lion hunts. We look forward to hunting with you.

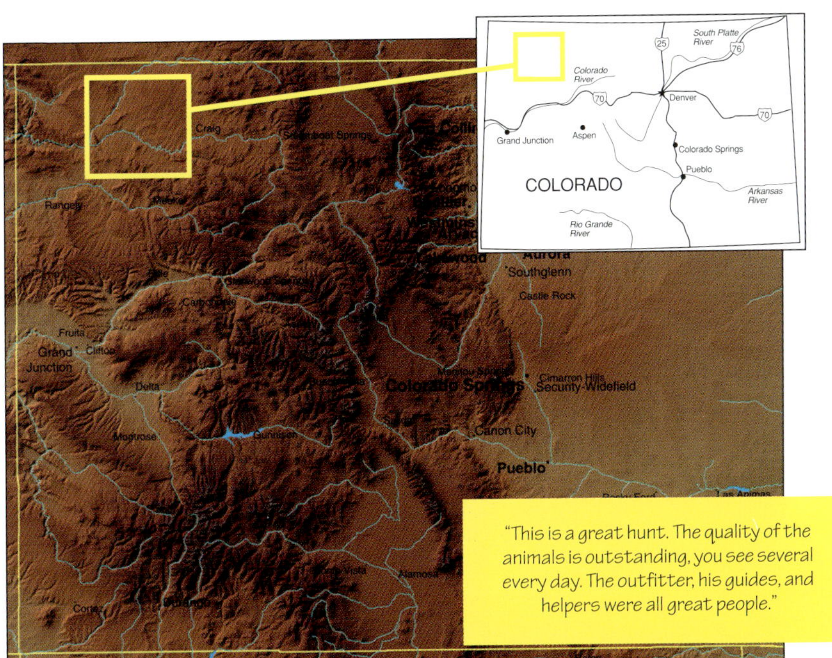

Samuelson Outfitters

Dick and Cathy Samuelson

P.O. Box 868 • Fraser, CO 80442
ph. (970) 726-8221 • Lic. #721

Samuelson Outfitters, a family business, has operated for more than 25 years in the Troublesome Basin.

It is one of the premiere elk hunting areas in Colorado and is noted for its considerable percentage of large bulls and abundance of wildlife. It is an area that one will remember for years to come and a place to which our family has grown very attached.

We offer fully-guided elk and mule deer hunts, drop-camps and pack service for archery, muzzleloader and rifle hunts. We also offer summer horsepack trips.

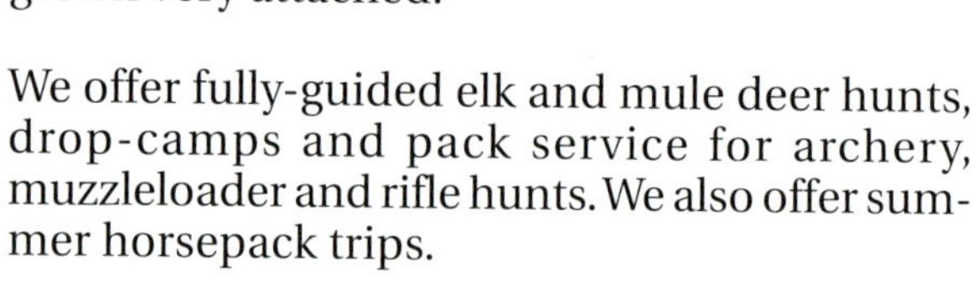

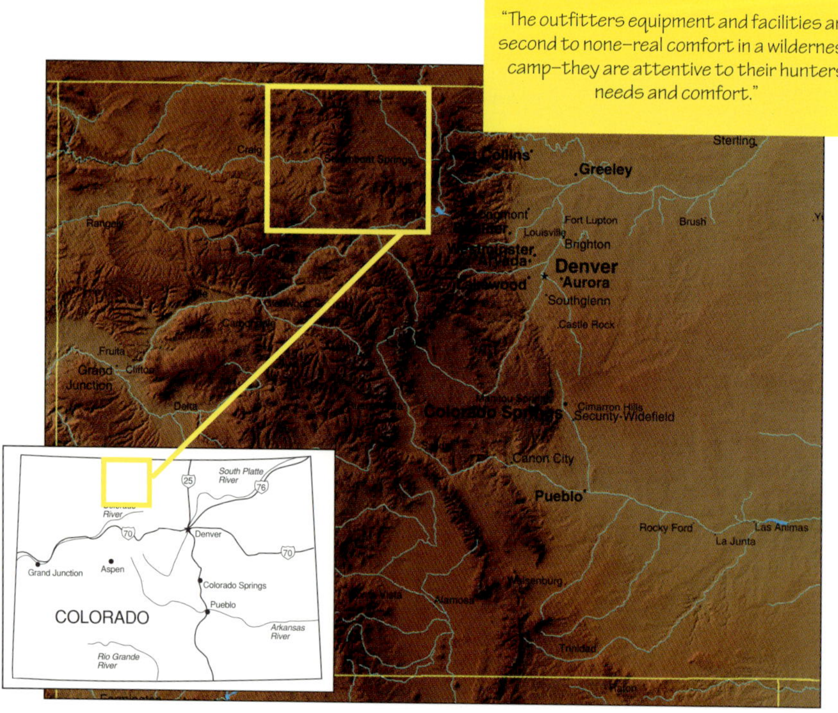

San Juan Outfitting, LLC

Tom and Cheri Van Soelen
186 C.R. 228 • Durango, CO 81301
ph. (970) 259-6259 • fax (970) 259-2652
email: sjo@frontier.net • Lic. #997

San Juan Outfitting (SJO) offers spring, summer and fall pack trips for a wide variety of services.

We are a full-time family-owned and operated outfitting company. Our permits are in the Weminuche Wilderness, Piedra area and San Juan National Forest. SJO offers fully-guided, semi-guided and drop-camps for rifle, archery, and muzzleloader hunters.

All camps are restricted to foot and horseback travel only. We believe in offering only high-quality hunts to a few hunters each year.

Enjoying not only the hunt, but all of God's country.

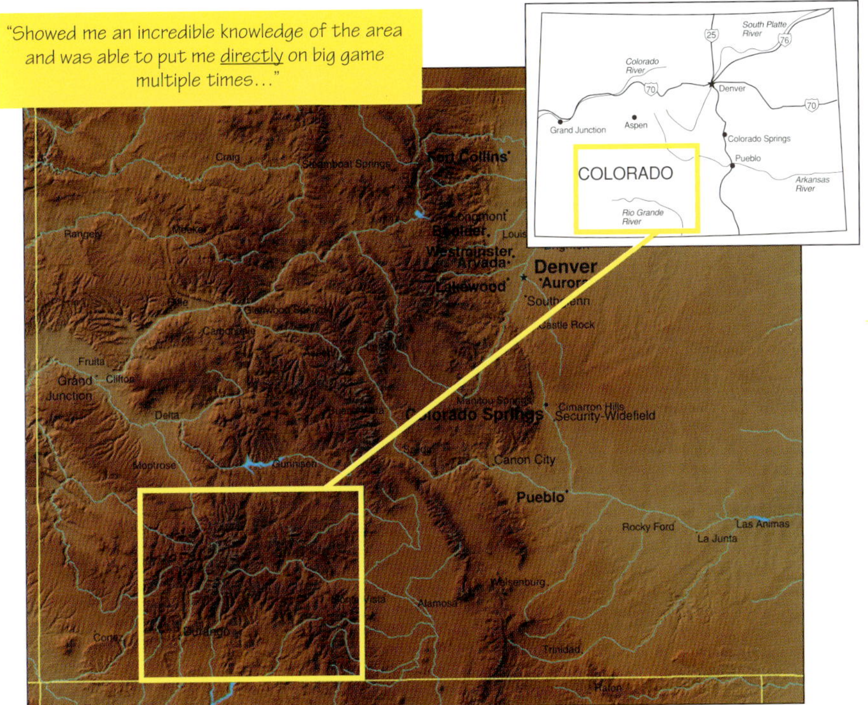

Spadafora Ranch Lodge

Roger Cesario
P.O. Box 1116 • Crested Butte, CO 81224
Home (970) 349-9836 • Ranch (970) 929-5201 • Lic. #711

Spadafora Ranch Lodge is located in Gunnison County and surrounded by Gunnison National Forest.

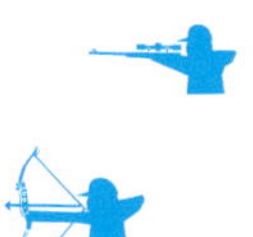

The ranch has been owned by the same family since 1929, and has had a hunting operation since early 1960s. Roger Cesario has been running the hunting operation as an outfitter since 1982 and received the Colorado Good Sportsman Award in 1992. Hunting is done from the lodge with jeeps to the hunting areas and on foot. Horses are utilized to pack the game.

We hunt both private land and Gunnison National Forest. Elk numbers of mature bulls on the ranch are excellent and mule deer number are also good.

The lodge is comfortable with hot showers, rooms for every two hunters, heat in the room, full kitchen and excellent elk hunting from the front door.

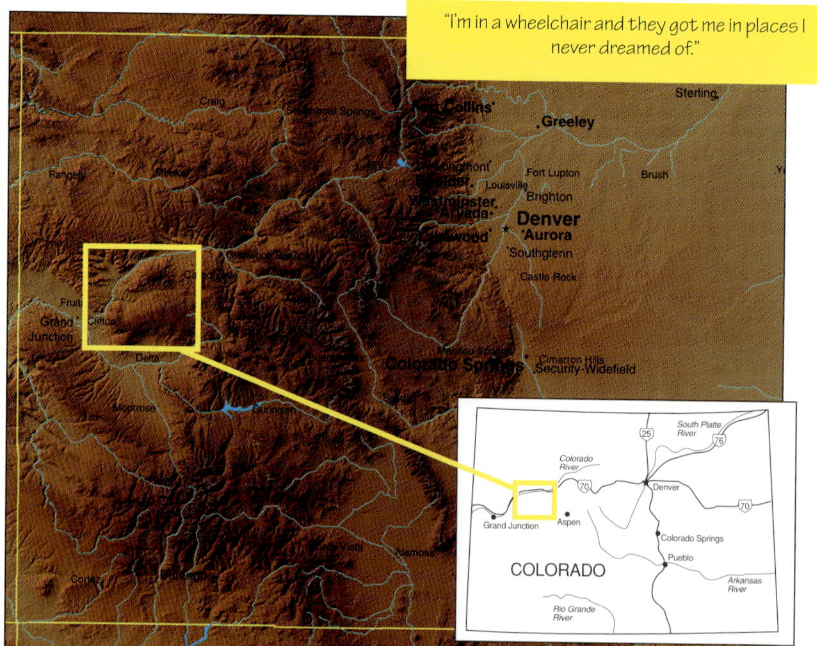

Idaho

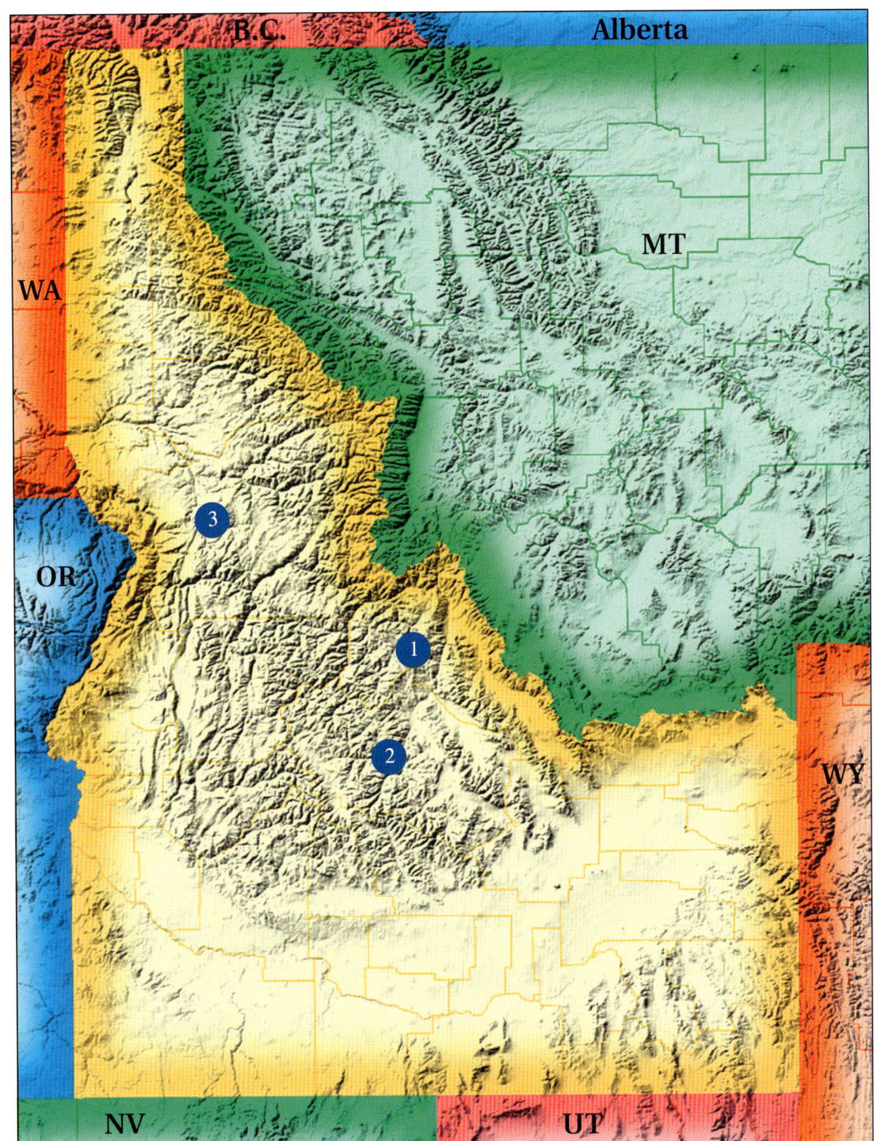

<u>Outdoor Professionals</u>

1 Castle Creek Outfitters
2 Horse Creek Outfitters
3 Renshaw Outfitting, Inc.

Useful information for the state of

Idaho

State and Federal Agencies

Outfitter & Guides Licensing Board
1365 N. Orchard, Room 172
Boise, ID 83706
phone: (208) 327-7380
fax: (208) 27-7382

Idaho Fish & Game Dept.
600 South Walnut
Boise, ID 83707
phone: (208) 334-3700

Forest Service
Northern Region
Federal Bldg.
PO Box 7669
Missoula, MT 59807-7669
phone: (406) 329-3616
TTY: (406) 329-3510

Clearwater National Forest
phone: (208) 476-4541

Idaho Panhandle, Coeur d'Alene-
Kaniksu-St. Joe National Forests
phone / TTY: (208) 765-7223

Nez Perce National Forest
phone: (208) 983-1950

Bureau of Land Management
Idaho State Office
1387 S. Vinnell Way
Boise, ID 83709-1657
phone: (208) 373-3896
or (208) 373-plus ext.
fax: (208) 373-3899

Office Hours 7:45 a.m. - 4:15 p.m.

Associations, Publications, etc.

Idaho Outfitters & Guides Association
PO Box 95
Boise, ID 83701
phone: (208) 342-1438

License and Report Requirements

• State requires licensing of Outdoor Professionals.

• State requires that every Outfitter be it bird, fish, big game, river rafting, trail riding or packing file a "Use Report" annually.

• Currently, no requirements for Guest/Dude Ranches.

Castle Creek Outfitters

Shane McAfee

P.O. Box 2008 • Salmon, ID 83467
phone: (208) 756-2548

Castle Creek Outfitters is owned and operated by Shane R. McAfee.

We have over 70,000 acres licensed to us by the State of Idaho in which Shane has been guiding hunters for over 24 years.

Castle Creek only takes a limited number of hunters each year in order to keep our hunts the highest quality.

We offer 2 types of hunts. You can hunt out of log cabin bunk houses from our back country ranch or you can pack into our deluxe tent camp.

We offer both 1 on 1, or 1 on 2, 8 day hunts from both locations.

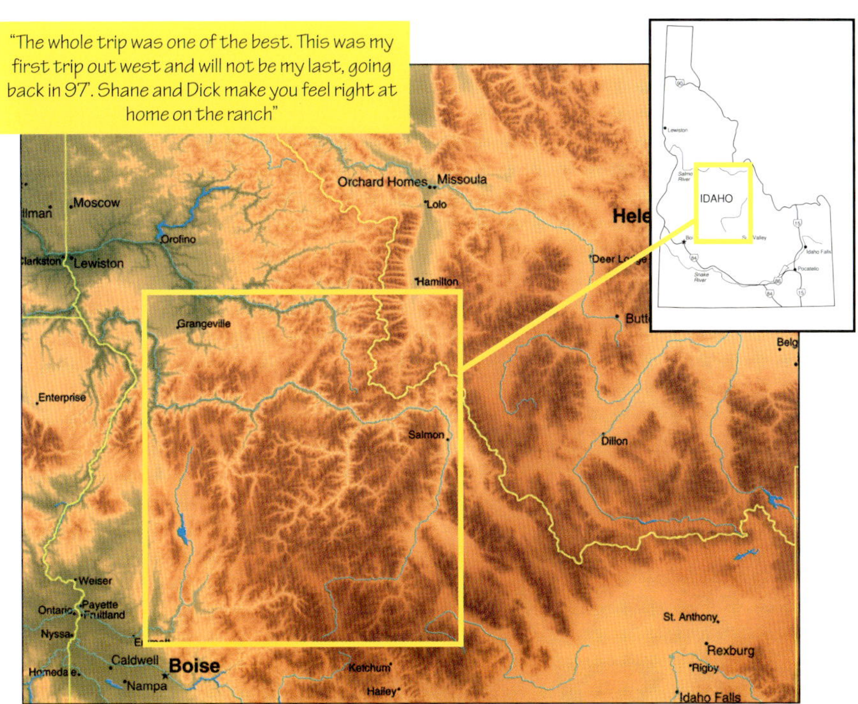

Horse Creek Outfitters

Jim Thomas - Ric Trusnovec

P.O. Box 950 • Challis, ID 83226
ph: J. Thomas (208) 879-5400 • R. Trusnovec (208) 879-4477

Horse Creek Outfitters is a full time, year around operation, and has been in business for 5 years.

We offer spring Bear hunting, summer family pack trips into high alpine lakes, fishing and sight-seeing, fall Elk and Deer hunts, and Lions in the winter. Our wilderness archery and rifle hunts are second to none. With three Pope & Young bulls taken the last three seasons and some fine rifle bulls from September through November. We operate three camps, a drive-in base camp and two pack-in camps personally run by the owner in each camp. Our wall tents are equipped with cots, foamies, lanterns and wood stoves.

You will find our personnel top notch, from guides and wranglers, to cooks that make home-style meals.

Your enjoyment and safety along with our hospitality is our goal.

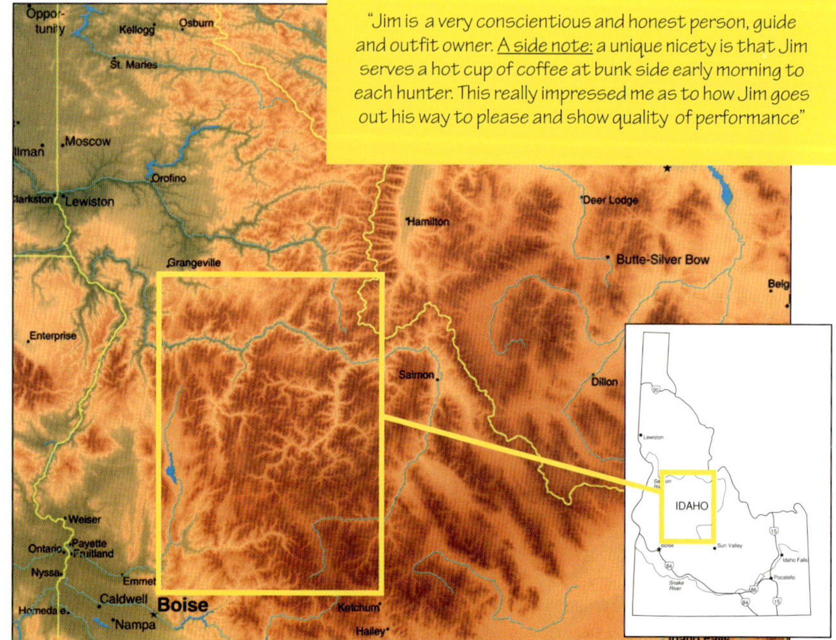

Renshaw Outfitting, Inc.

Jim Renshaw

PO Box 1165 • Kamiah, ID 83536-1165
ph. (208) 935-0726 • (926) 4520 • (800) 452-2567

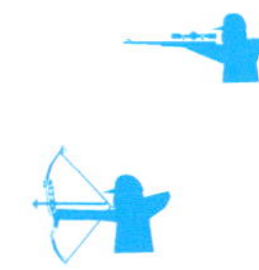

"Go with the best and most experienced outfitter in the state of Idaho."

Licensed and bonded the longest in Idaho. Offering the following fully-guided deluxe hunts: spring black bear (different color phases) in May and June; deluxe fall bugle archery elk hunts (tree stand available); deluxe guided rifle elk hunts; and late fall whitetail hunts on private land in November.

All hunts are fully guided and everything is furnished except personal gear and licenses. If you book an hunt early, the license and tags can be purchased from Idaho's outfitter set-aside pool. Facilities are deluxe tent camps with floored tents, wood heat, running water, hot showers, and lights. We serve home style meals.

Please call for further information, or to book a hunt.

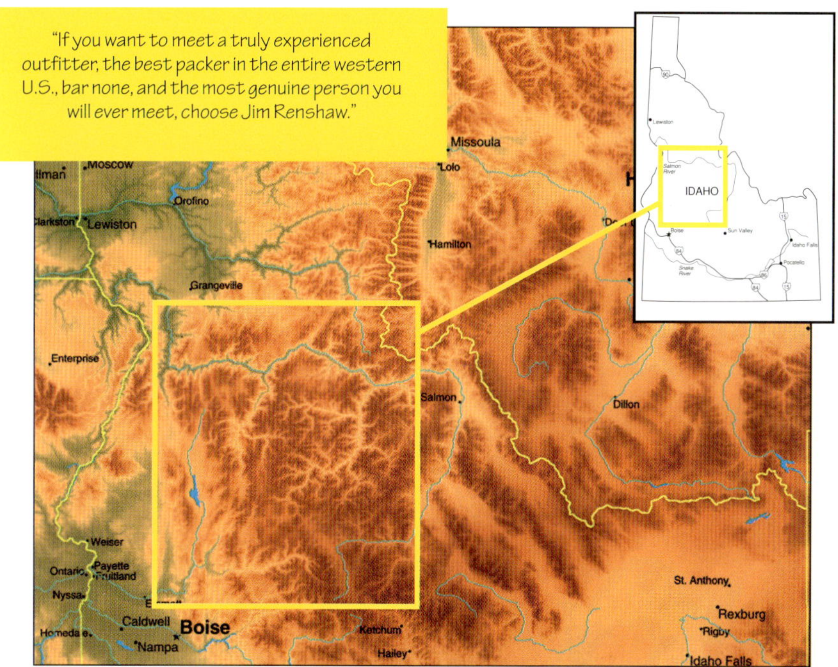

Maine

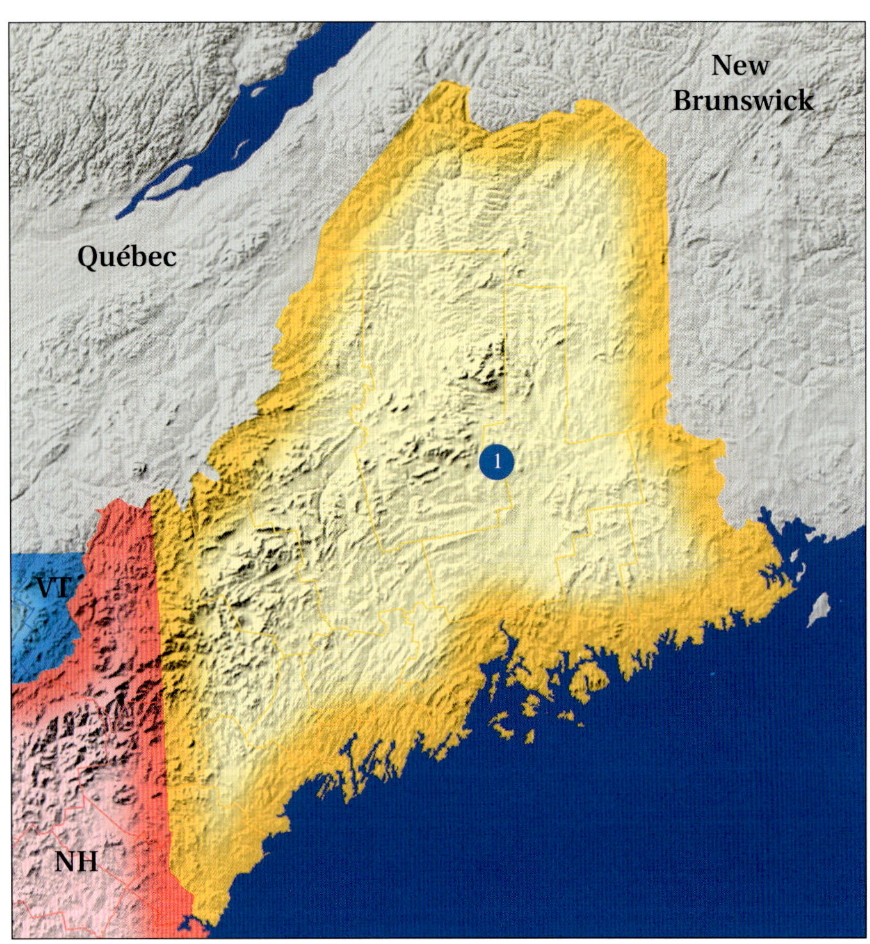

<u>Outdoor Professionals</u>

1. God's Country Guide Service

Maine

State and Federal Agencies

Maine Dept. of Fish & Wildlife
284 State St. Station #41
Augusta, ME 04333
phone: (207) 287-8000

Forest Service
Eastern Region
310 West Wisconsin Ave. Rm. 500
Milwaukee, WI 53203
phone: (414) 297-3646
TTY: (414) 297-3507

White Mountain National Forest
Federal Building
719 North Main Street
Laconia, NH 03246
phone: (603) 528-8721

Bureau of Land Management
Eastern States
7450 Boston Boulevard
Springfield, Virginia 22153
phone: (703) 440-1660
or (703) 440- Plus Extension
fax: (703) 440-1599

Office Hours: 8:00 a.m. - 4:30 p.m.

Eastern States
Milwaukee District Office
310 W. Wisconsin Ave., Suite 450
(P.O. Box 631 53201-0631)
Milwaukee, Wisconsin 53203
phone: (414) 297-4450
fax: (414) 297-4409

National Parks

Acadia National Park
phone: (207) 288-3338

Associations, Publications, etc.

Sportsman's Alliance of Maine
RR 1, Box 1174
Church Hill Road
Augusta, ME 04330-9749
phone: (207) 622-5503

Maine Professional Guide Association
phone: (207) 785-2061

The Maine Sportsman
phone: (207) 287-3995

License and Report Requirements

• State requires licensing of Outdoor Professionals.

• Monthly Head Fee Guides Report required for Whitewater River Companies.

• No report required for Hunting and Fishing Professionals.

God's Country Guide Service

Leonard Coover

RFD #1, Box 5460 • Brownville, ME 04414
ph. (207) 965-8139

God's Country Guide Service is a family-owned and operated business with each family member taking pride in the job they do. Len and his two sons, Matt and Adam, are registered Maine guides and provide fully-guided moose, bear and deer hunts in north central Maine. Pat, Louis' wife, provides three home-cooked meals each day.

Lodging in clean new cabins, transportation to and from your stand, and complete trophy care, completes your hunting package. Our outfitting business has earned the reputation for producing fall black bear in both quantity and quality.

Black bears killed at our camps hold the Maine state record for both 1995 and 1992. Maine whitetail are in a class of their own both for antler size and body weight. Buck shot at our camps are in excess of 200 pounds field-dressed.

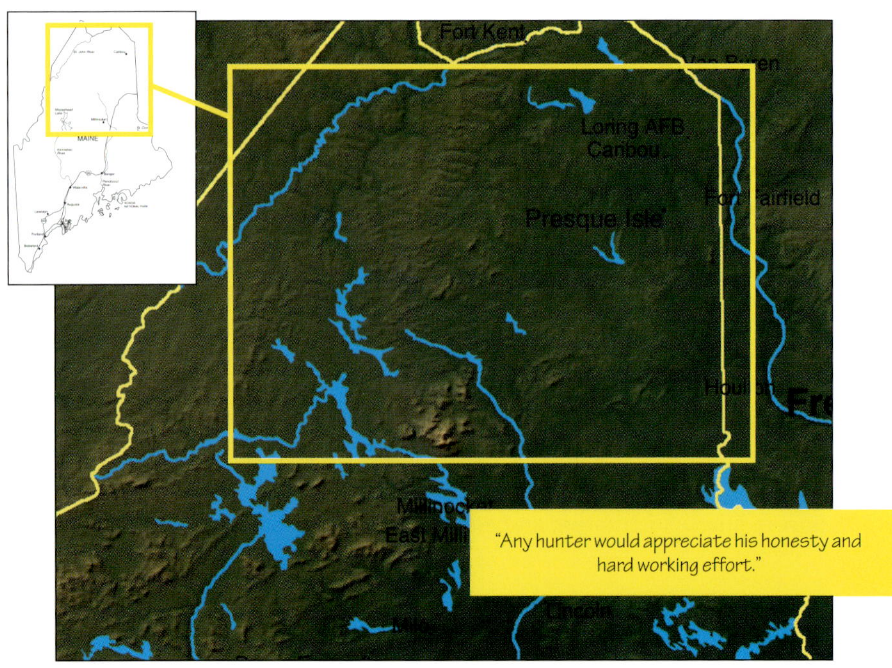

"Any hunter would appreciate his honesty and hard working effort."

Montana

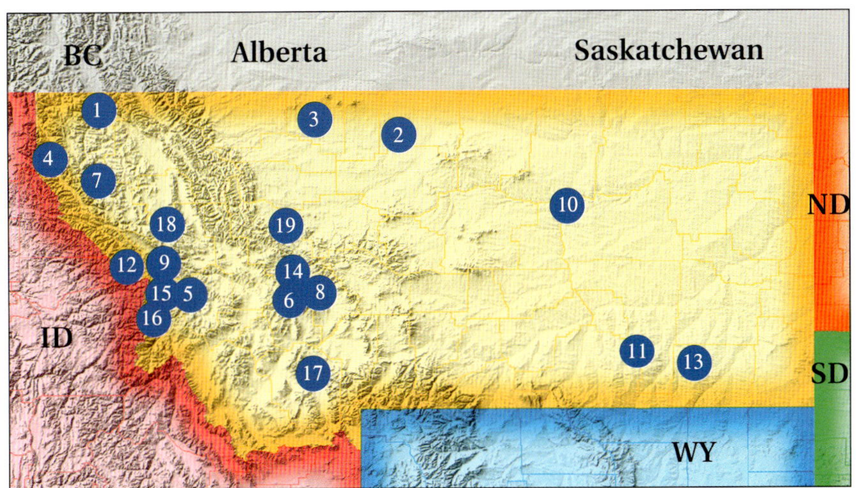

Outdoor Professionals

1. Buckhorn Ranch Outfitters
2. Chase Hill Outfitters
3. Cow Creek Outfitters
4. Elk Creek Outfitting
5. Esper's Under Wild Skies Lodge & Outfitters
6. EW Watson & Sons Outfitting
7. Flat Iron Outfitting
8. Hidden Hollow Hideaway
9. JM Bar Outfitters
10. Kibler Outfitting
11. Lakeview Resort & Outfitters
12. Lone Tree Outfitting
13. Mitchell Outfitting
14. Ramshorn Outfitters
15. Rick Wemple Outfitting
16. R.L. Sourbrine Outfitters & Sons
17. S&W Outfitters
18. White Tail Ranch/WTR Outfitters, Inc.
19. Wild West Outfitters

Useful information for the state of

Montana

<u>State and Federal Agencies</u>

Montana Board of Outfitters
Dept. of Commerce
Arcade Building - 111 North Jackson
Helena, MT 59620-0407
phone: (406) 444-3738

Montana Dept. of Fish, Wildlife & Parks
1420 East 6th
Helena, MT 59620
phone: (406) 444-2535

Forest Service
Northern Region
Federal Building
PO Box 7669
Missoula, MT 59807-7669
phone: (406) 329-3616
TTY: (406) 329-3510

Bitterroot National Forest
phone: (406) 363-7117

Custer National Forest
phone / TTY: (406) 657-6361

Flathead National Forest
phone: (406) 755-5401

Gallatin National Forest
phone / TTY: (406) 587-6920

Helena National Forest
phone: (406) 449-5201

Kootenai National Forest
phone: (406) 293-6211

Lewis & Clark National Forest
phone: (406) 791-7700

Lolo National Forest
phone: (406) 329-3750

Bureau of Land Management
Montana State Office
Granite Tower
222 North 32nd Street
P.O. Box 36800
Billings, Montana 59107-6800
phone: (406) 255-2885
fax: (406) 255-2762
Email - mtinfo@mt.blm.gov
Office Hours: 8:00 a.m. - 4:30 p.m.

<u>National Parks</u>

Glacier National Park
phone:(406) 888-5441

<u>Associations, Publications, etc.</u>

Montana Outfitters & Guides Assoc.
PO Box 1248
Helena, MT 59604
phone: (406) 449-3578

Rocky Mountain Elk Foundation
PO Box 8249
Missoula, MT 59807-8249
phone: (406) 523-4500
fax: (406) 523-4550

Boone & Crockett Club
Old Milwaukee Depot, 250 Station Dr.
Missoula, MT 59801
phone: (406) 542-1888
fax: (406) 542-0784

<u>License and Report Requirements</u>
- State requires licensing of Outdoor Professionals.
- State requires an "Annual Client Report Log" for all Hunting and Fishing Outfitters.
- State does not regulate River Guides.
- Guest/Dude Ranches need to get an Outfitter license only if they take guest to fish or hunt on land that they do not own.

Buckhorn Ranch Outfitters

Harry and Claire Workman

Box 84 • Eureka, MT 59917
ph. (406) 889-3762

Harry and Claire Workman's Buckhorn Ranch Outfitters, is a family-owned and operated outfit with 30 years in the Bob Marshall Wilderness and a lifetime experience in beautiful northwestern Montana. Buckhorn Ranch 10-day wilderness hunts take place in the Silvertip Creek drainage of the Bob Marshall Wilderness, Flathead National Forest. Most of the summer pack trip and the deer, moose, and bear hunts are near our home ranch in Eureka, Montana. Silvertip City's remote wilderness hunting camp has been in continuous operation for more than 50 years with the "over 80" retired outfitter, who established the camp, still helping out!

From this camp we hunt primarily elk but also mule deer, black bear, goats and moose.

Whether it is a day ride from the ranch or a 10-day wilderness hunt, Buckhorn Ranch's Montana outing is an exciting, enjoyable adventure.

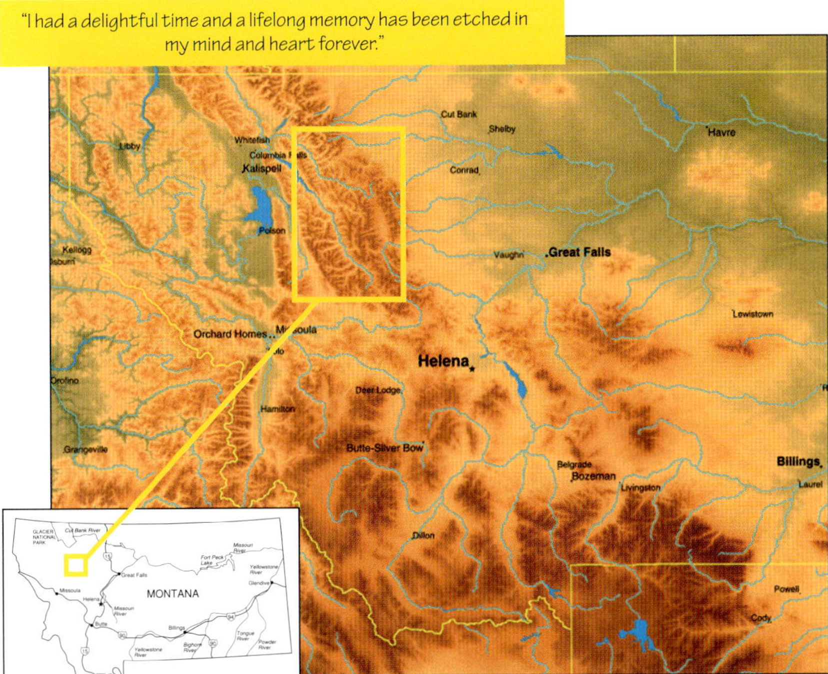

Chase Hill Outfitters

Bill and Renita Brown

HC77 Box 851 • Big Sandy, MT 59520
ph. (406) 386-2447 • fax (406) 386-2435

Chase Hill Outfitters specializes in Pope and Young bull elk, trophy deer and varmint safaris. The quantity and quality of animals is tremendous with one-to-one doe-buck ratio on the mule deer end the with the elk rated No. 1 in North America.

Our guides are all professionals; courteous, ambitious and knowledgeable. Our fleet vehicles consist of 4x4 4-door trucks and Suburbans. The hunts are all guided on more than 100,000 acres of exclusively-leased or owned private land, and 2 million acres of public land.

We have very spacious ranch-style accommodations with a large recreation room, three bedrooms and two bathrooms. The meals are big, hearty, all-you-can-eat, with homemade breads and gourmet desserts.

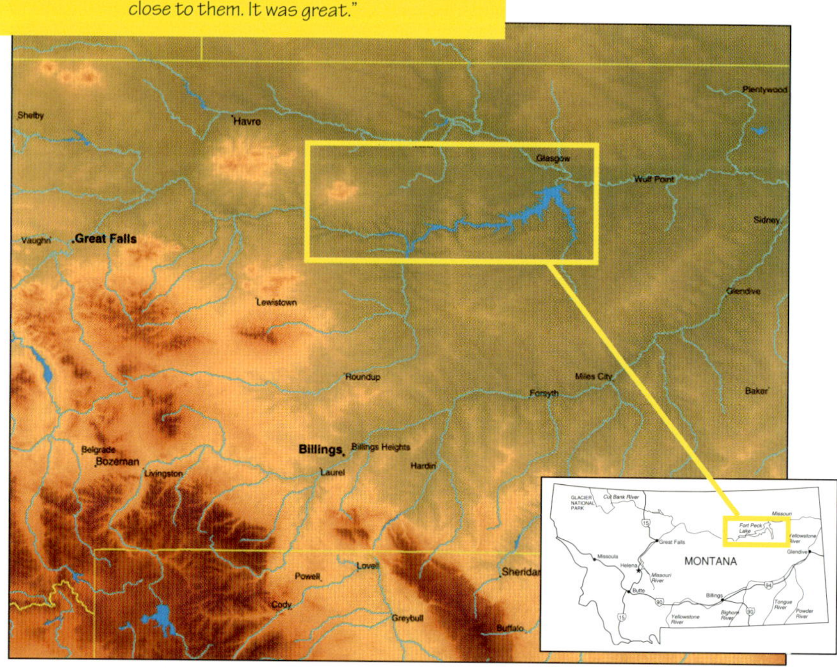

Cow Creek Outfitters

John Fritz

Box 280 • Chester, MT 59522

ph./fax (406) 432-2755

Cow Creek Outfitters is located on a working cattle ranch 47 miles south of Chinook, Montana.

We do not advertise but in the eight years we have been professionally guiding, we have depended completely on the recommendations of our past clients.

I am proud to say we offer some of the best mule deer and antelope hunting in Montana. We have good elk and bighorn sheep populations with permits by drawings. We hunt a huge area of approximately 20-square miles.

The area consists of the Bear Paw Mountains on the north and the Badlands and canyons of the Missouri River Breaks on the south.

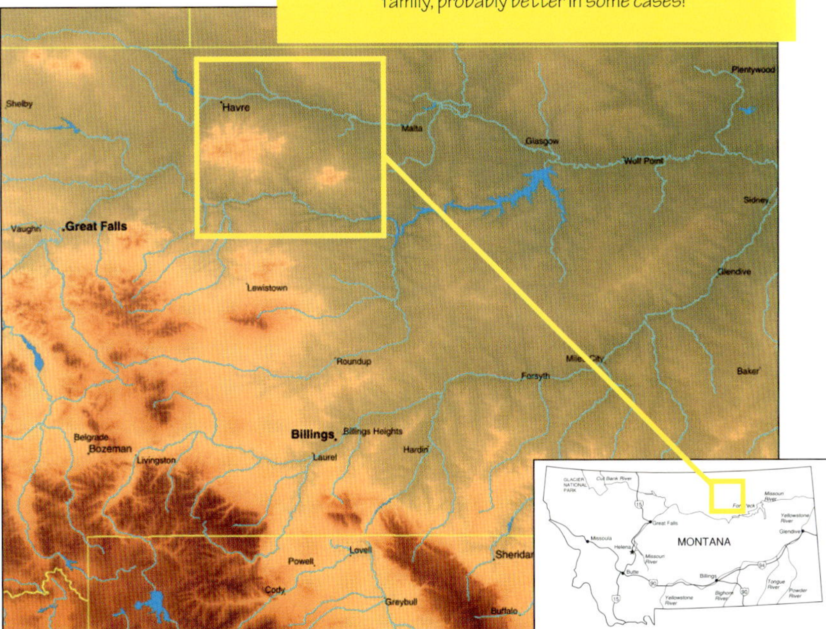

Elk Creek Outfitting

Brent and Kathy Fitchett

20 W. Elk Creek Road • Heron, MT 59844
ph. (406) 847-5593

Welcome to Elk Creek Outfitting located in the mountainous border between Northwestern Montana and Northeastern Idaho.

With a comfortable lodge, cozy cabins and home-cooked meals, owners and operators Brent and Kathy Fitchett will make your stay memorable. Elk Creek Outfitting is licensed and bonded to hunt big game animals in Montana and Idaho.

For a wide variety of hunts Elk Creek Outfitting has rifle, archery and muzzleloader hunts for elk, bear, mountain lion, whitetail and mule deer (moose and sheep available by special drawings). Elk Creek Outfitting also hunts on the Kootenai National Forest in Montana, and on the Panhandle National Forest in Idaho, and they offer exclusive trophy whitetail deer hunts on private land in Montana.

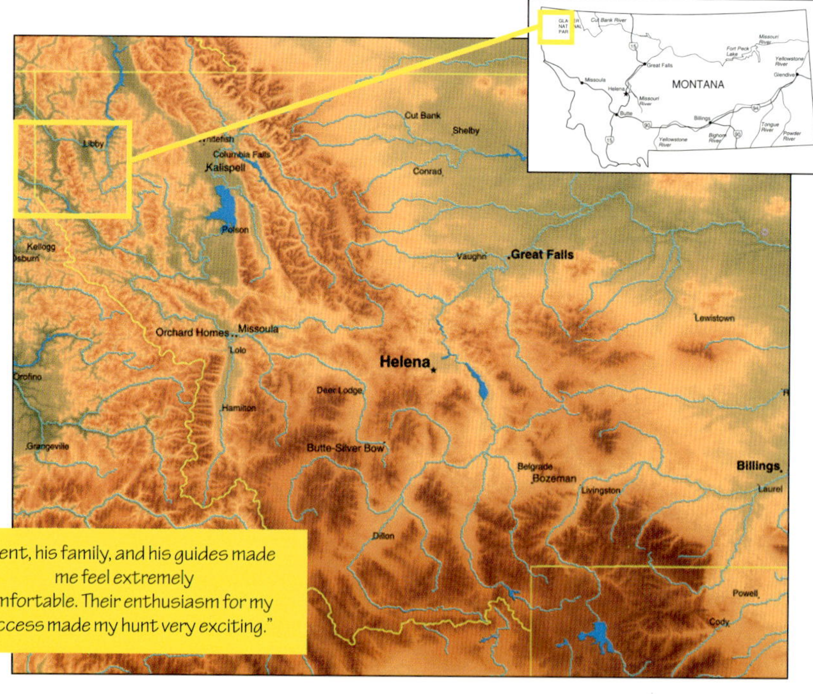

Esper's Under Wild Skies Lodge and Outfitters

Vaughn Esper
P.O. Box 849 • Philipsburg, MT 59858
ph. (406) 859-3000

Under Wild Skies Lodge & Outfitters is located in Anaconda Pintler Wilderness and surrounding Deer Lodge and Beaverhead National Forests. It has exclusive hunting rights in 300,000 acres of some of the best hunting in Southwestern Montana.

Our courteous, trained, licensed and seasoned guides are professionals with the highest standards. They take great pride in their abilities and success rates. At Under Wild Skies, we pay meticulous attention to every detail and make every effort to make your hunt productive and memorable, and it shows.

At the end of the trail where the mountains meet the sky, you will find "the last best place"…Under Wild Skies.

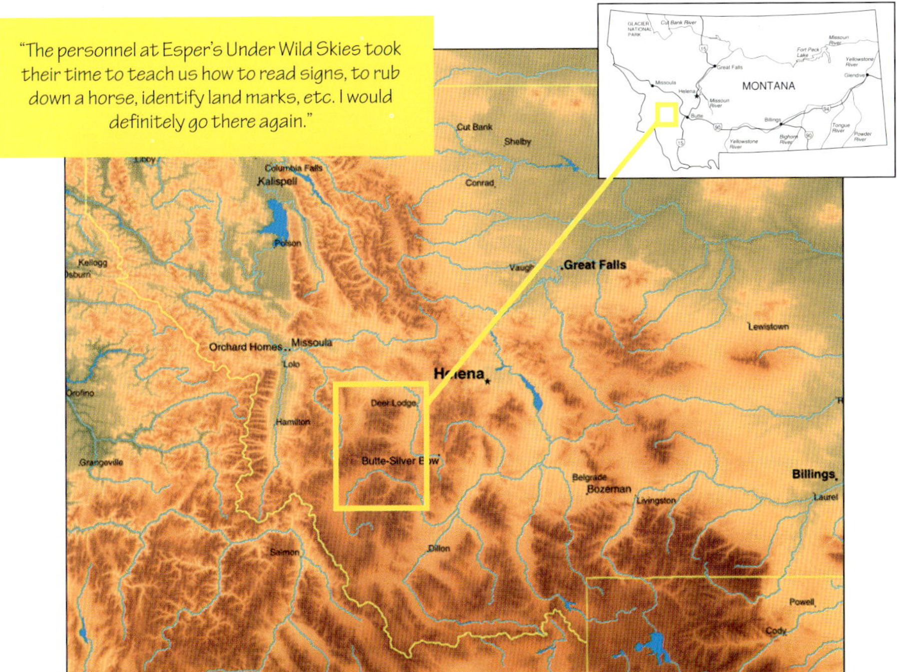

EW Watson & Sons Outfitting

Ed and Wanda Watson

7837 U.S. Hwy. 287 • Townsend, MT 59644
phone: (800) 654-2845 • fax: (406) 266-4498

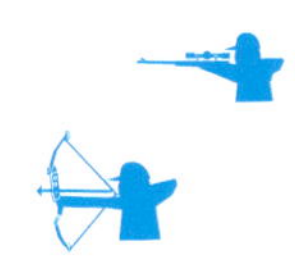

Ours is a family-owned and operated business which specializes in custom outdoor adventures. This is traditional elk/deer hunting at its finest.

Sixteen years of guiding and pack experience have given us the extra ability it takes to produce trophies for our clients. Service and quality are our main goals!

The unique geography of our area in the Lee Metcalf Wilderness in the Beaverhead National Forest of the Madison Mountain Range near Ennis, Montana, makes for very little hunting pressure and excellent game opportunities. This is one hunt you don't want to miss.

We look forward to a quality hunting experience with you.

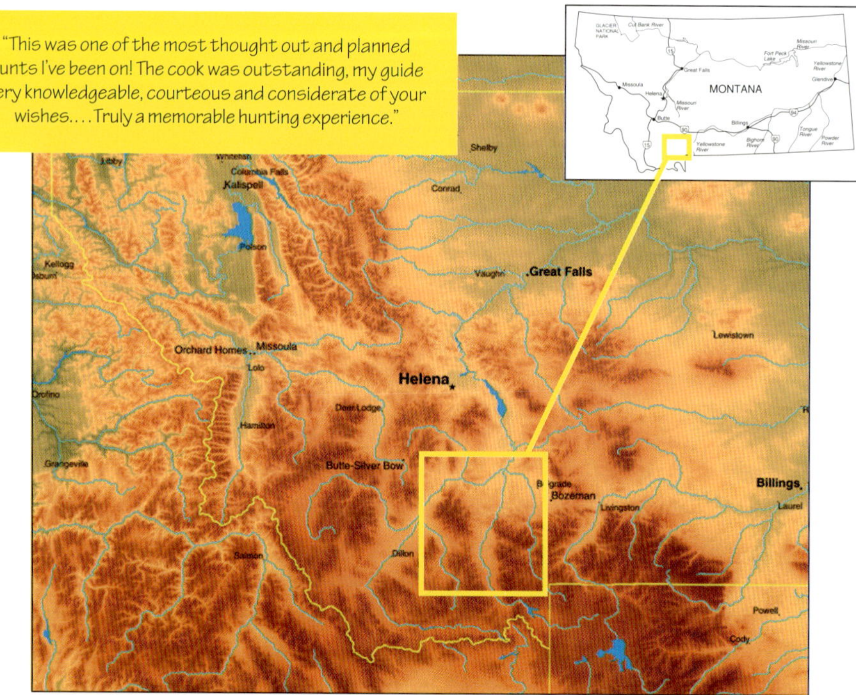

Flat Iron Outfitting

Jerry C. Shively
3 Golf Course Rd. • Thompson Falls, MT 59873
ph. (406) 827-3666

Flat Iron Outfitting provides a very unique and personal service for hunters and fisherman and other people who want to experience the very best of western Montana.

We have a flatland lease which produces some of the finest whitetails in Montana.

The largest whitetail taken on a guided hunt in this state was taken here. Our Forest Service permit area has an excellent elk, bear, and cougar population.

Our high mountain lake fishing, photo trips and day hikes in the mountains make for a lifetime of unforgettable memories.

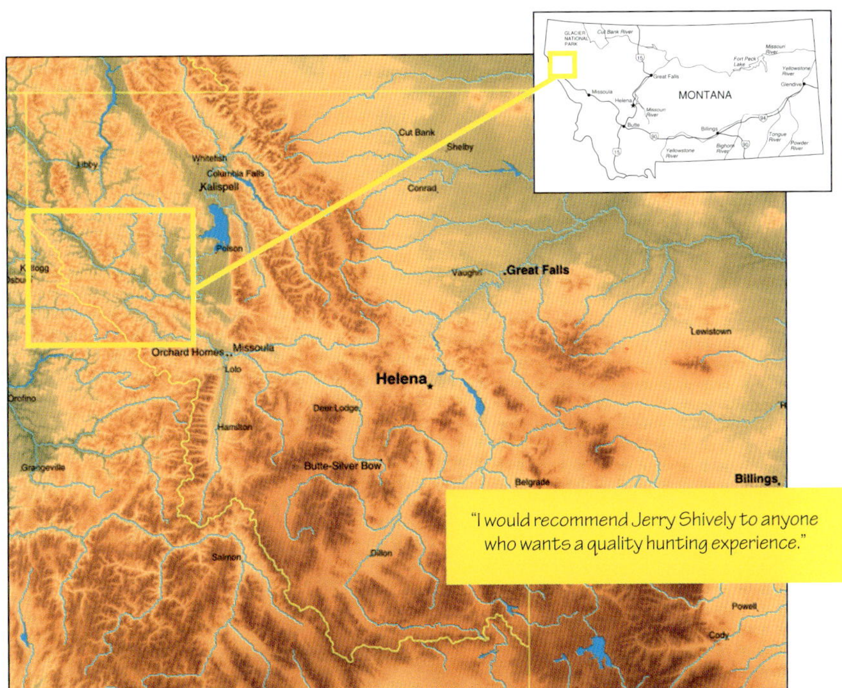

Hidden Hollow Hideaway

Kelly and Jill Flynn

Box 233 • Townsend, MT 59644
ph. (406) 266-3322

"I enjoyed what has to be the one of the most delightful, enchanting, picturesque and successful Elk and Deer hunts in the United States." This quote certainly describes Hidden Hollow Hideaway.

For hunters looking for a great <u>combination</u> deer and elk hunt, the Hideaway offers a wonderful opportunity. With more than 20 years in the same area, the Hideaway team hunts more than 20,000 acres of private ranch land in conjunction with a proposed wilderness area. In 1994, one of the hunters harvested a whitetail buck that was a Safari Club world record.

In the past 10 years archery and rifle hunters have enjoyed a better than 50% success on 4 pt., 5 pt., and 6 pt. bull elk.

The Hideaway offers the hunt of a lifetime.

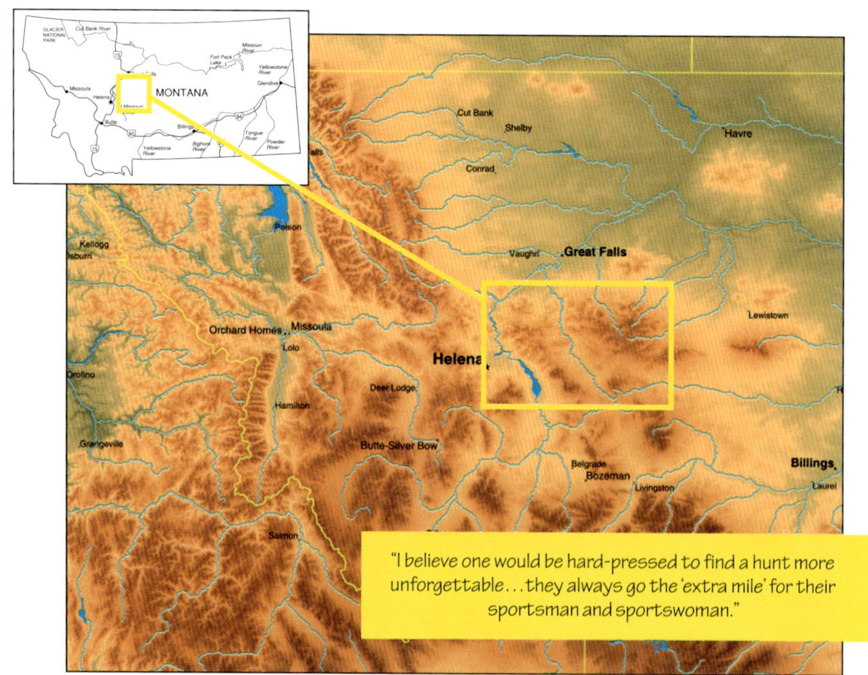

JM Bar Outfitters

Jeff and Maria Freeman
23945 Bonita Road • Clinton, MT 59825
ph. (406) 825-3230 • fax (406) 825-3050

We have been providing outdoor experience for sportsman and vacationers since 1975.

We are located on Rock Creek, a blue ribbon trout stream, in the Long John Mountain Range, 30 miles east of Missoula, Montana.

We operate a full-time, year-round family out-fitting business. There is abundant wildlife in the surrounding mountain including a large wild sheep population.

We aim to give you as much information about our hunt as possible, and we always enjoy talking to a fellow hunter.

Feel free to call us anytime.

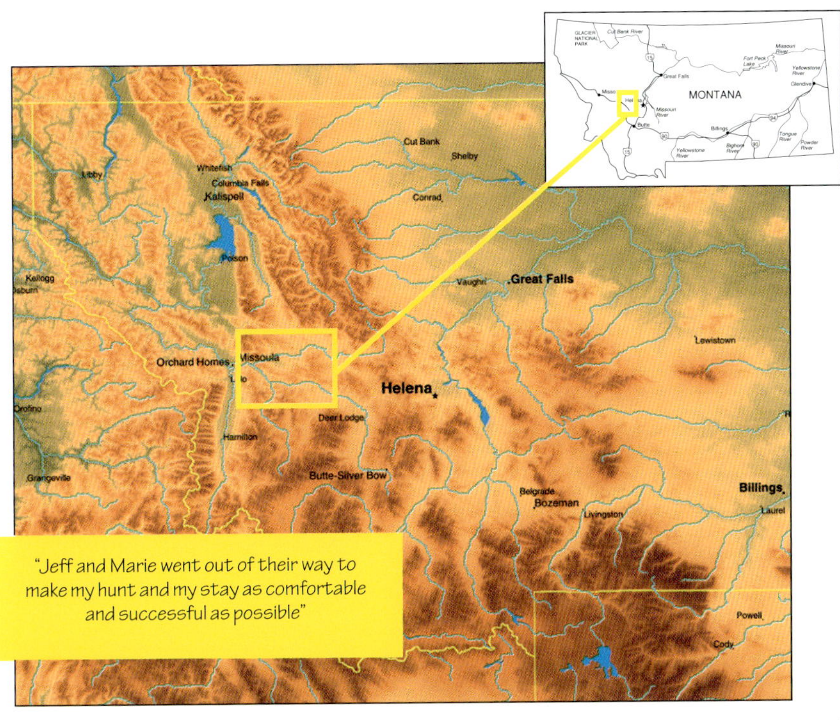

> "Jeff and Marie went out of their way to make my hunt and my stay as comfortable and successful as possible"

Kibler Outfitting

Myron and Mary Beth Kibler

Box A-6 • Sand Spring, MT 59077
ph. (406) 557-2503

Our hunting areas are located 26 miles south of Sand Spring Montana. We hunt both private and BLM lands depending on the species, for a total of approximately 45,000 acres.

The limits we place upon ourselves keep the quality and quantity of our game superb. Our specialized service to our clients make return business such that we do not do paid advertising. Word of mouth advertising has served us well, having only 25-30 hunters per year. This keeps our attitude fresh and makes your vacation a very special one.

It would be our pleasure to have you and your friends hunt with us!

If you have any questions, please feel welcome to contact us at anytime.

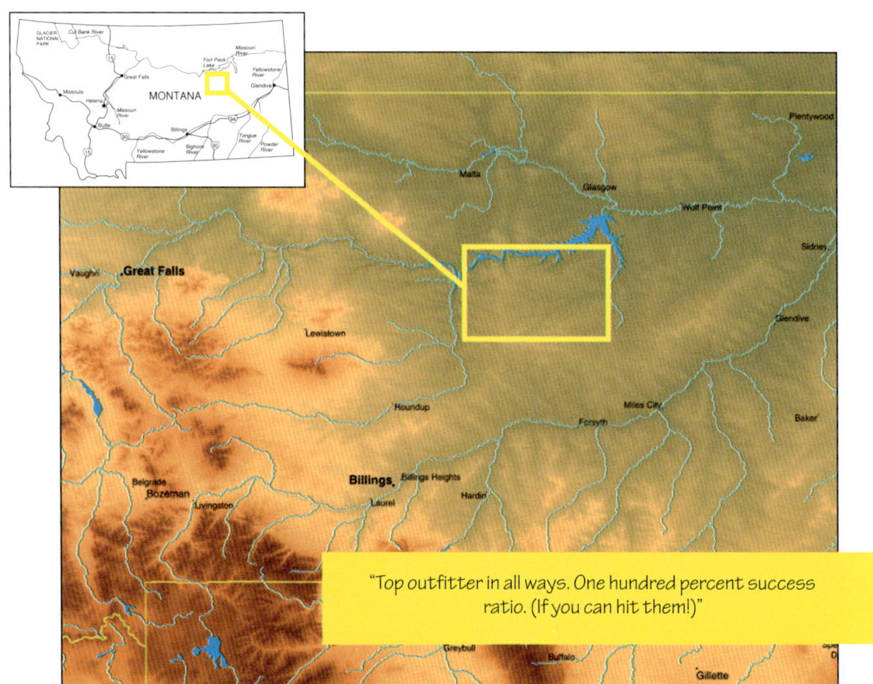

Lakeview Resort & Outfitters

Dan Murphy
P.O. Box 1000 • Lake City, CO 81235
ph. (800) 456-0170 • 970-944-2401 • fax: 970-944-2925

Our Montana trophy mule deer hunt offers an exclusive private land trophy opportunity.

Our 37 years of combined guide experience in the field, new jeeps, fully-equipped camps, limited hunters and high number of trophy deer creates a hunt that sells itself.

We also hunt in Colorado where our wilderness area and horse camps are top quality. Each archery, muzzleloader or rifle combo deer and elk hunt are limited to four to six hunters with three guides per season.

These small camps allow time for personal treatment and room to move.

"We're in the business of making memories."

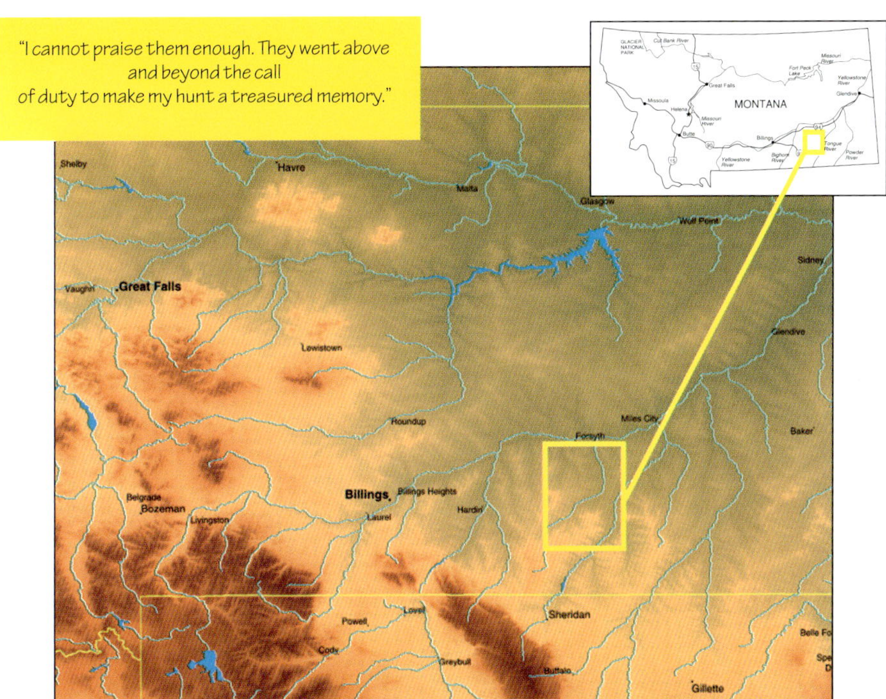

Lone Tree Outfitting

Larry Pendleton

1531 Iron Cap Rd. • Stevensville, MT 59870
ph. (406) 777-3906

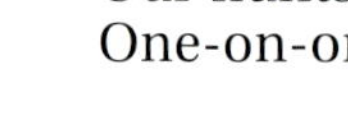

We at Lone Tree Outfitting offer a wide variety of hunting opportunities and species of big game to hunt. These are ranch-style hunts based on private property leased by us for our clients' use only, thus ensuring privacy and quality.

We average 80% an our elk hunts. We have a full-time cook and several great home-cooked meals.
Our hunts are run with two clients per guide. One-on-one hunts cost extra.

Eighty percent of our annual client base are return clients or referrals from past clients.

We also assist clients in procuring licenses to hunt with us.

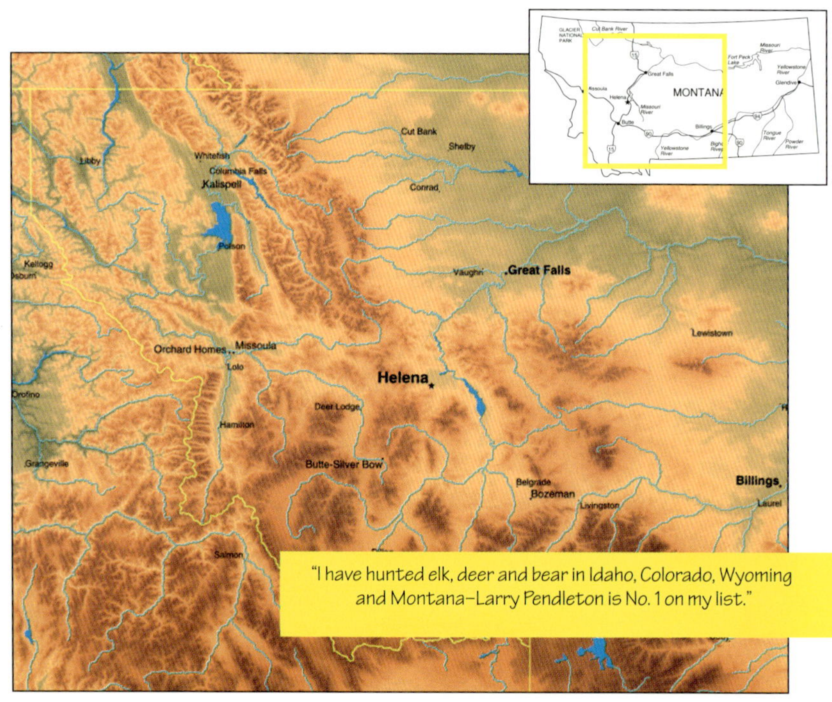

Mitchell Outfitting

Floyd Mitchell

PO Box 228 • Broadus, MT 59317
ph. (406) 436-2522 • Camp (406) 427-5810

Floyd Mitchell, owner of Mitchell Outfitting, has been in the Outfitting business for 18 years.

We specialize in mule deer, whitetail, antelope, prairie dogs, varmint calling, turkey, upland game birds and family vacation packages. Our guided hunts take place on beautiful and scenic private ranches in Powder River and Carter counties. We have modern facilities with showers, and home-cooked meals provided.

We take pride in offering exceptional hunting with experienced guides.

You will not find a better average of good bucks taken right here in Eastern Montana.

We guarantee you will be more than pleased, not only with the hunting, but with all aspects of our service.

"Floyd Mitchell and his guide are of the quality that makes them the best in the business. The hunting cabin is rustic, but hell, that makes it all for the better."

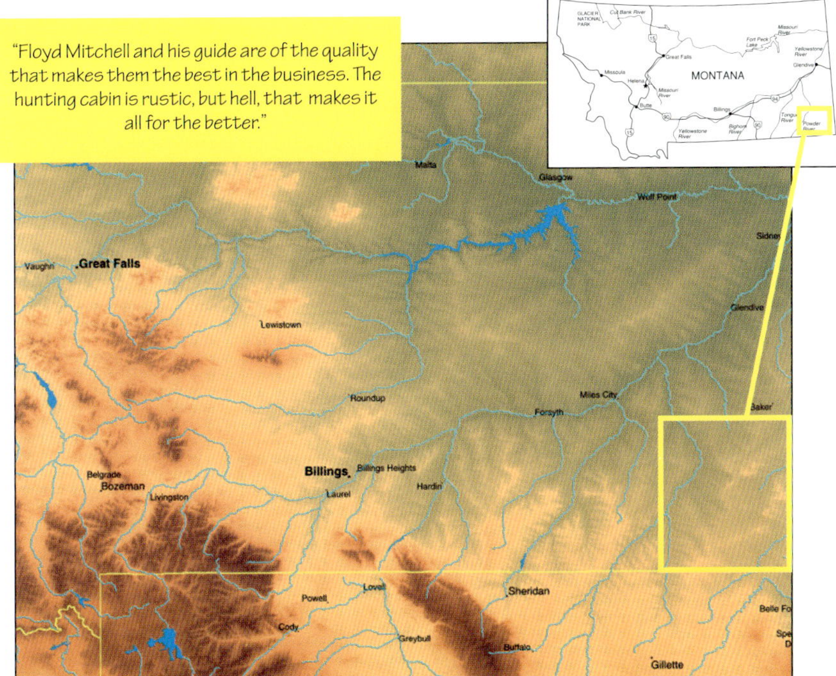

Ramshorn Outfitters

Audie and Vivianne Anderson

P.O. Box 662 • Townsend, MT 59644
ph. (406) 266-3095

Ramshorn Outfitters offers a large variety of hunts to suit most hunters and their personal goals.

You can hunt high alpine areas for elk or lower more varying terrain for mule deer or whitetail deer or test your stalking skills against a sharp-eyed antelope. Vivianne and I pride ourselves in providing a quality trip and polished camp. Food and accommodation are top-notch.

We specialize in quality trips and I personally believe every hunting trip should be treated as a once-in-a-lifetime experience; let us make yours a great one.

Our high rate of repeat clients says it all!

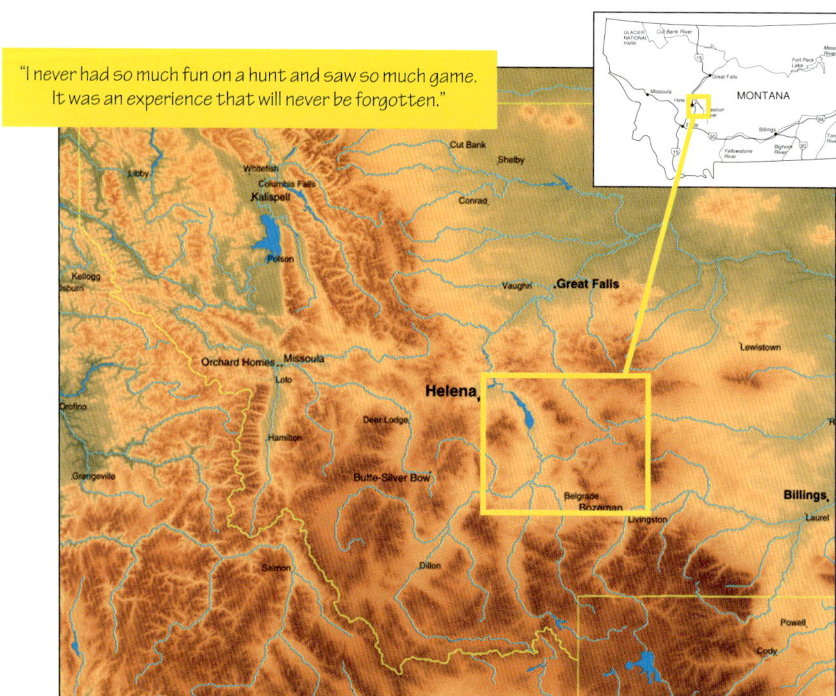

Rick Wemple Outfitting

Rick Wemple

1765 Pleasant View Drive • Victor, MT 59875
ph. (406) 642-3869

Extreme hunts for trophies, that is what I offer. Only the fit need apply.

I will hunt my hunters until they either kill or quit. I provide all the equipment, food and transportation of hunters and game. I offer hunts that are physical and in any kind of weather. Overnight in the woods, on the trail of trophies means we take what we need to survive and continue hunting the next day.

I have spent my entire life in Western Montana and in the Selway Wilderness area. I started guiding in 1974 and got my outfitter license in 1982. All I know is hunting, guiding and outfitting. I know my area and game. I try as hard as possible to get my clients the game they seek. My hunts are tailored and priced for the hunters who are looking for true fair chase trophies in Idaho or Montana.

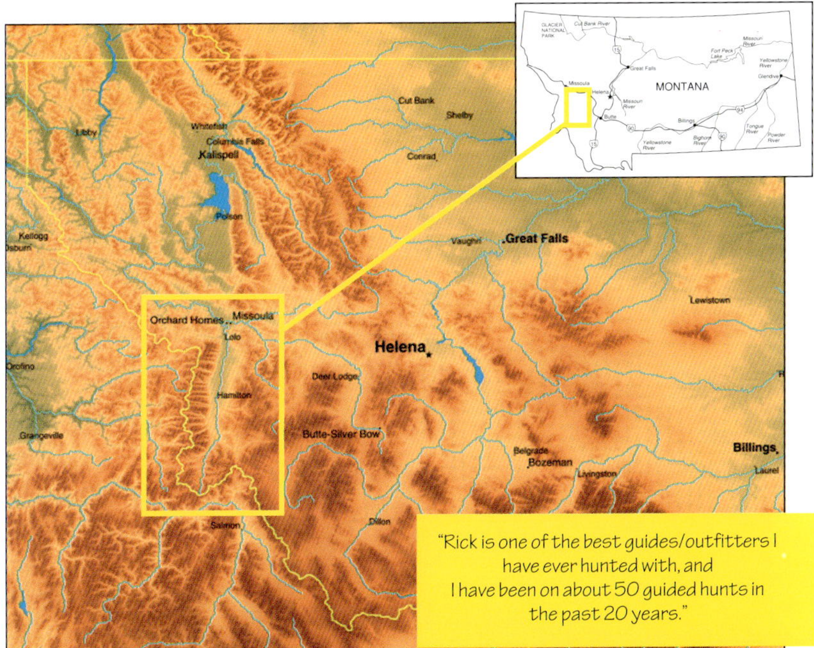

R.L. Sourbrine Outfitters and Sons

Richard Sourbrine

2019 Meridian Road • Victor, MT 59875
ph. (406) 642-3251

Family-owned and operated with 16 years in the business.

We offer hunts for elk, deer, black bear, goat, sheep, moose in the heart of the Bitteroot Valley. Day hunts, accommodations included. Guest cabin. Four hunters to a party.

Private ground and national forest land. Transportation to and from Missoula airport included. Local meat processing available.

Some of the best taxidermists are in the area. Clients should make reservations January of the year they want to hunt. Private ranch available for elk, mule deer and buffalo.

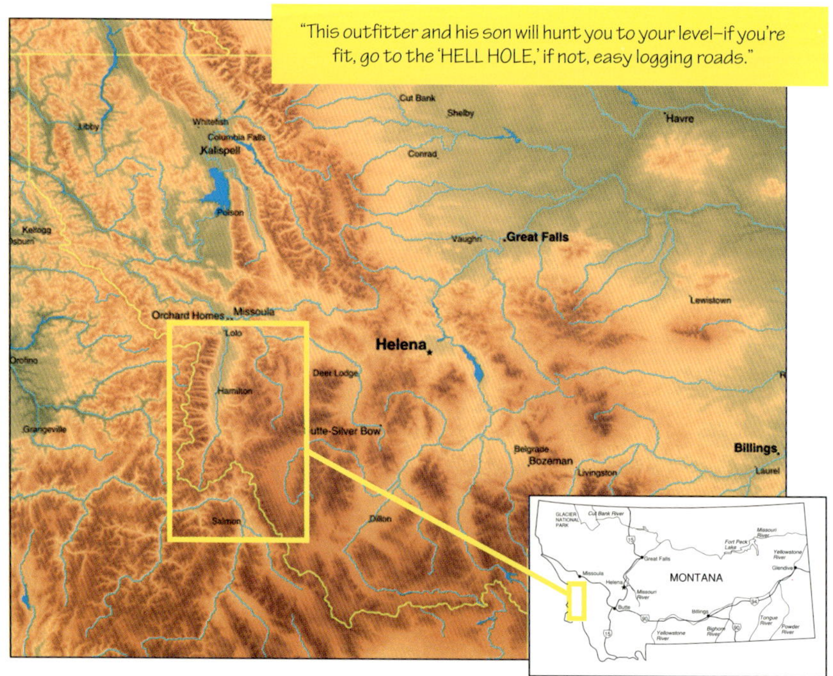

S&W Outfitters

Brad Hanzel

PO Box 160520 • Big Sky, MT 59716
ph.(406) 995-2658 • Sept.-Nov (406) 538-4864

Howard Seymour

PO Box 76 • Sandy Creek, NY 13145
ph.(315) 387-5806 • Sept.-Nov. (406) 538-4864

S&W Outfitters was established in 1981 with the idea of treating clients with the same consideration and respect that we would like if in their place.

Our goal is to provide our clients with a first-class hunt and very memorable experience, to be remembered long after their trophy mounts have faded and lost their splendor.

We would like to express our gratitude for your interest in S&W Outfitters.

We hope you will join us next year for the hunt of your dreams.

Please call us to discuss any questions you may have about our hunts.

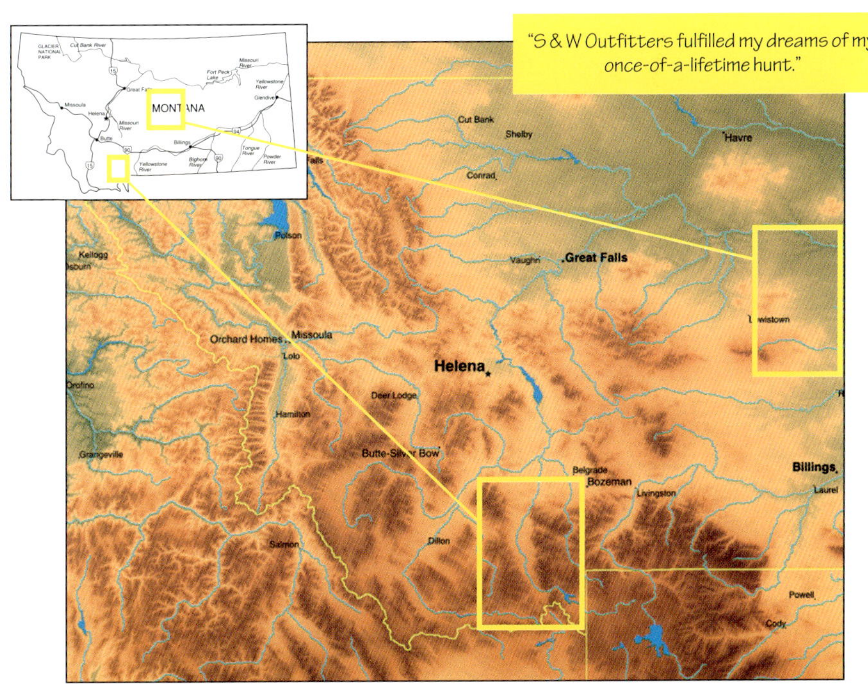

White Tail Ranch/WTR Outfitters, Inc.

Jack and Karen Hooker
520 Cooper Lake Rd. • Ovando, MT 59854
ph. (406) 793-5666 • (888) WTR-5666
email: wtroutfitters@montana.com • www.recworld.com/wtro

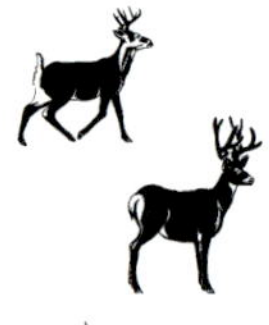

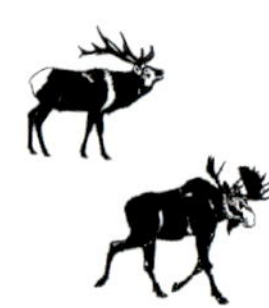

White Tail Ranch Outfitters has been specializing in summer wilderness education pack trips and big game hunting since 1940.

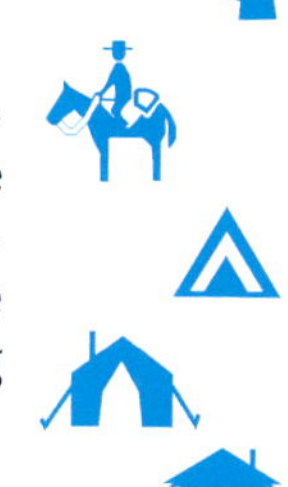

Over the years our main hunt schedule has consisted of guided parties. We provide a deluxe camp with everything furnished. We also provide outfitted drop camp service. Our camps are between 9 and 21 miles, by horse and packstring from our trailhead.

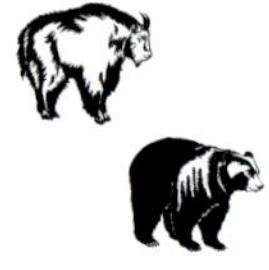

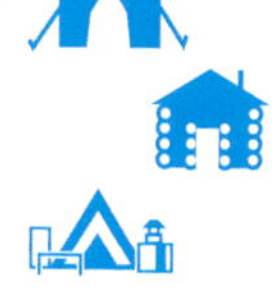

We have a high rate of success with the percentage of opportunities being even higher.

We are in Montana to service our guest from far and wide.

"These are real wonderful people with a real professional outfit."

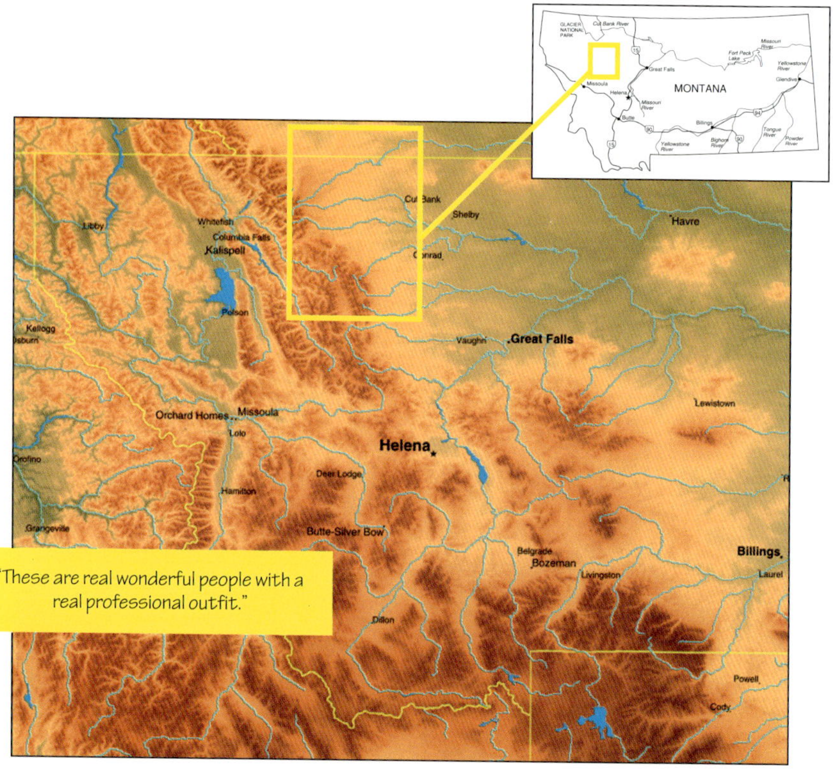

Wild West Outfitters

Michael A. Goyins

2595 York Rd. • Helena, MT 59601
ph. (406) 449-6549

Wild West Outfitters offers some of the finest elk, deer and bear hunting in the state of Montana. Specializing in elk archery hunts, our goal is to be the best at what we do.

All hunting is done on private land. The animals are wild and free, each presenting a unique hunting challenge.

Wild West Outfitters offers not only memorable hunts, but also an opportunity to experience Montana's high-mountain beauty and develop friendships that will last a lifetime.

We guarantee an adventure you won't soon forget.

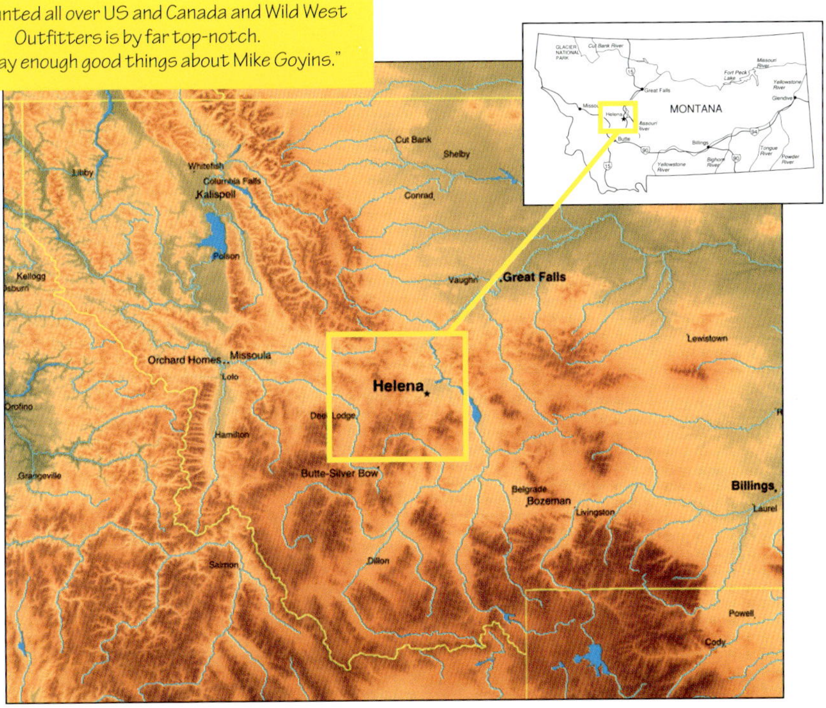

New Mexico

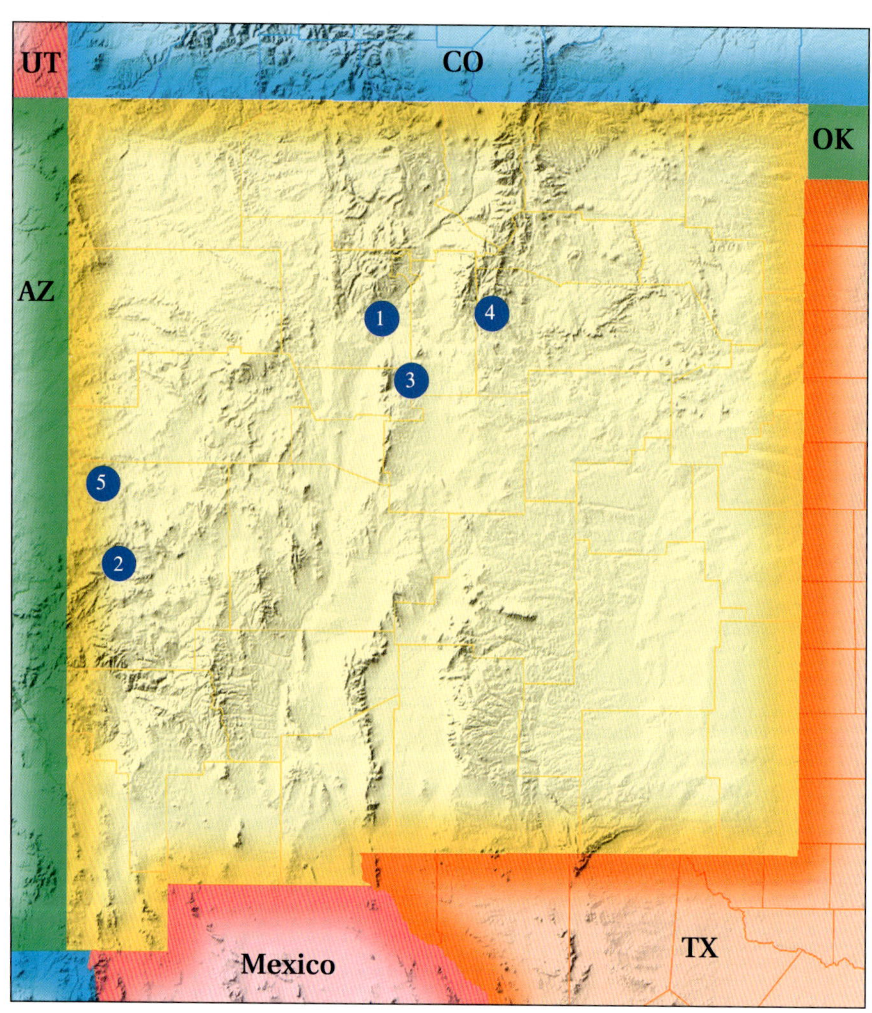

Outdoor Professionals

1. Cecil Ralston Guide & Outfitters
2. Double J Outfitters
3. Pusch Ridge Outfitters
4. Terrero General Store & Riding Stables
5. Timberline Outfitters

Useful information for the state of

New Mexico

State and Federal Agencies

New Mexico Game & Fish Dept.
Villagra Building
Santa Fe, NM 87503
phone: (505) 827-7975

Forest Service
Southwestern Region
Federal Building
517 Gold Avenue SW
Albuquerque, NM 87102
phone: (505) 842-3300
TTY: (505) 842-3898

Carson National Forest
phone: (505) 758-6200

Cibola National Forest
phone / TTY: (505) 761-4650

Gila National Forest
phone: (505) 388-8201

Lincoln National Forest
phone: (505) 434-7200

Santa Fe National Forest
phone: (505) 438-7840

Bureau of Land Management
New Mexico State Office
1474 Rodeo Road
Santa Fe, NM 87505

Mailing Address:
P.O. Box 27115
Santa Fe, NM 87502-0115

Information Number: (505) 438-7400
fax: (505) 438-7435
Public Lands Information Center (PLIC):
(505) 438-7542

Office Hours: 7:45 a.m. - 4:30 p.m.

National Parks

Carlsbad Caverns National Park
3225 National Parks Hwy.
Carlsbad, NM 88220
phone: (505) 785-2232

Associations, Publications, etc.

New Mexico Council of Outfitters &
Guides, Inc.
160 Washington SE #75
Albuquerque, NM 87108
phone: (505) 764-2670

License and Report Requirements

• State requires that Hunting Outfitters be licensed.

• State requires the filing of an "Annual Report of Outfitters' Clients" for hunting only.

• "Use Permit" required for Fish and River Outfitters using BLM and Forest Service lands. They are not required to file any reports.

Cecil Ralston Guides and Outfitters

Cecil and Jodie Ralston

P.O. Box 1510 • Bernalillo, NM 87004
ph. (505) 867-2191

We offer hunts for mule deer, black bear, mountain lion, antelope, javelina, Barbary sheep, bighorn sheep, oryx and ibex.

We have a two-on-one guide system, while arrangements can be made for anyone who requests a personal guide. We hunt both public and private land, using horses, 4x4 trucks, fourrunners, and some on foot. Most all of our hunts are based on five days; some are longer and some are two to three days. Our camps are comfortable, wall tents, lights, cots and stoves. All meals are good and wholesome, family style home cooked meals all you can eat. We cater to our hunters as much as possible.

Our main interest is you. If you drive out you can come here to our house, or the ones that fly can be picked up at the Albuquerque International Airport.

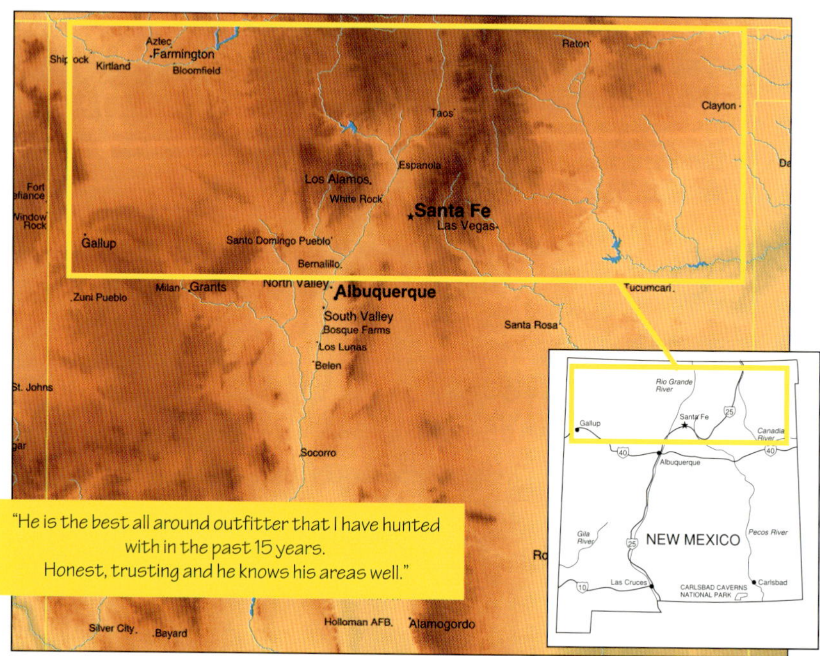

Double J Outfitters

Jimmy and Jenny Heap

P.O. Box 990 • St. Johns, AZ 85936
phone: 520-337-2339 • 505-533-6515

We are Jimmy and Jenny Heap of the NH Ranch. We are small and intend to stay that way.

We specialize in friendly, personalized service and superior quality hunts. This is not your run-of-the-mill hunting trip.

We have been in business three years and offer private landowner and public hunts. Our guides have been screened and especially   selected. Ratios are one-to-one.

Prices are fair with no "extra" fees. We promise wonderful food, hot showers and warm and comfortable beds. Our services are unsurpassed.

Come hunt with Double J and get set for good times, great hunting and big bulls.

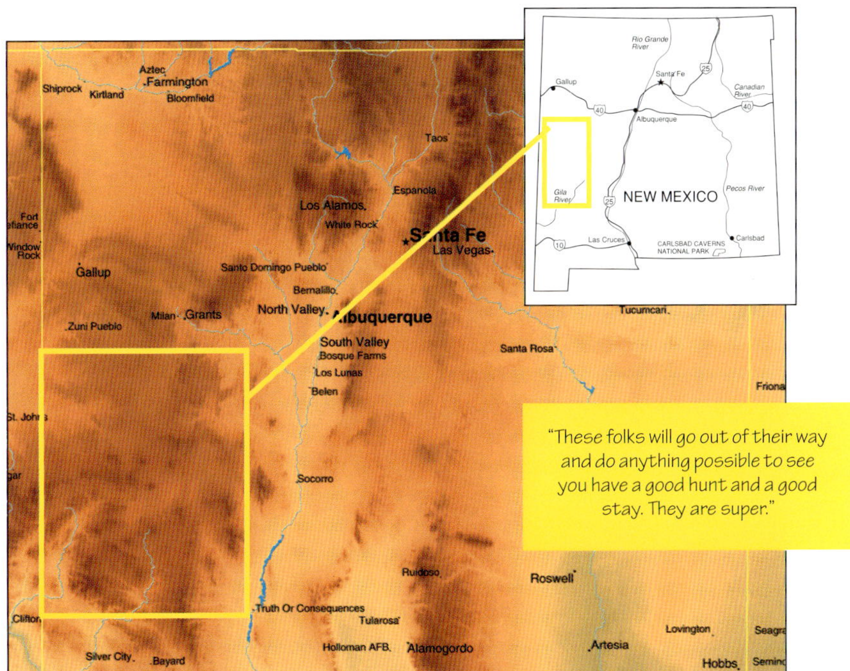

"These folks will go out of their way and do anything possible to see you have a good hunt and a good stay. They are super."

Pusch Ridge Outfitters

Kirk and Roxane Kelso

10260 N. Hardage Lane • Oro Valley, AZ 85737
ph. (520) 544-0954

Kirk Kelso of Pusch Ridge Outfitters is noted as one of the premiere outfitters in the country for Coues' whitetail. The hunt area has produced some of the top heads in Boone & Crockett, SCI, Pope & Young and the Longhunter record books.

Hunters take a number of bucks scoring more than 100 points every year, including a buck in 1995 that scored 121-plus points!

They are also noted for their success hunting antelope, elk, desert bighorn sheep, Rocky Mountain, desert mule deer and javelina. They hunt antelope and elk in both Arizona and New Mexico with high scoring trophies taken every year.

Their New Mexico antelope lease produced four Boone & Crockett heads out of eight hunts in 1995!

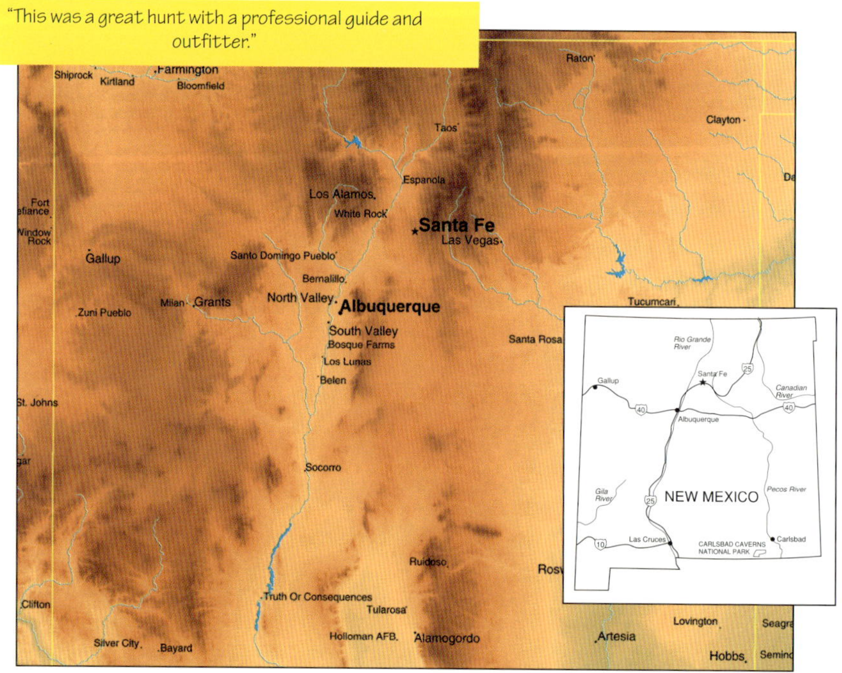

Terrero General Store and Riding Stables, Inc.

Huie Ley

P.O. Box 12 • Terrero, NM 87573
ph. (505) 757-6193

This is a family-owned and operated business. My father, Happy Ley, started the business working for a guest ranch at Cowels in 1927.

We outfit into the Santa Fe National Forest and the Pecos Wilderness. The Wilderness encompasses approximately 230,000 acres which, in turn, is surrounded by approximately 300,000 acres of national forest. The Pecos Wilderness is located in both Carson and Santa Fe national forests. Elevation runs from 6,000 feet in the foothills to over 13,000 feet at the summit of Truchas Peak.

Primitive conditions are preserved for the use, enjoyment and spiritual refreshment of the people. For more information give us a call.

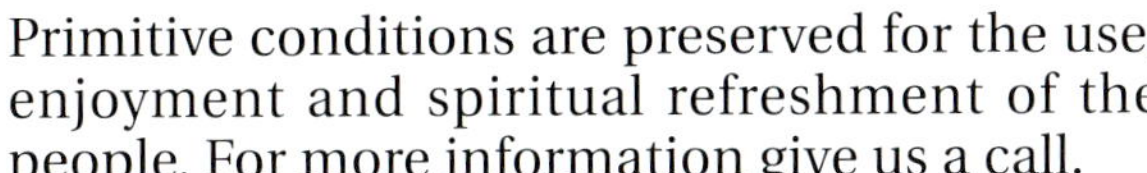

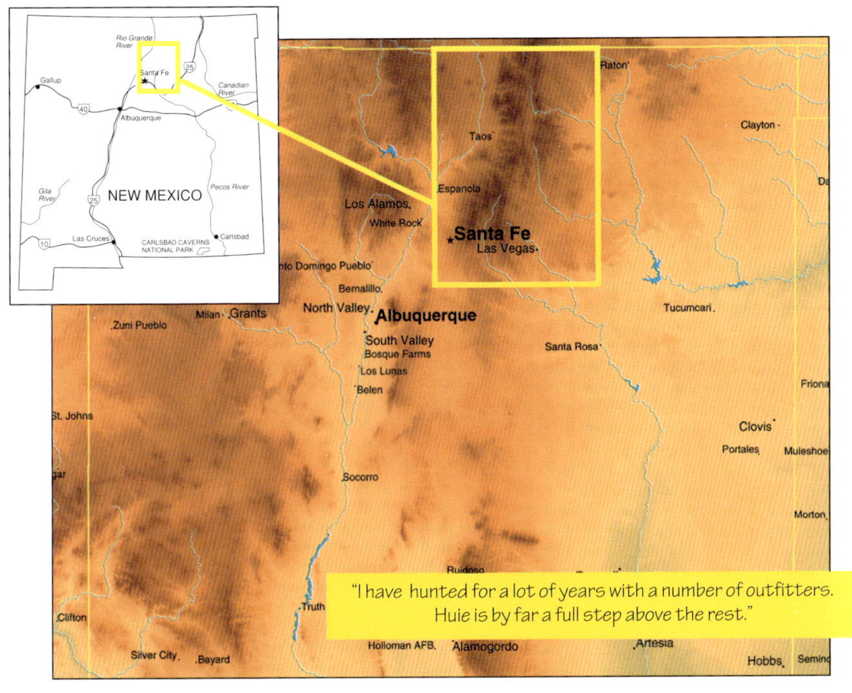

Timberline Outfitters

Perry and Brenda Hunsaker

19831 E. Warner Rd. • Higley, AZ 85236
ph. (505) 547-2413 and (602) 988-9654

I am Perry Hunsaker, the owner of Timberline Outfitters. All clients are guided one-on-one unless otherwise arranged. Our guides are seasoned hunters and know what it takes to get you on your trophy.

It's no secret that the areas we hunt are considered by most experts the best in North America. New Mexico and Arizona are the hot spots. If your dream is a trophy-class animal, you are in the right spot. Our meals consist of roast beef and turkey with all the trimmings. You will not go hungry in this camp. Camps range from ranch headquarters with individually-heated rooms to comfortable tent camps.

We want your trip to be a success. You have my word we will do our best so that your stay will be a memorable and rewarding experience.

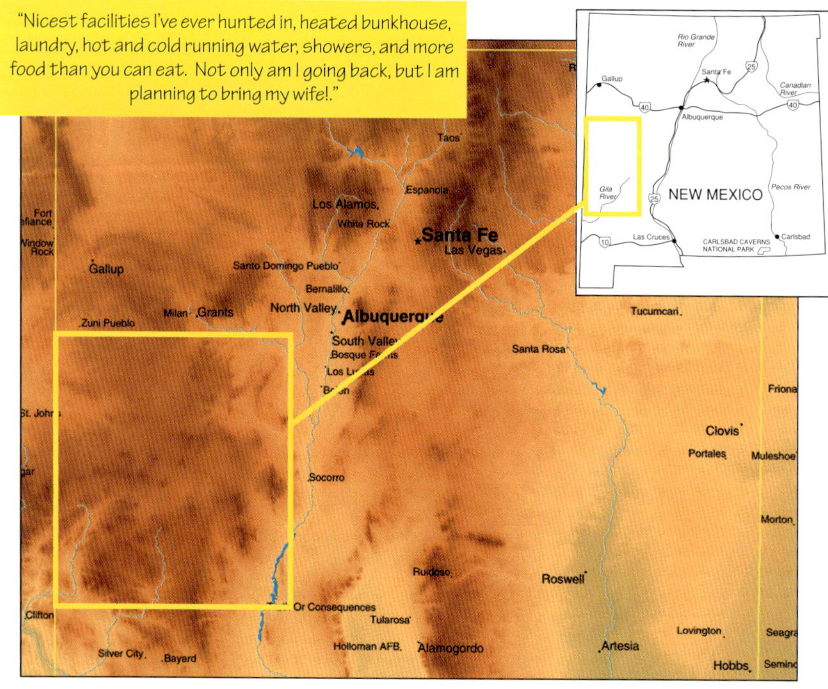

Oregon

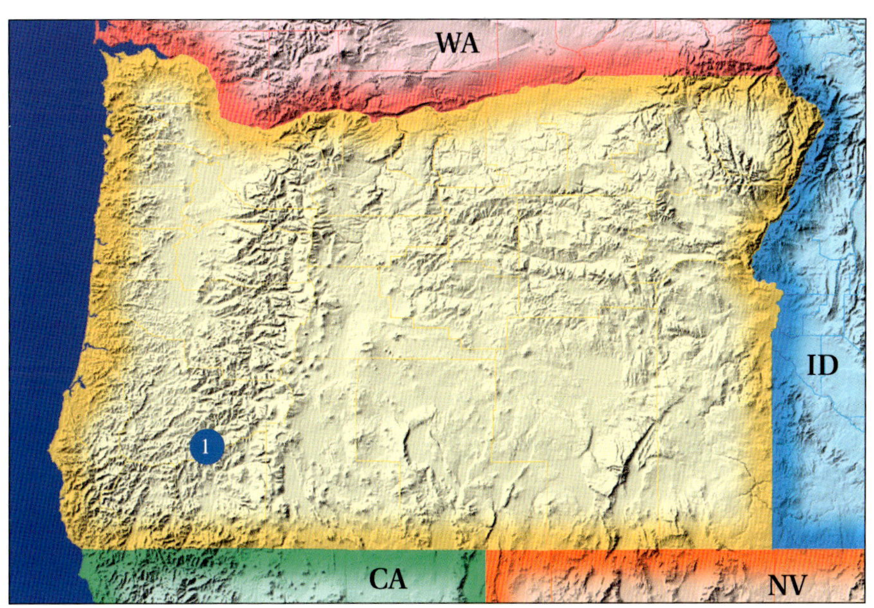

Outdoor Professionals

1 Arrow Five Outfitters

Useful information for the state of
Oregon

State and Federal Agencies

Oregon Dept. of Fish & Wildlife
PO Box 59
Portland, OR 97207
phone: (503) 872-5268

Oregon Marine Board
435 Commercial St. NE
Salem, OR 97310
phone: (503) 373-1405
or (503) 378-8587

Columbia River Gorge Ntl. Scenic Area
902 Wasco Avenue, Ste 200
Hood River, OR 97031
phone: (541) 386-2333

Forest Service
Pacific Northwest Region
333 SW 1st Avenue
PO Box 3623
Portland, OR 97208
phone: (503) 326-2971
TTY: (503) 326-6448

Rogue River National Forest
phone: (541) 858-2200

Siskiyou National Forest
phone: (541) 471-6500

Siuslaw National Forest
phone: (541) 750-7000

Umpqua National Forest
phone: (541) 72-6601

Winema National Forest
phone: (541) 883-6714

Bureau of Land Management
Oregon State Office
(serves Washington also)
Information Access Center
1515 SW 5th Ave.
P.O. Box 2965
Portland, OR 97208-2965
phone: (503) 952-6001
or (503) 952-Plus Extension
fax: (503) 952-6308
Tdd: (503) 952-6372

Electronic mail
General Information:
or912mb@or.blm.gov
Webmaster: orwww@or.blm.gov

National Parks

Crater Lake National Park
PO Box 7
Crater Lake, OR 97604
phone: (541) 594-2211

Associations, Publications, etc.

Oregon Outdoor Association
PO Box 9486
Bend, OR 97708-9486
phone: (541) 382-9758

License and Report Requirements

• State requires licensing of Outdoor Professionals.

• State requires a "Year-End Report" for Outfitters hunting and/or fishing on BLM
   land.

Arrow Five Outfitters

Jim Schaafsma

Star Route 1 • Box 64A, Zenia, CA 95595
ph./fax (707) 923-9633

Arrow Five Outfitters has been owned and operated by Jim Schaafsma since 1981.

Roosevelt elk and blacktail deer hunts are provided in Medford and Myrtle Creek, Oregon and Coues' deer hunts in Sonora, Mexico.

Our blacktail deer, black bear, boar and turkey hunts are in both Humboldt and Trinity counties, located in Northern California.

We have a 100% success on our rifle deer hunts in California and 98% success on archery.

Our hunts offer an excellent chance for record book SCI, P&Y, and B&C.

All our hunts are one-to-one fully guided on private property.

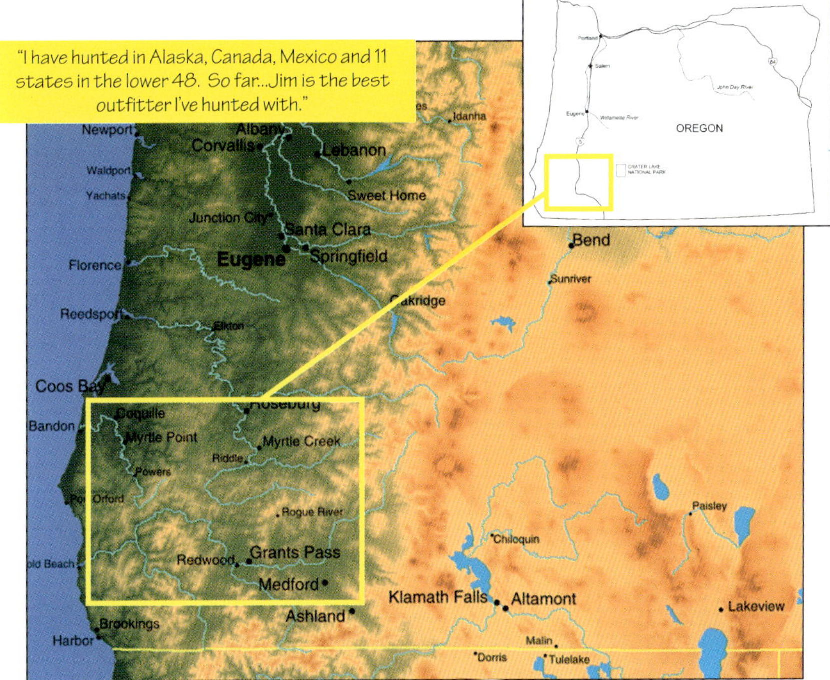

Texas

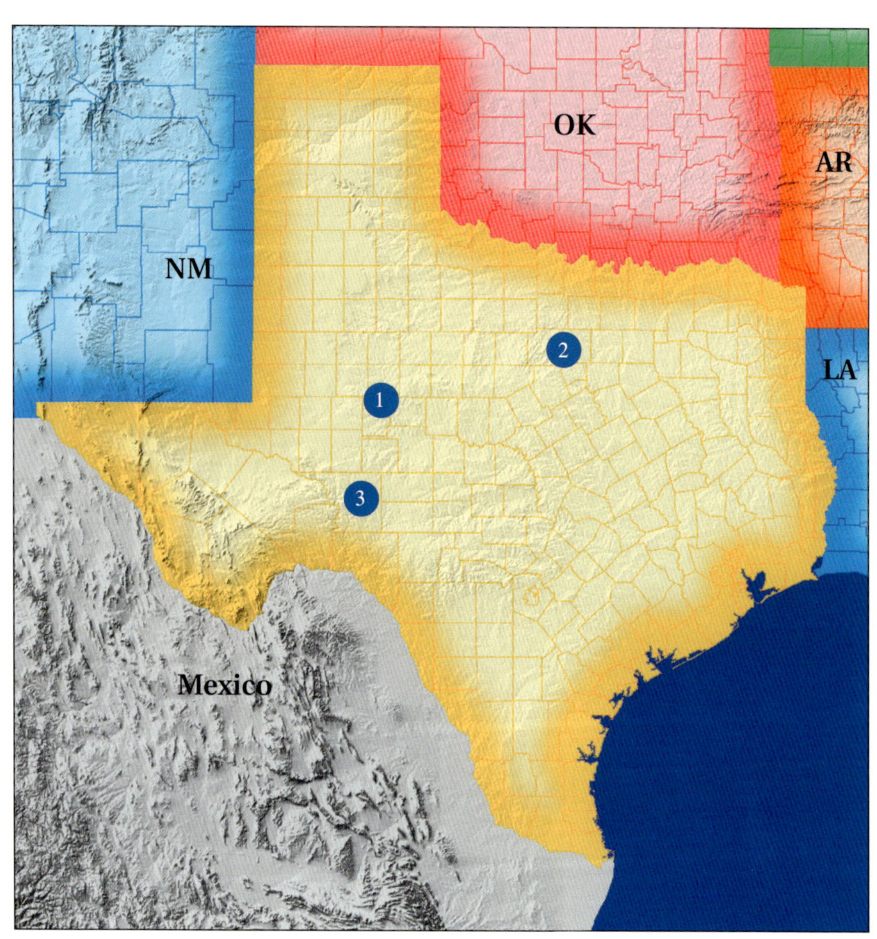

Outdoor Professionals

1 Adobe Lodge Hunting Camp
2 Cutbirth Cattle Company, Ltd.
3 Lone Star Trail Outfitters

Texas

State and Federal Agencies

Texas Parks & Wildlife Dept.
4200 Smith School Rd.
Austin, TX 78744
phone: (512) 389-4800

Texas Tourism
phone: (800) 888-8839

Forest Service
Southern Region
1720 Peachtree Road NW
Atlanta, GA 30367
phone: (404) 347-4177
TTY: (404) 347-4278

Angelina-Davy Crockett-Sabine-Sam
Houston National Forests
Homer Garrison Federal Bldg.
701 North First Street
Lufkin, TX 75901
phone / TTY: (409) 639-8501

Bureau of Land Management
New Mexico State Office
(serves Kansas, Oklahoma & Texas)
Street Address:
1474 Rodeo Road
Santa Fe, NM 87505

Mailing Address:
P.O. Box 27115
Santa Fe, NM 87502-0115

Information Number: (505) 438-7400
fax: (505) 438-7435
Public Lands Information Center (PLIC):
(505) 438-7542

Office Hours: 7:45 a.m. - 4:30 p.m.

National Parks

Big Bend National Park
Big Bend National Park, TX 79834
phone: (915) 477-2251

Guadalupe Mountains National Park
HC 60, Box 400
Salt Flat, TX 79847-9400
phone: (915) 828-3351

Associations, Publications, etc.

Texas Wildlife Association
1635 NE Loop 410, Ste 108
San Antonio, TX 78209
phone: (512) 826-2904
phone: (800) 460-5494

Wildlife Society Texas Chapter
PO Box 207 Lampasas, TX 76550
phone: (512) 556-4172

International Professional Hunters'
Association
PO Box 17444
San Antonio, TX 78217
phone: (512) 824-7506

License and Report Requirements

• State does not license or register Outfitters, Guides, or Lodges.

• State has no report requirements.

Adobe Lodge Hunting Camp

Skipper Duncan

9660 US 67 South • San Angelo, TX 76904
ph. (915) 942-8040

Rookies and world-class veterans alike consistently describe their Adobe Lodge experience in the same way — their most FUN hunt ever.

You will hunt 100% private land which has a long tradition of super whitetail and turkey hunting.

Nationally known since 1987 as a hunting operation that has it all — good accommodations, good food, superb hunting and a well-run camp.

Adobe Lodge Hunting Camp enjoys a high level of repeat clients and word-of-mouth referrals.

Booking a hunt is easy — just call Skipper Duncan.

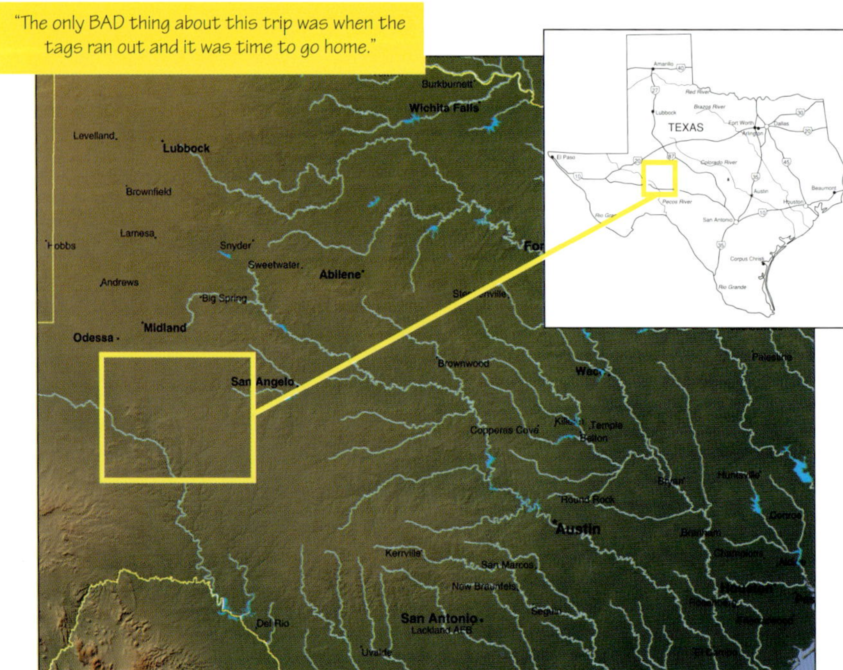

Cutbirth Cattle Co., Ltd.

Treldon and Minnie Cutbirth

Rt. 3 Box 178 • Brownwood, TX 76801
ph. (915) 646-3356

Cutbirth Cattle Co., Ltd. offers some of the best whitetail deer hunts in Texas.

Our operation is 2,400 acres of family-owned land that is located 10 miles south of Brownwood on FM Rd. 45.

The terrain is rolling live Oak hills with some post oak, Spanish oak, mesquite and cedar.

We use ground blinds and elevated blinds that are located at natural crossings, at corn feeder pens and at grain fields.

We also do still-hunting and rattling.

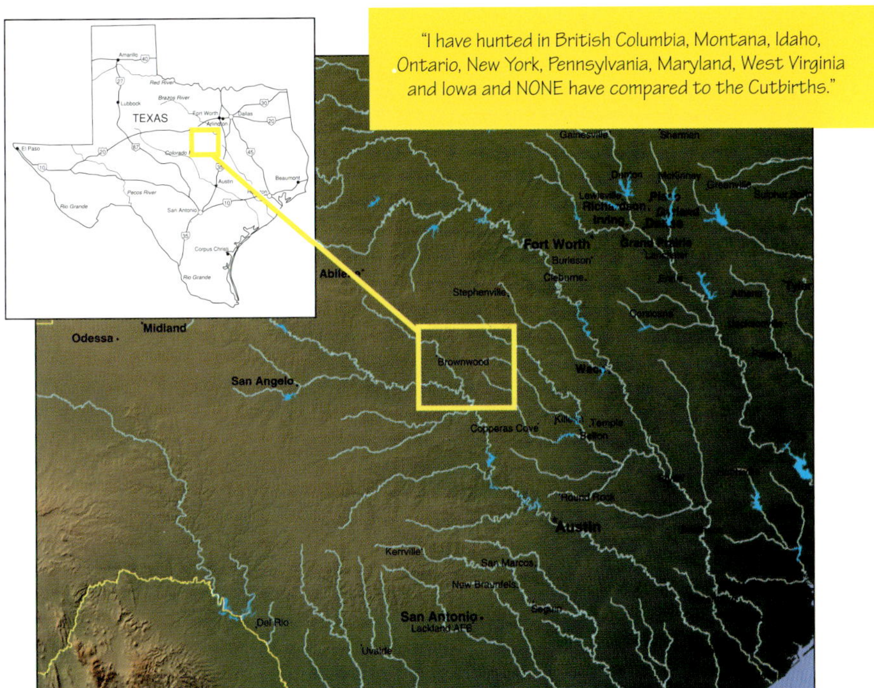

Lone Star Trail Outfitters

Trent Huckaby

PO Box 268 • Fort Stockton, TX 79735
Res. (915) 336-5028 • Ranch ph. (915) 395-2243 • Lodge ph. (915) 395-2936

This West Texas hunt offers a five-day combination whitetail and desert mule deer package hunt on four ranches that total 50,000 acres.

Our country is a beauty of the Southwest with its rolling hills, deep canyons, brushy creek beds, and wide-open spaces.

We do not allow the hunter to "rough it." Three meals are prepared daily and a four-bedroom, two-bath lodge is provided for accommodations. Meat is quartered, heads are caped, and a large walk-in cooler is provided for storage.

With our intensive management program and the opportunity to hunt assorted exotic animals we provide the hunter with a hunt of a lifetime.

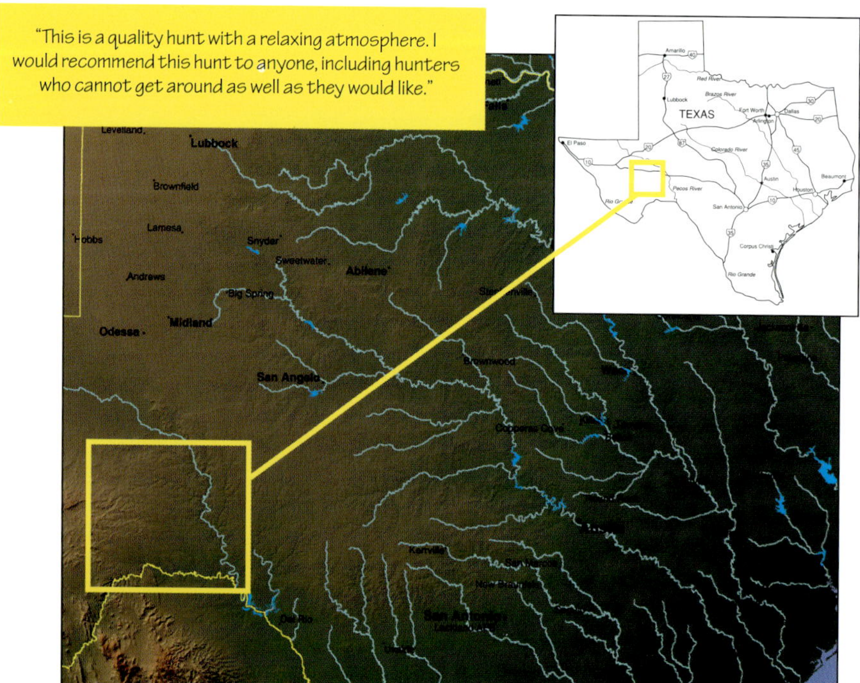

Wisconsin

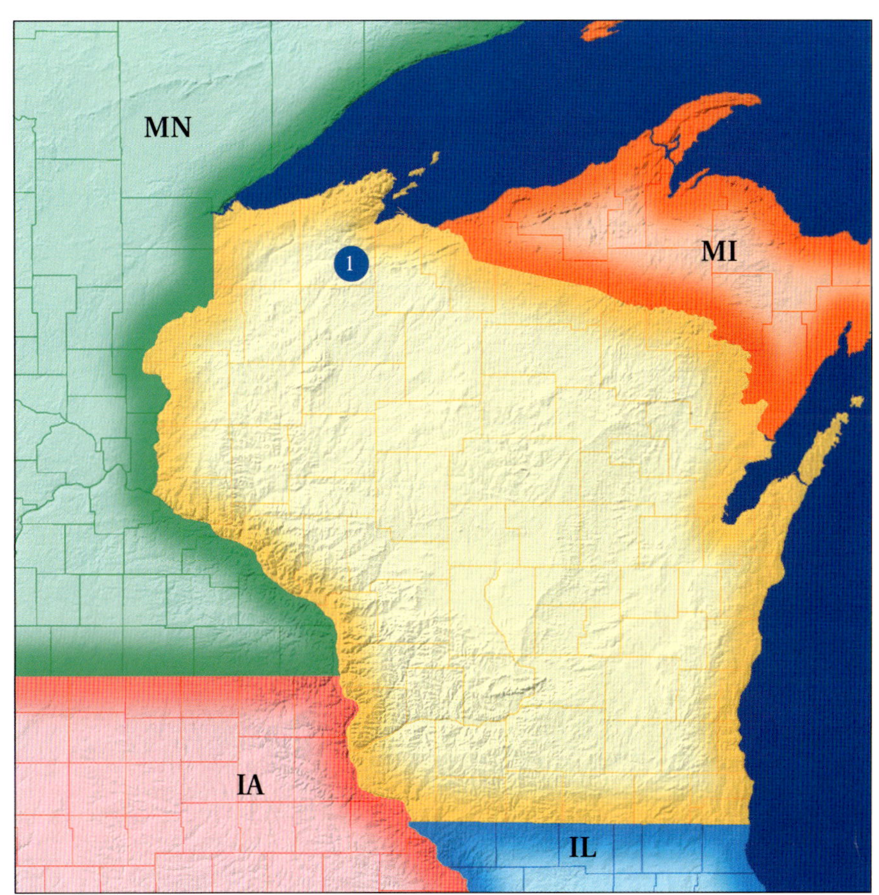

Outdoor Professionals

1 Chip's Call of the Wild Guide Service

Wisconsin

State and Federal Agencies

Wisconsin Dept. of Natural Resources
Box 7921
Madison, WI 53707
phone: (608) 266-2621

Department of Tourism
phone: (608) 266-2161

Forest Service
Eastern Region
310 W. Wisconsin Ave., Room 500
Milwaukee, WI 53203
phone: (414) 297-3946
TTY: (414) 297-3507

Chequamegon National Forest
1170 4th Avenue South
Park Falls, WI 54552
phone: (715) 762-2461
TTY: (715) 762-5701

Nicolet National Forest
Federal Building
68 South Stevens Street
Rhinelander, WI 54501
phone: (715) 362-1300

Bureau of Land Management
Eastern States
7450 Boston Boulevard
Springfield, Virginia 22153
phone: (703) 440-1660
or (703) 440- Plus Extension
fax: (703) 440-1599

Office Hours: 8:00 a.m. - 4:30 p.m.

Eastern States
Milwaukee District Office
310 W. Wisconsin Ave., Suite 450
(P.O. Box 631 53201-0631)
Milwaukee, Wisconsin 53203
phone: (414) 97-4450
fax: (414) 297-4409

Associations, Publications, etc.

Whitetails Unlimited, Inc.
PO Box 720
Rhode Island Street
Sturgeon Bay, WI 54235
phone: (414) 743-6777
fax: (414) 743-4658

Recreation Guide to Wisconsin

License and Report Requirements

• State does not license or register Outfitters, Guides or Lodges.

• State has no report requirements.

Chip's Call of the Wild Guide Service

Erroll "Chip" Mosser

N 3267 Highway 17 • Merrill, WI 54452

ph. (715) 536-5784

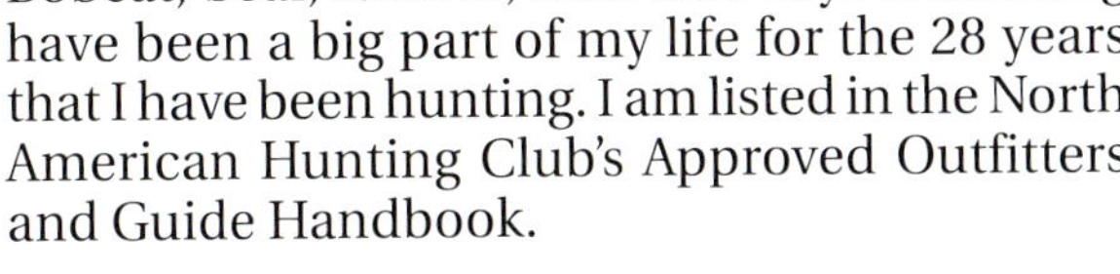

Bobcat, bear, racoon, deer and coyote hunting have been a big part of my life for the 28 years that I have been hunting. I am listed in the North American Hunting Club's Approved Outfitters and Guide Handbook.

These hunts are very exciting and I enjoy sharing them with others. I guide on familiar land and use techniques which have been acquired throughout my hunting career. In addition to my memberships in the Wildlife Legislative Fund of America and National Rifle Association, I write a monthly article for the Wisconsin Bear Hunters Association in Full Cry Magazine.

If you wish to contact my past clients, hunters' addresses and phone numbers are available for your reference. I hope that you will join me in the beautiful northwoods to watch my hounds in action.

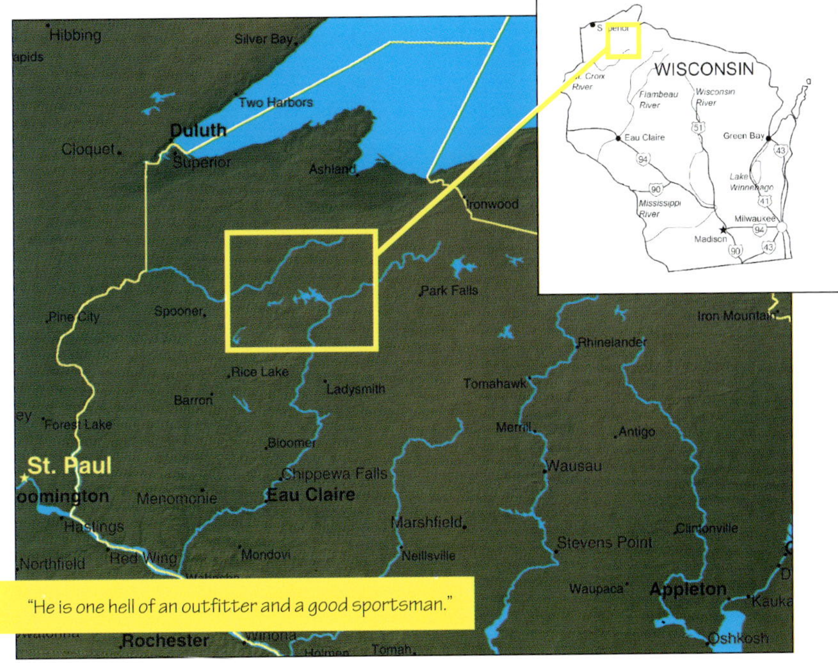

Wyoming

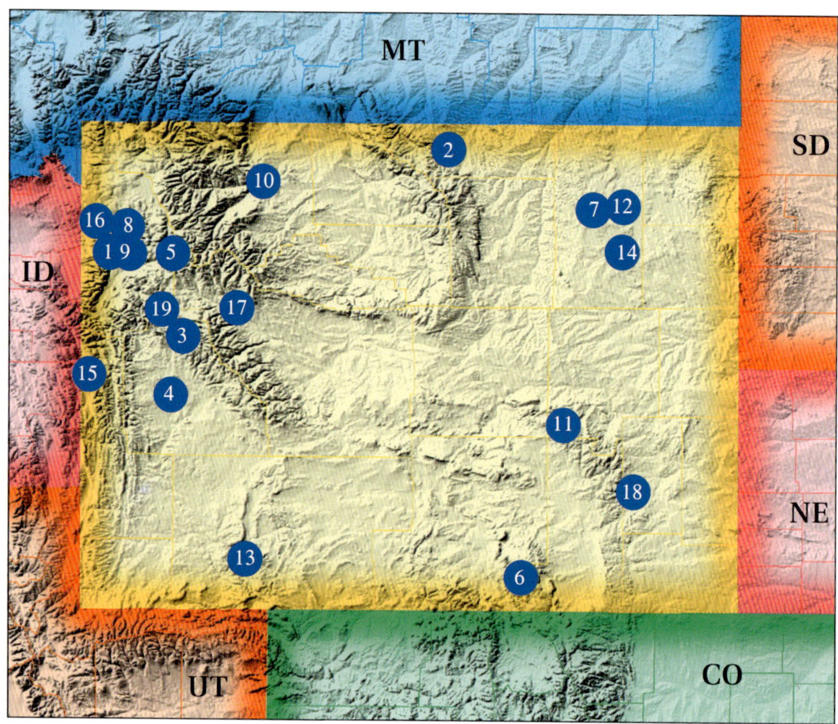

Outdoor Professionals

1. Arrowhead Outfitters
2. Beaver Creek Outfitters
3. Boulder Lake Lodge
4. Darby Mountain Outfitters
5. Darwin Ranch
6. Grand & Sierra Outfitters
7. Greer Outfitters
8. Hidden Basin Outfitters
9. John Henry Lee Outfitters
10. K Bar Z Guest Ranch & Out.
11. Lightning Creek Ranch
12. P Cross Bar Ranch
13. Red Desert Adventures
14. River S Enterprises
15. Swift Creek Outfitters
16. T Lazy T Outfitters
17. Triangle C Ranch
18. Twin Pine Ranch
19. Western Wyoming Trophy Hunts

Useful information for the state of

Wyoming

State and Federal Agencies

Wyoming Dept. of Commerce
Board of Outfitters
1750 Westland Rd.
Cheyenne, WY 82002
(800) 264-0981
phone: (307) 777-5323
fax: (307) 777-6715

Wyoming Game & Fish Dept.
5400 Bishop Blvd.
Cheyenne, WY 82002
phone: (307) 777-4601

Forest Service
Intermountain Region
Federal Building
324 25th Street
Ogden, UT 84401-2310
phone: (801) 625-5306
TTY: (801) 625-5307

Bridger-Teton National Forests
Forest Service Building
340 North Cache
PO Box 1888
Jackson, WY 83001
phone: (307) 739-5500
TTY: (307) 739-5064

Bureau of Land Management
Wyoming State Office
(serves Nebraska also)
Information Access Center
5353 Yellowstone

P.O. Box 1828
Cheyenne, WY 82003
phone: (307) 775-6BLM or 6256
fax: (307) 775-6082
Office Hours: 7:45 a.m. - 4:30 p.m.

National Parks

Grand Teton National Park
PO Drawer 170
Moose, WY 83012
phone: (307) 739-3610

Yellowstone National Park
PO Box 168
Yellowstone National Park, WY 82190
phone: (307) 344-7381

Associations, Publications, etc.

Wyoming Outfitters & Guides Assoc.
PO Box 2284
239 Yellowstone Ave., Suite C
Cody, WY 82414
phone: (307) 527-7453
fax: (307) 587-8633

Jackson Hole Outfitters & Guide Association
850 W. Broadway
Jackson Hole, WY 83001
phone: (307) 734-9025

Foundation for North American Wild Sheep
720 Allen Avenue
Cody, WY 82414

License and Report Requirements

• State requires licensing of Outdoor Professionals.

• State requires that Big Game Outfitters file a "Year-End Report".

• Fishing Outfitters need to get a permit to fish on BLM land.

• Outfitters and Guest/Dude Ranches must file a "Use" or "Day Report" with the Wyoming Forest Service if they Fish, Hunt or Raft on Forest Service Land.

Arrowhead Outfitters

Robert Lowe
P.O. Box 835 • Jackson Hole, WY 83001
ph. (307) 733-5223

Bobby Lowe has been guiding/outfitting in Wyoming since 1976. He takes pride being able to offer hunters a top-quality, personalized hunt.

He services a low volume of hunters to keep success and satisfaction at a maximum.

Arrowhead Outfitters operates two Bridger Wilderness area camps. Guides are friendly, experienced and knowledgeable.

Excellent mountain horses and mules accommodate even inexperienced riders. Tents, saddles and equipment are all in top shape. Game populations in the areas are some of the best in Wyoming to give you the best chance possible to take home your trophy animal. Color brochure available.

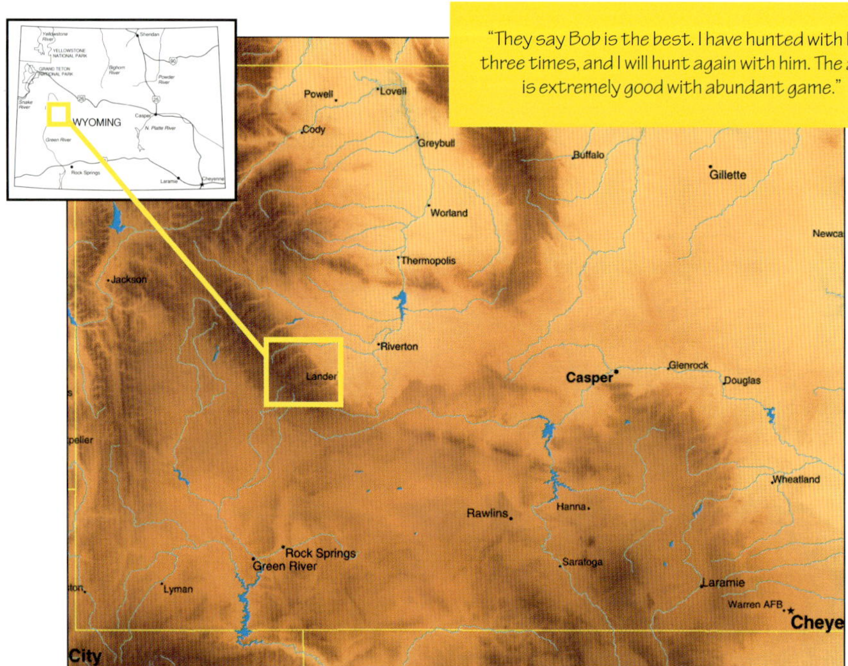

"They say Bob is the best. I have hunted with him three times, and I will hunt again with him. The area is extremely good with abundant game."

Beaver Creek Outfitters

Steve Kobold

PO Box 7337 • Sheridan, WY 82801
ph. (307) 672-0008

Beaver Creek Outfitters have been in business for 13 years. We offer elk, antelope and mule deer and, occasionally, buffalo and moose hunts. We take a limited number of hunters each year as we want to assure our customer the best possible hunt.

Over the last three years, our elk have an average score of 341, with two making the Boone and Crockett record book. All of our hunts are on private land consisting of more than 250,000 acres near historic Hole-in-the-Wall district of Northern Wyoming.

We are very close to our hunting areas so our hunters stay in a motel. We gladly accommodate handicapped hunters.

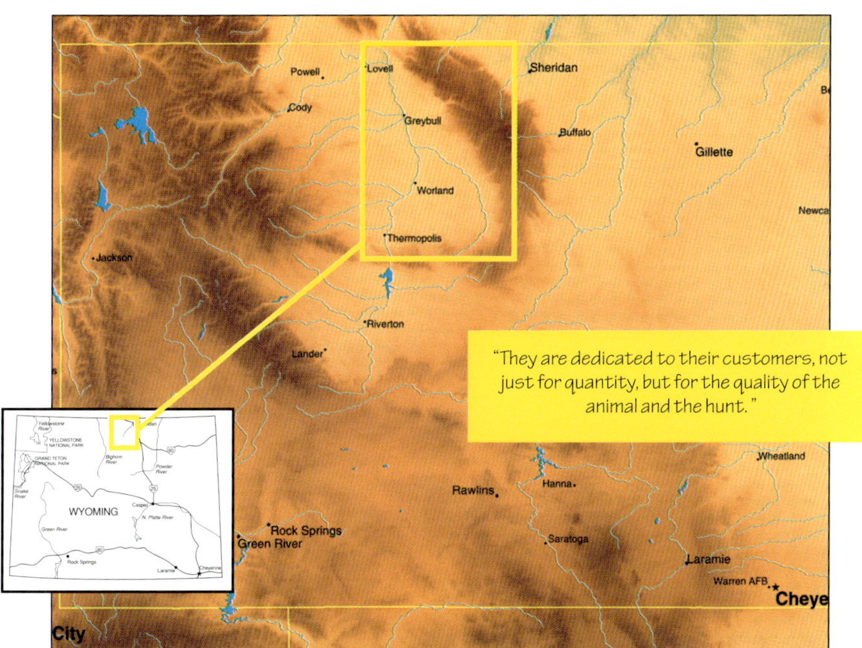

Boulder Lake Lodge

Kim Bright

Box 1100 • Pinedale, WY 82941
ph. (307) 537-5400 or (800) 788-5401

The Boulder Lake Lodge is one of the oldest and most successful hunting-outfitting operations in the state of Wyoming. It is located in the heart of the Bridger National Forest in the Wind River Range of the Rocky Mountains.

The ranch features a beautiful and rustic lodge, which serves as base camp for hunting operations.

It is located in the center of some of the state's finest big game areas. Boulder Lake Lodge not only provides the best hunting and hunting areas, but you also receive fine food, accommodations and hospitality.

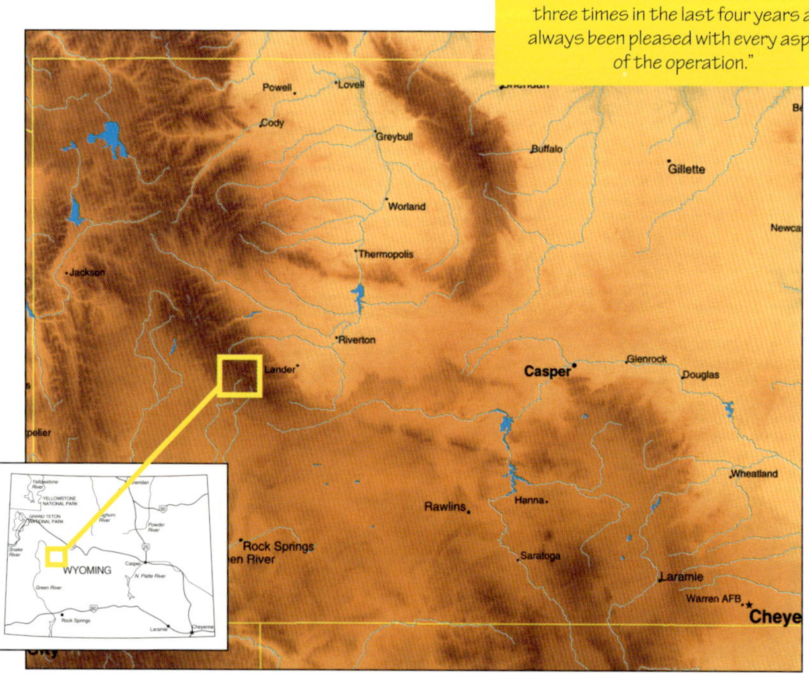

Darby Mountain Outfitters

John Harper and Chuck Thornton
Box 447 • Big Piney, WY 83113
ph. (307) 386-9220 • (307) 276-3934

Come to beautiful Wyoming and enjoy quality, first-class full service hunting at an affordable price. All hunts include food, comfortable wall tent lodging, bath tent, airport shuttle, trophy care, experienced and gentle mountain horses with tack.

Our guides (with two hunters per guide) are dedicated professionals who work hard to ensure a successful hunt. At Darby Mountain Outfitters we put forth the extra effort (experience blended with personal service) to assure you will enjoy your stay with us.

We want you to enjoy your vacation and want it to be an experience worth returning to.

We do our very best to show you success and good time.

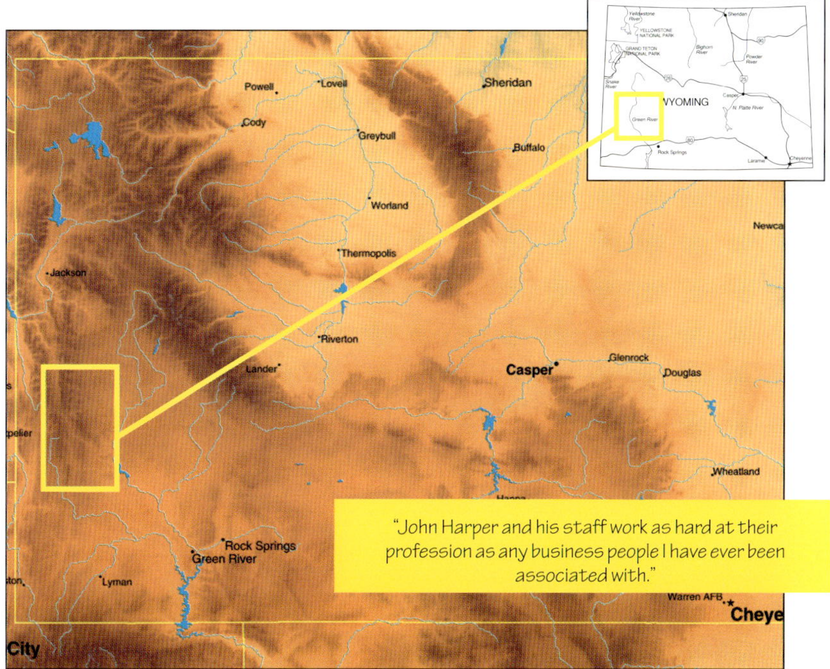

"John Harper and his staff work as hard at their profession as any business people I have ever been associated with."

Darwin Ranch

Loring Woodman
PO Box 511 • Jackson, WY 83001
ph. (307) 733-5588 • Fax (307) 739-0885

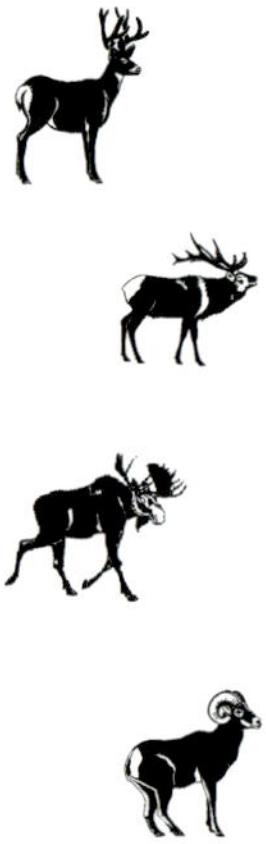

The Darwin Ranch has been catering to hunters ever since 1965 when Loring Woodman started renovating the old log cabins along the original, now obliterated, pioneer wagon track into Jackson Hole.

We are 22 miles inside the Teton National Forest and have this last, totally isolated section of the Gros Ventre River to ourselves, giving us excellent access to the area's resident elk and moose populations.

Maximum of six hunters at a time with one guide for every two hunters.

A wilderness hunt with success rates of 80-85% on elk and 100% on moose in the last 30 years.

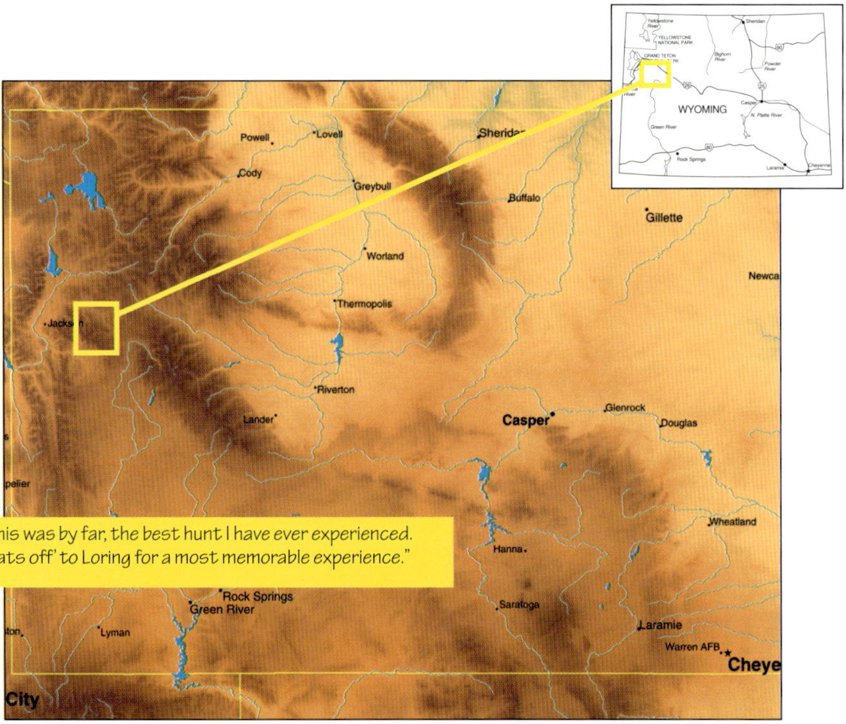

Grand and Sierra Outfitters

Glen Knotwell
PO Box 312 • Encampment, WY 82325
ph. (307) 327-5200 or (307) 327-5107

Skyler Knotwell
2200 S. 558W. • Oakley, ID 83346
ph. (208) 862-3872

Grand and Sierra Outfitters is a family owned business of forty years, that is based out of Encampment Wyoming.

We conduct our big trophy and game hunts on both private and public lands.

Hunts are from the lodge or tent camps depending on what species hunted or where you are going to hunt.

Fall-Big Game hunts Deer, Elk, Antelope and Sheep (remember that all Wyoming non-resident big game hunts are by drawing).

For more information, give us a call.

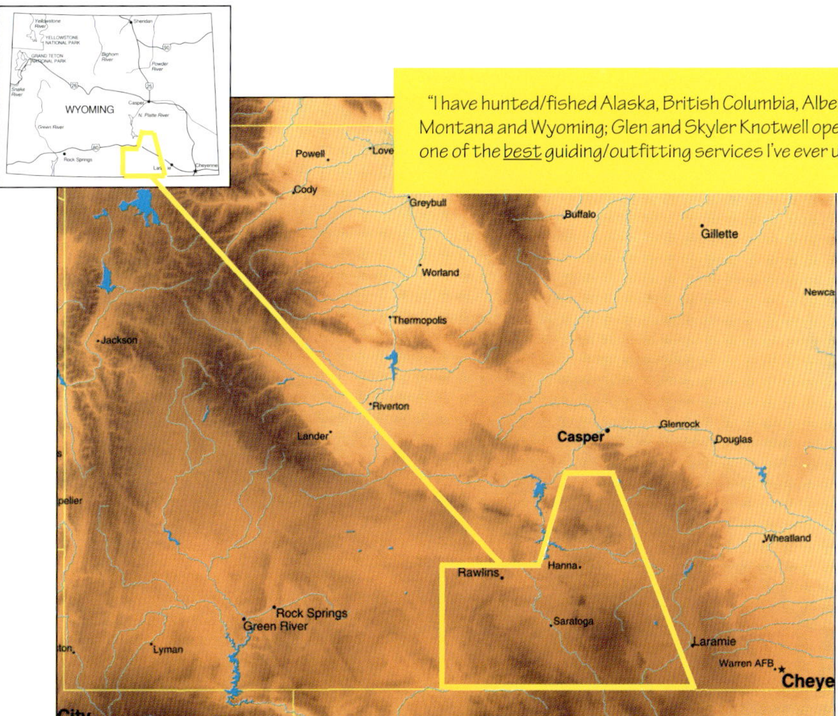

Greer Outfitters

Randy and Lora Greer

PO Box 38 • Gillette, WY 82717

ph. (307) 687-7461

Greer Outfitters is a family operation established in 1952 . We offer exceptional Trophy Antelope, Mule Deer, Whitetail and Buffalo hunting.

We control 300,000 acres of PRIVATE property taking only a select amount of hunters every season. Our success rate is excellent on both rifle and archery. We offer professionally guided hunts as well as drop camps.

Not only is our quantity exceptional but our quality as well with an average season producing Mule Deer , 24" 5x5 up to 30", Antelope ranging from 14" to 16", and Whitetail 16" 5x5 up to 20".

We cater to individual needs and parties depending on ability and circumstances. We also offer private game bird hunting, trout fishing and welcome non-hunters.

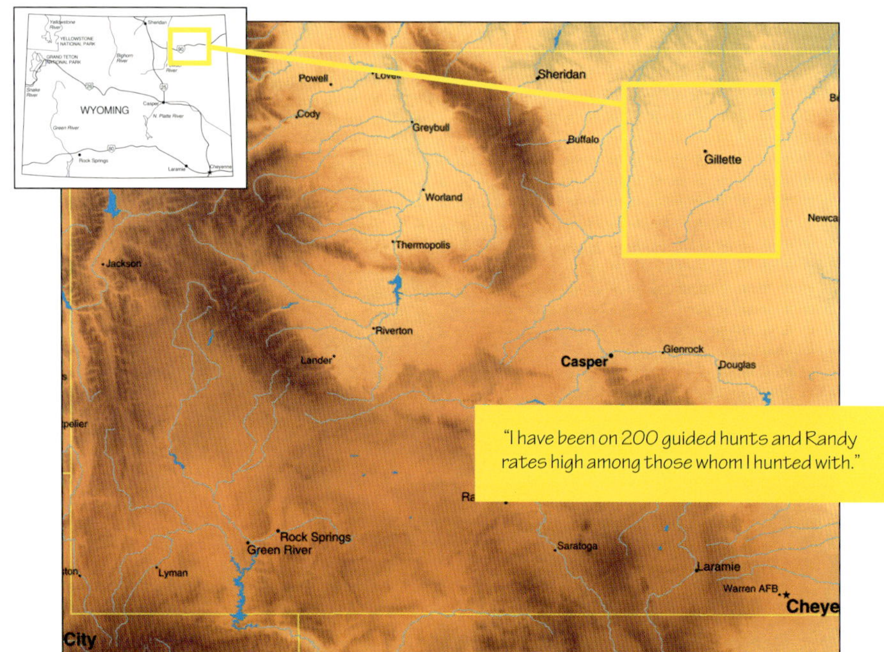

Hidden Basin Outfitters

Phillip Engler — George Engler

P.O. Box 1146 • Jackson, WY 83001

ph. business: (307) 733-7980 • residence: (307) 733-1108

Hidden Basin is owned and operated by brothers who are lifetime natives of the area. Both have been hunting guides for more than 20 years.

Our camp is accessible by 4-wheel drive which makes it a very comfortable setup.

We are located on the Wyoming/Idaho border. When Idaho's season opens, it gives us a mid-season boost, driving the game back over to our area. In the summer months, we give horseback tours, which help us keep a close eye on the game.

Our camp is full with six hunters which helps to maintain a high success rate. We have a two-hunter to one-guide policy.

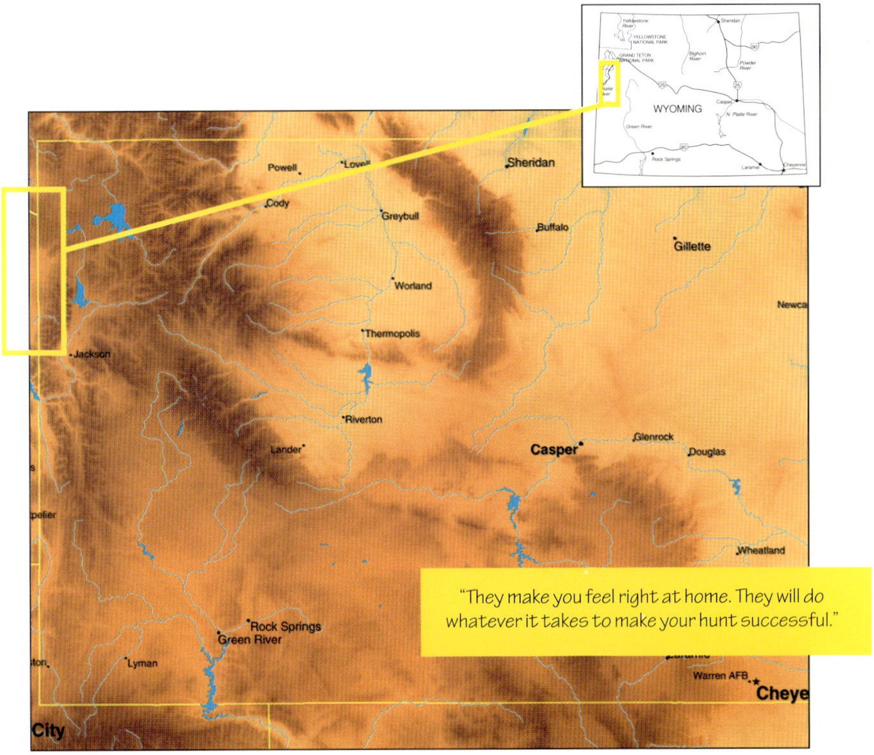

"They make you feel right at home. They will do whatever it takes to make your hunt successful."

John Henry Lee Outfitters, Inc.

John Lee
Box 8368 • Jackson, WY 83002
ph. (307) 733-9441 or (800) 3-JACKSON

Quality guided pack-in horseback hunts in the Teton Wilderness area, below Yellowstone Park. Camp is located 16 miles into the wilderness area.

Hunting for elk, deer, moose, sheep and bear. Also hunting late season elk migrating from Yellowstone Park to Jackson Hole. These hunts are based from the town of Jackson and hunting is done in the Teton National Park. Archery hunts are done in the wilderness camp. We also offer summer pack-in flyfishing trips and scenic pack trips.

Friendly professional guides, great meals, gentle horses. Outfitter has 14 years guiding experience in these areas.

For a free color brochure call or write.

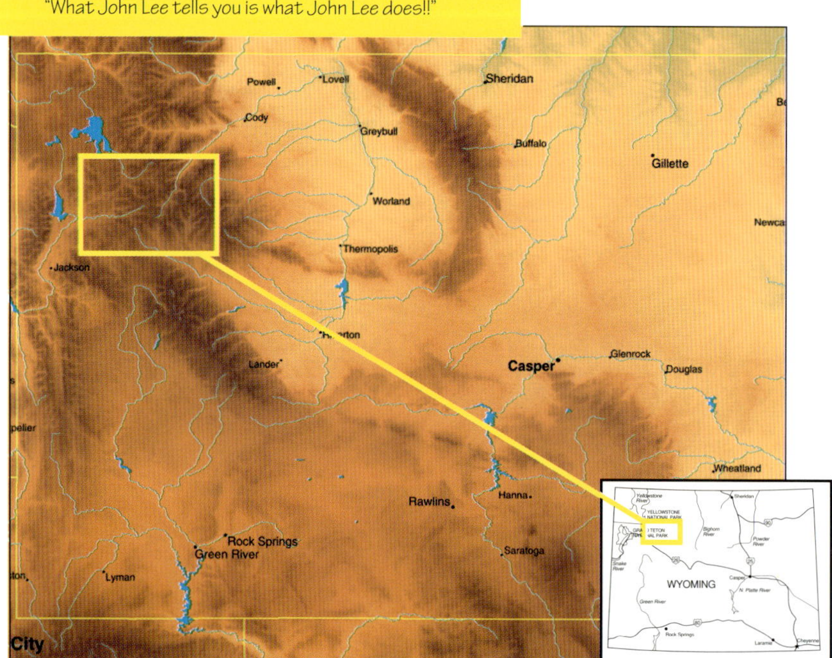

K Bar Z Guest Ranch and Outfitters

Dave Segall and Dawna Barnett
P.O. Box 2167 • Cody, WY 82414
ph. (307) 587-4410 • fax (307) 527-4605

K Bar Z is a family-owned operation nestled in the heart of the Rockies in Northwest Wyoming. They have two wilderness camps and a comfortable lodge located in the Shoshone National Forest.

Our guides specialize in providing the type of hunt you want and will work hard to find the game you are looking for. Our hunt area is located just east of Yellowstone Park and is a major migration route for elk, mule deer and bighorn sheep.

This is some of the most rugged and wild country in the lower 48 states. With the top-notch guides at the K Bar Z, you could have the opportunity to bag the big one of a lifetime.

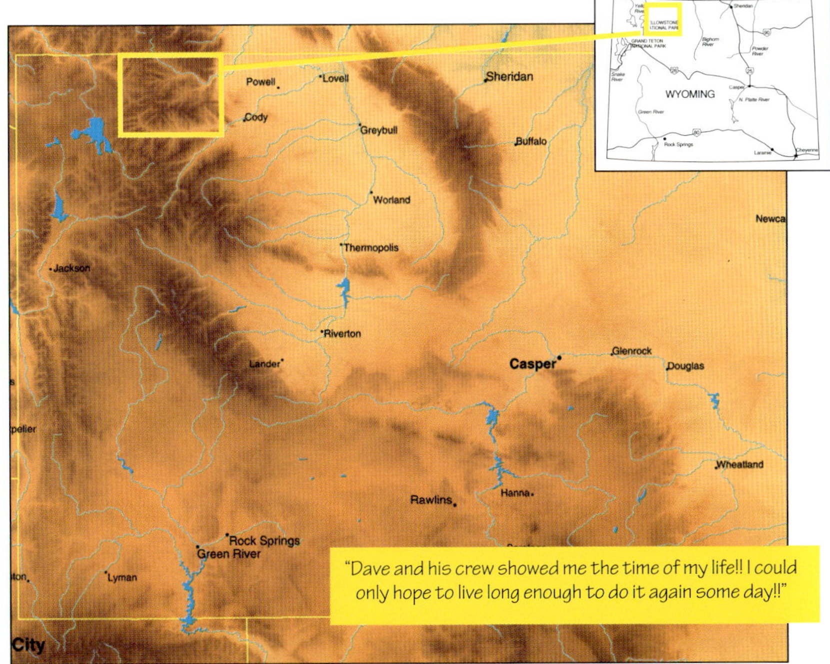

Lightning Creek Ranch

Jim Werner
1713 Walker Creek Rd. • Douglas, WY 82633
ph. (307) 358-2633

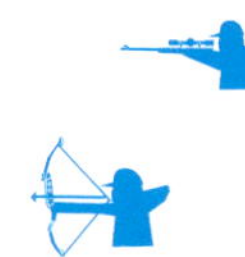

Our hunts are run on our family-owned ranches and hunters stay right in the ranch houses. With only six-to-eight hunters at a time on our 12,000-acre ranch, this makes for a good hunt with a personal touch.

The September bow hunts for antelope have averaged better than 85% success in the last ten years with 65% of the trophies making Pope and Young. Rifle deer and antelope hunts are in the first three weeks of October.

These hunts are by 4x4 spotting, then stalking by foot. Rifle elk hunts are in November.

If you are looking for a hunt with a small group and a personal touch, give us a try.

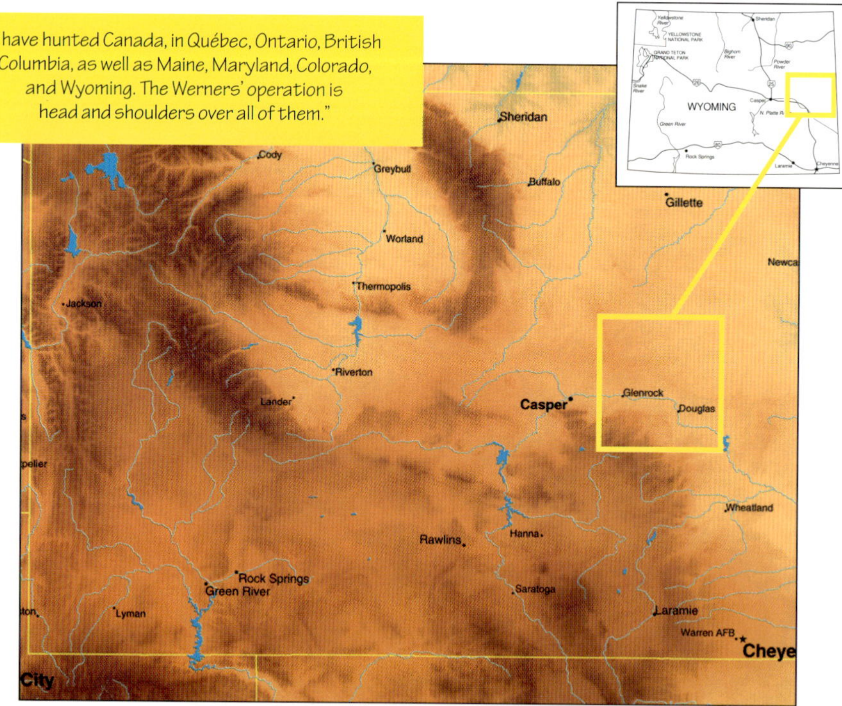

P Cross Bar Ranch

Marion and Mary Scott

8585 North Highway 14 -16 • Gillette, WY 82716
ph. (307) 682-3994 • fax (307) 682-3684

Safari Club International's 1993 North American Professional Hunter's of the Year, Marion and Mary Scott have been serving the hunting public for almost 45 years.

We work hard to make every hunt a quality experience. Our experienced guides cover 200,000 acres of private ranches located in beautiful wildlife-filled Northeast Wyoming.

Family hunts, youth hunts, handicapped hunts and alternative weapon hunts are encouraged and are very successful.

With the able help of longtime guides such as Dudley Mackey, Mick Shober and Dan Hunsaker, Marion and Mary have produced many outstanding-award winning trophies for their clients.

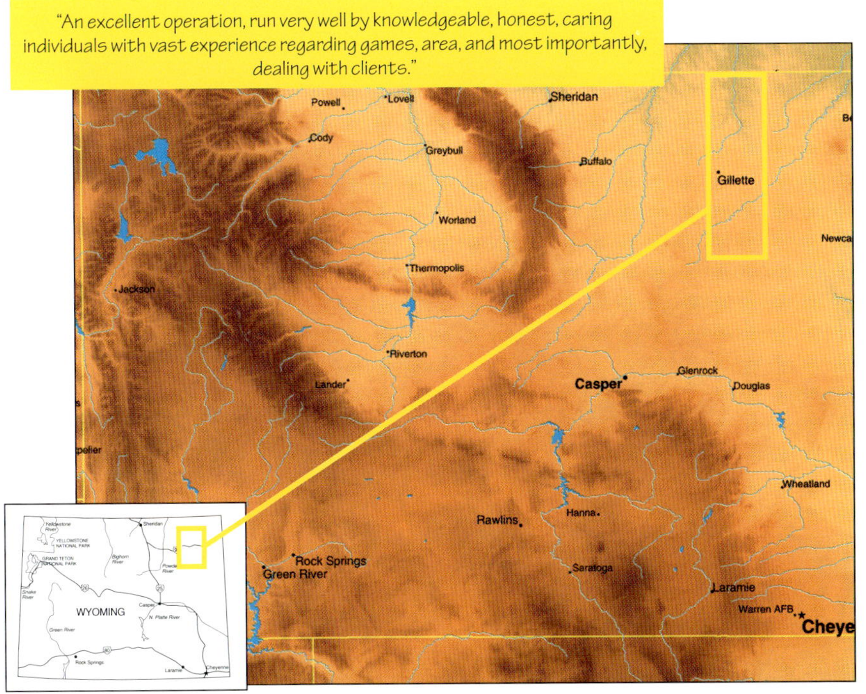

Red Desert Adventures

Vic R. Dana

PO Box 2324 • Rock Springs, WY 82902-2324
ph. (307) 362-8056

I am proud to offer the serious hunter some of the finest pronghorn antelope, mule deer, elk, and Shiras moose in Wyoming today. I feel I can provide the best hunting available because I extensively scout my areas throughout the year by taking my own personal survey.

I am a lifetime resident of the Rock Spring area of Southwest Wyoming. I have outfitted and personally hunted this area for more than 25 years.

This experience enables me to select only the best areas for my clients and give them the best possible chances for success.

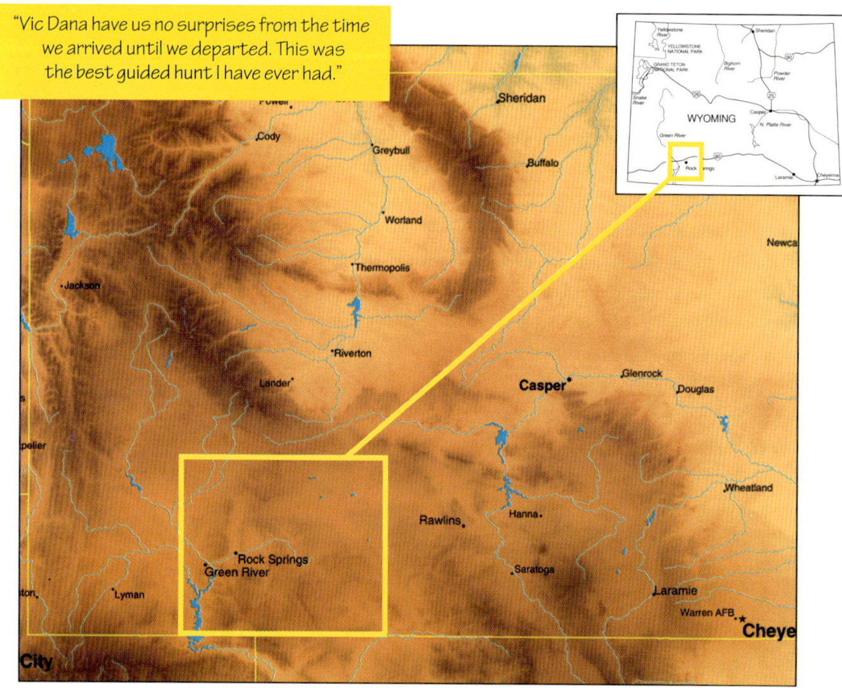

River S Enterprises

Mike and Debbie Schwiebert

P.O. Box 286 • Santa Margerita, CA 93453
ph. (805) 466-7741 • fax (805) 466-9903 • mobile (805) 440-0109

River S Enterprises is owned and operated by Mike and Debbie Schwiebert. All hunts are conducted under exclusive lease on quality, well-managed private concessions in California and Wyoming.

Meals are excellently prepared, nutritious and plentiful. Hunts are conducted with one guide for two hunters.

Guides are experienced professionals who are committed to their clients' success. Mike and Debbie are dedicated to providing the finest quality outdoor experience possible. It is their policy to provide each client with a safe, successful and enjoyable outdoor experience.

They put forth 100% to meet these objectives. "Should a client feel that we have not fulfilled our efforts, we will refund 100% of the cost."

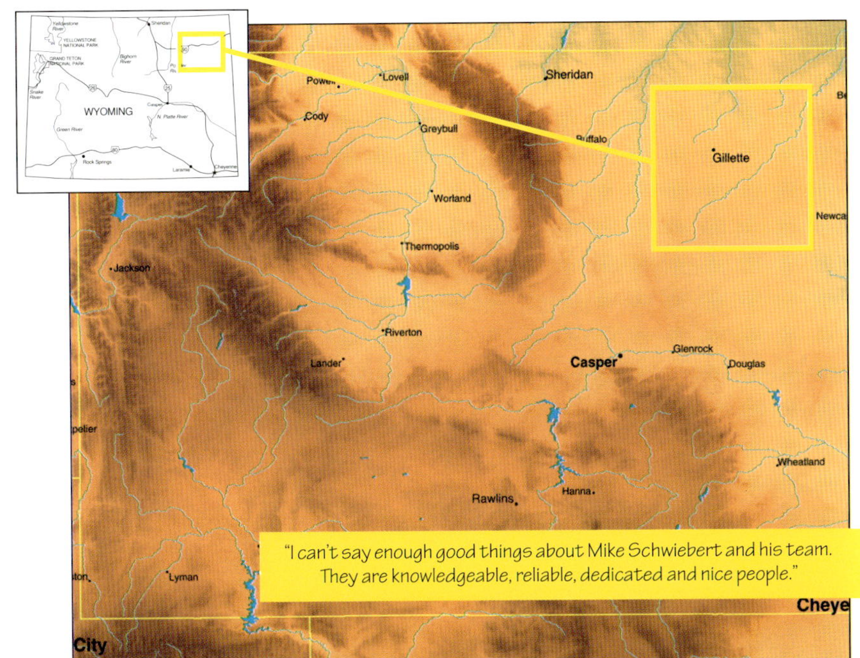

Swift Creek Outfitters

B.J. and Vicki Hill

PO Box 1472 • Afton, WY 83110

ph. (307) 886-5470

Swift Creek Outfitters is owned by the Hill family in Afton, Wyoming. Our Jackson Hole elk camp has, in the past few years, held at 26 bulls per 100 cows postseason count.

Our bull elk season starts in September in the height of the rut. Our Greys River-Salt River Range mule deer camp has held at 30 bucks per 100 does. We have taken several 30-inch-plus bucks out of this camp. We also offer November–December late snow hunts for elk and moose.

We pack high-quality binoculars and hunt hard for our clients.

Our reputation is very important to us. A free color brochure is available on request.

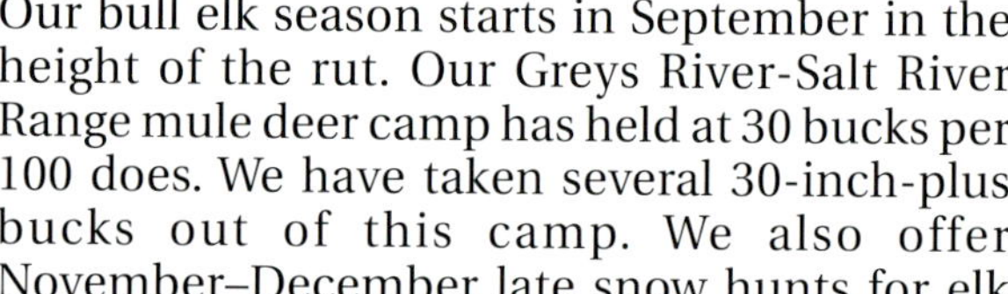

T Lazy T Outfitters

Tom Toolson Outfitters

Box 1288 • Jackson Hole, WY 83001
ph. (307) 733-4481

T Lazy T Outfitters is family-operated, and has been doing business for the past 29 years.

With approximately 80 hunting days, a maximum of 20 hunters, and one of the largest area authorizations in Northwest Wyoming (which enables us to move with the game), we are able to specialize your hunt. We spike camp for sheep and moose.

Outfitting and guiding year-round is my only business. Year-end reports furnished upon request.

Consistently high harvest is my personal guarantee for a rewarding hunt.

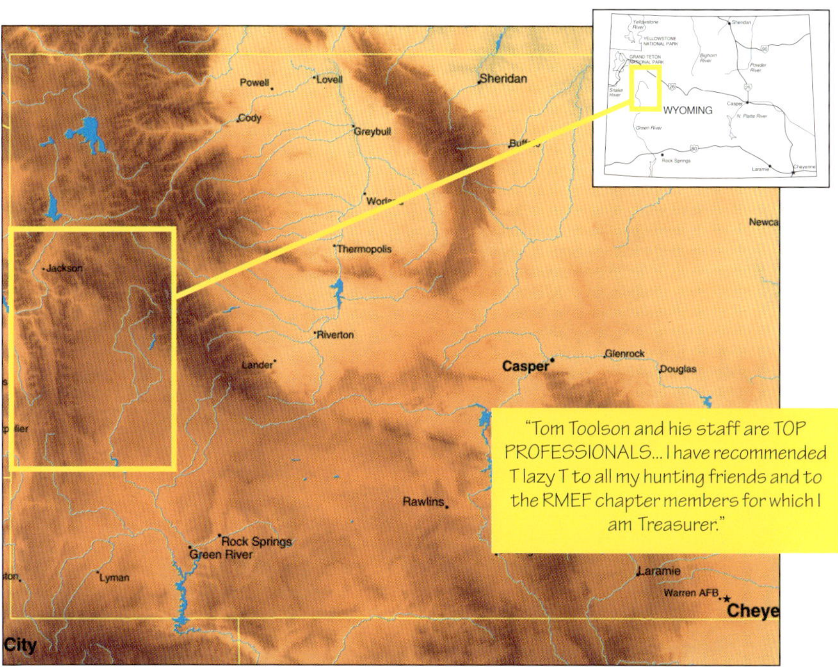

"Tom Toolson and his staff are TOP PROFESSIONALS... I have recommended T lazy T to all my hunting friends and to the RMEF chapter members for which I am Treasurer."

Triangle C Ranch

Cameron Garnick

3737 US Highway 26 • Dubois, WY 82513
ph. (307) 455-2225 • fax (307) 455-2031

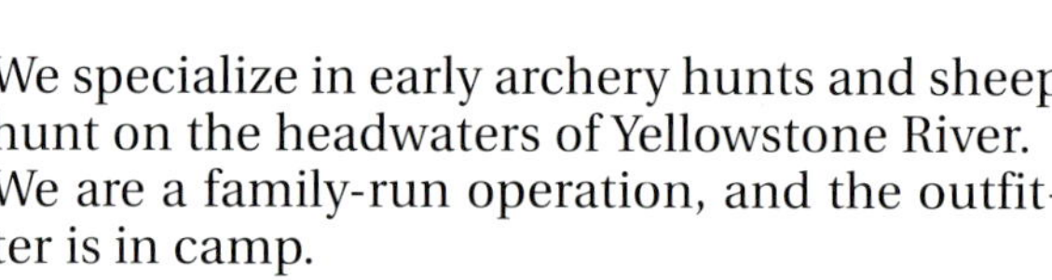

We are a fair chase outfit, hunting big bulls in Jackson Hole and Shosohone National Forest.

We specialize in early archery hunts and sheep hunt on the headwaters of Yellowstone River. We are a family-run operation, and the outfitter is in camp.

Our guides have worked with us for years and have the country in their bones.

We pride ourselves in good beds, great food and the best company.

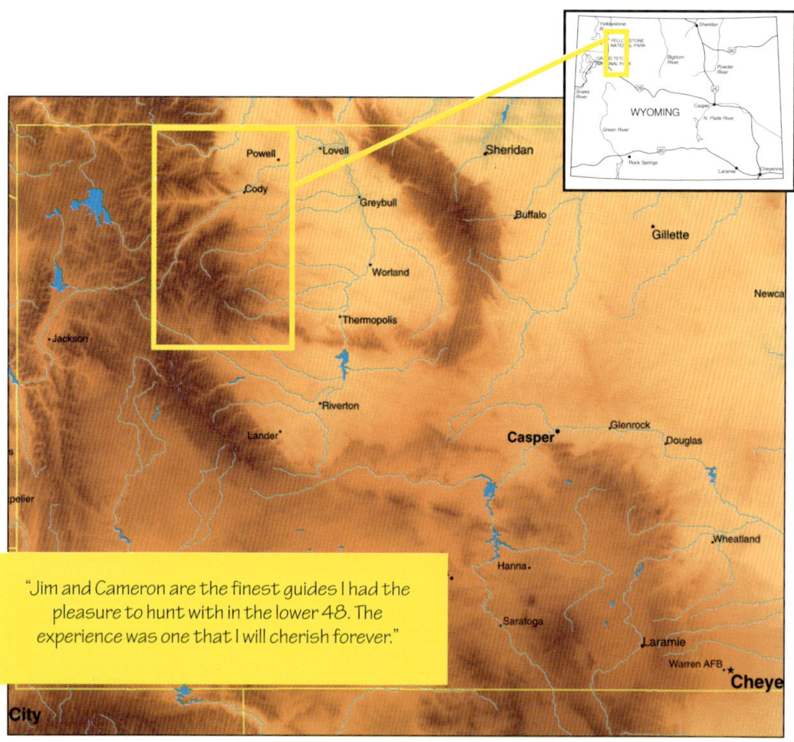

Twin Pine Ranch

Larry and Peg Gerke

644 Harris Park Rd. • Wheatland, WY 82201
ph. (307) 322-2485

The Twin Pine Ranch, a private cattle ranch in beautiful mountain surroundings, has been offering a guided hunting program since 1984 with very high hunter success rates.

As we guide on our 13,000 acres of private land only, the game is big and plentiful and you are assured of exclusive hunting, using 4-wheel drive vehicles.

We work hard to provide excellent guiding service, top-notch meals and clean comfortable lodging.

Our many returning hunters seem to feel at home where our friendly and caring program does make a difference.

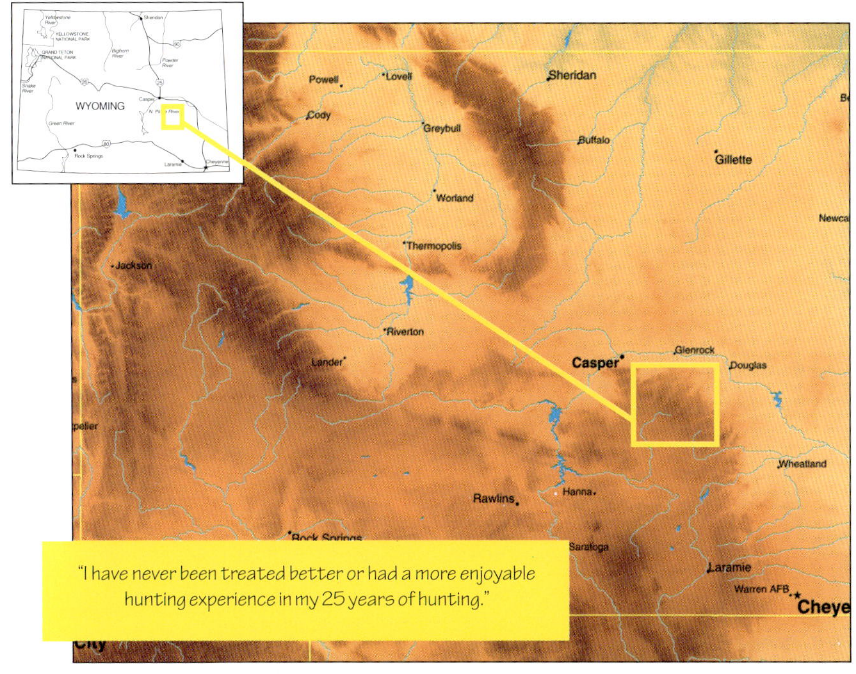

Western Wyoming Trophy Hunts

Levi Lozier

Box 100 • Cora, WY 82925
ph. (800) 822-8466 • (307) 367-4868 • fax (307) 367-6260

Come join Levi Lozier, a fifth generation outfitter, and his experienced crew for some of the finest elk, mule deer, antelope, bighorn sheep and Shiras moose hunting in Wyoming.

We are located on the west slope of the Wind River Mountain Range. First-class service and accommodations coupled with 45 years of quality hunting and excellent success are the pride of Western Wyoming Trophy Hunts.

One of only a few places in the Western U.S. where you can hunt elk with a rifle (Sept. 20) while the elk are bugling and in the heat of the rut.

Call now for more information.

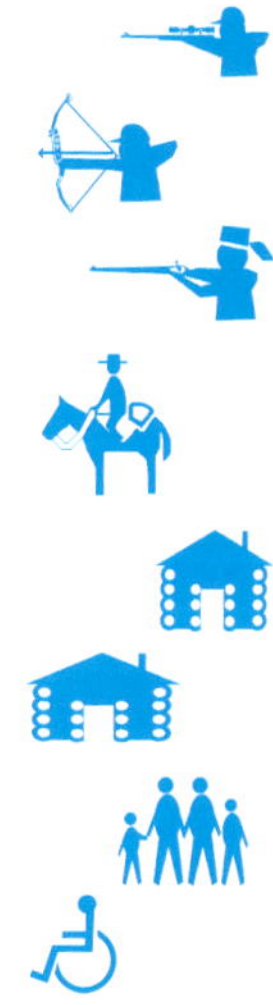

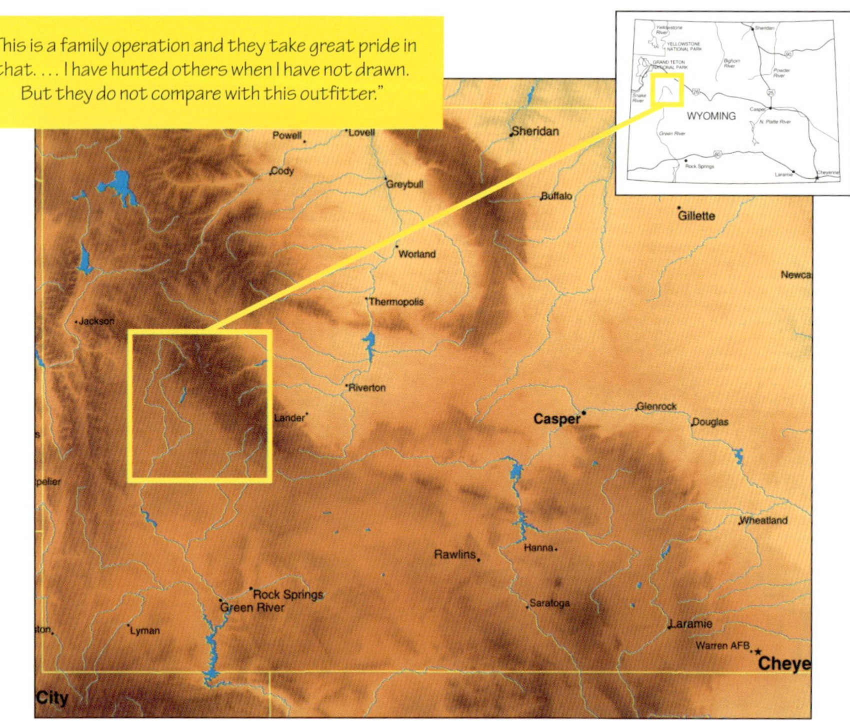

Arrow Five Outfitters

Jim Schaafsma

Star Route 1, Box 64A • Zenia, CA 95595
ph./fax (707) 923-9633

Arrow Five Outfitters has been owned and operated by Jim Schaafsma since 1981. We feature Coues' deer, desert mule deer, and javelina hunts in Sonora, Mexico.

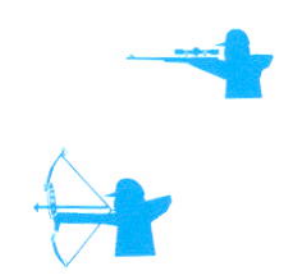

Our blacktail deer, black bear, boar and turkey hunts are in both Humboldt and Trinity counties, located in Northern California. We have a 100% success on our rifle deer hunts in California, and 98% success on archery.

We also provide Roosevelt elk and blacktail hunts in Medford and Myrtle Creek, Oregon. Our hunts offer an excellent chance for record book for SCI, Pope & Young, and Boone & Crockett.

All of our hunts are fully-guided, one-to-one, on private property.

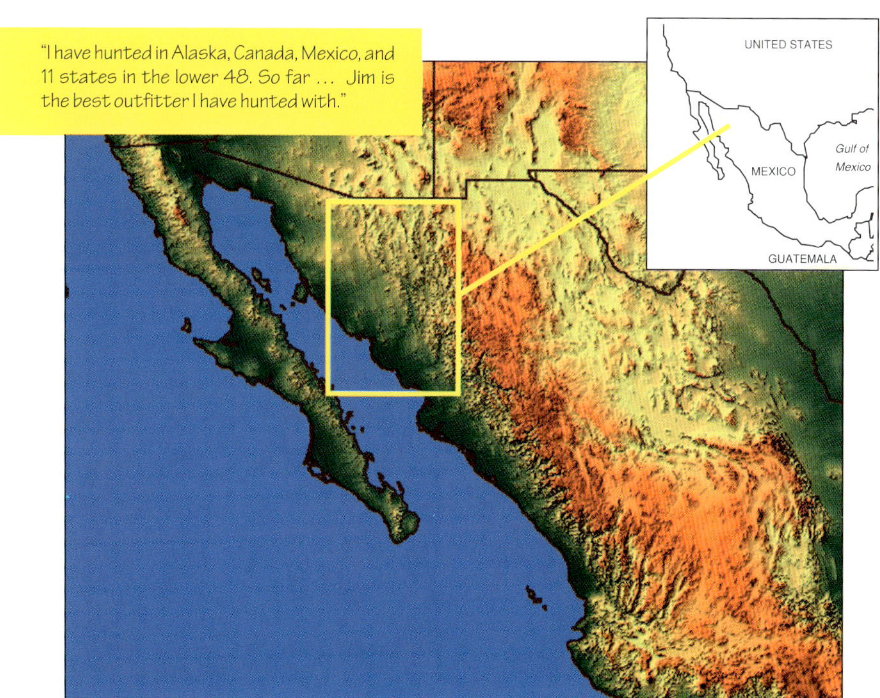

Canada

Outdoor Professionals

1. A/Z Outfitters, Ltd.
2. Big Rack Adventures
3. Blind Creek Outfitters
4. Bonnet Plume Outfitters
5. Cariboo Mountain Outfit.
6. E&D Outfitters
7. Herbert's Guide Service
8. Love Bros. & Lee, Ltd.
9. Moose Valley Outfitters
10. N.W.T. Outfitters, Ltd.
11. Stricker Outfitting
12. Tom Scott Outfitting
13. Western Guiding Service

Canada

Outdoor Professionals

14 Camp Michi Wawa

15 George River Lodge, Inc.

16 Ida Patey & Sons

17 Jack Hume Adventures, Inc.

18 Portland Creek Outfitters

19 Safari Caribou du Nouveau Québec

20 Sam's Hunting & Fishing Camps

Useful information for the provinces of
Canada

Alberta:
Ministries and Agencies

Dept. of Environmental Protection
9945-108 Street
Edmonton, Alberta, Canada T5K 2C6
phone: (403) 427-8636
fax: (403) 422-6339
email: Lfunke@env.gov.ab.ca

Natural Resources Service
9945-108 Street
Edmonton, Alberta, Canada T5K 2C6
phone: (403) 427-6749

Land and Forest Service
phone: (403) 427-3541

Associations, Publications, etc.

Alberta Outfitters Association
Box 277
Caroline, Alberta, Canada T0K 0M0
phone/fax: (403) 722-2692

Professional Outfitters Association of
Alberta
PO Box 67012 Meadowlark Park
Edmonton, Alberta, Canada T5R 5Y3
phone: (403) 486-3050
fax: (403) 484-4942

The Alberta Fish & Game Association
6924-104 Street
Edmonton, Alberta, Canada T6H 2L7
phone: (403) 437-2342
fax: (403) 438-6872

The Outdoor Edge (publication)
5829-97 Street
Edmonton, Alberta, Canada T6E 3J2
phone: (403) 448-0381
fax: (403) 438-3244

British Columbia:
Ministries and Agencies

Ministry of the Environment
810 Blanshard St., 4th Floor
Victoria, B.C. Canada V8V 1X4
phone: (604) 387-9422

Ministry of Small Business Tourism &
Culture
1117 Wharf St.
Victoria, B.C. Canada V8V 2Z2
phone: (604) 387-1683

Associations, Publications, etc.

Guide Outfitters Association of British
Columbia
PO Box 94675
Richmond, B.C. Canada V6Y 4A4

Newfoundland:
Ministries and Agencies

Department of Natural Resources
PO Box 8700
St. John's, NF Canada A1B 4J6
phone: (709) 729-4715

Department of Tourism, Culture &
Recreation
PO Box 8730
St. John's, NF, Canada A1B 4J6
phone: (709) 729-2830
fax: (709) 729-1965
email: info@tourism.gov.nf.ca

Northwest Territories:
Ministries and Agencies

Department of Resources, Wildlife &
Economic Development
Government of the NW Territories

Canada

Scotia Centre, Box 21
600 5102 - 50 Avenue
Yellowknife, N.T. Canada X1A 3S8
phone: (403) 69-2366
fax: (403) 873-0169

Manitoba:
Ministries and Agencies

Department of Natural Resources
Legislative Building, Room 333
Winnipeg, MB Canada R3C 0V8
phone: (204) 945-3730

Dept. of Industry, Trade & Tourism
Travel Manitoba, Dept RH7
1515 Carlton St.
Winnipeg, MB Canada R3C 3H8
phone: (204) 945-3777/ext. RH7
fax: (204) 945-2302

Associations, Publications, etc.

Manitoba Lodges & Outfitters Assoc.
23 Sage Crescent
Winnipeg, MB Canada R2Y 0X8
phone: (204) 889-4840

Ontario:
Ministries and Agencies

Ministry of Natural Resources
Toronto, Ontario, Canada M7A 1W3
phone: (416) 314-2301

Associations, Publications, etc.

The Ontario Federation of Anglers and
Hunters, Inc.
4601 Guthrie Drive, Box 2800
Peterborough, Ont., Canada K9J 8L5
phone: (705) 748-6324
fax: (705) 748-9577
email: ofah@oncomdis

Northern Ontario Tourist Outfitters
Association
269 Main St. West, Suite 408
North Bay, Ontario, Canada P1B 2T8
phone: (705) 748-6324
fax: (705) 748-9577
email: noto@onlink.net
http://virtualnorth.com/noto/

Québec:
Ministries and Agencies

Dept. of Recreation, Fish & Game
Place de la Capitale 150 Blvd.
Rene-Levesque Est, Québec
Canada G1R 4Y1
phone: (418) 643-6527

Associations, Publications, etc.

Federation of Québec Outfitters
2485 Boul Hamel
Québec, Canada G1P 2H9
phone: (418) 877-5191

Yukon Territories:
Ministries and Agencies

Dept.of Renewable Resources
Box 2703
Whitehorse, Y.T. Canada 71A 2C6
phone: (403) 667-5460

Associations, Publications, etc.

Yukon Fish & Game Association
PO Box 4434
Whitehorse, Y.T. Canada Y1A 3T5
phone: (403) 667-2843

Yukon Outfitters Association
Box 4548
Whitehorse, Y.T. Canada Y1A 2R8
phone: (403) 668-4118

Big Rack Adventures

Blair and Kathy Trout

Box 98 • Newbrook, Alberta, Canada T0A 2P0
ph. (403) 576-2394

We, Blair and Kathy, offer one of the finest quality whitetail deer and black bear hunts in Alberta. We have been in the business since the early '80s, maintaining only the highest hunting and fair chase ethics.

We provide our clients with top-quality service, attending to the smallest of details. Our lodge provides real home-like atmosphere. We hunt the fringe area between agricultural and big bush country on public and private land. Extensive scouting and shed-antler hunting enables us to determine the location and the quality of the game in our area. We had previously picked up at least one shed from half of the bucks taken in the '95 season.

We provide complete trophy care. Our overall goal is for a top quality hunt and a top quality trophy.

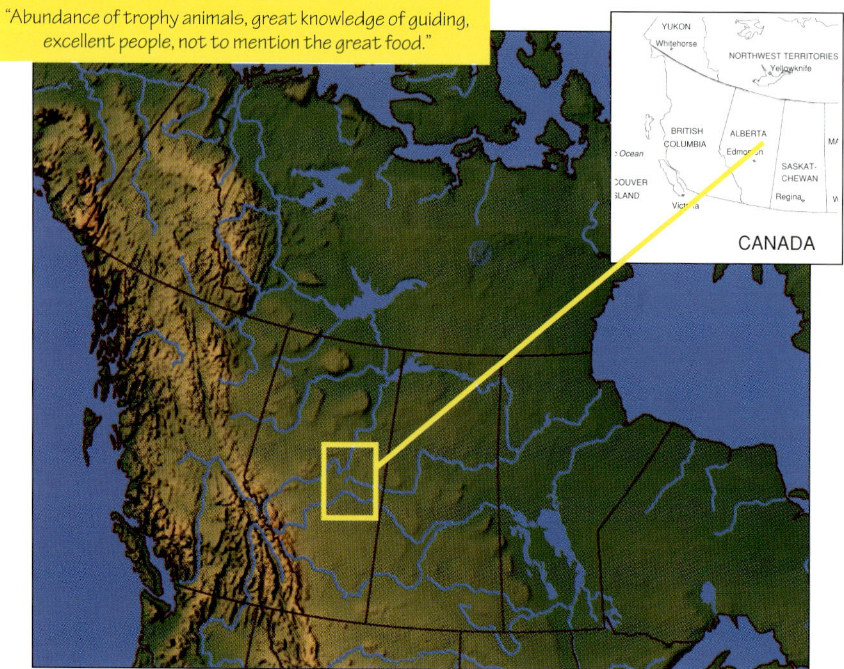

Hebert's Guide Service

Joe and Doreen Hebert

Box 234 • Valleyview, Alberta, Canada T0H 3N0
ph. (403) 524-2417 • fax (403) 524-4725

We operate a family guide service at Little Smoky, a very small but active community with mostly farming and oil field work. Our farm is ten miles northwest of Little Smoky where we have our clients meet us.

Our hunts consist of parties of four or six people at one time, however, our facilities will accommodate more if required. Camp consist of three sleepers and a cookhouse with a fireplace. We use quads and Argos in wildlife management Unit 54 for elk, moose whitetail and mule deer, spring and fall bear. Also goose hunting in the early fall. Summer photography and scenic quad trips available. All guides are experienced.

We are licensed and bonded members of the P.O.A.A., Safari Club and fish and game. For your memorable hunting trips call or fax us in Alberta.

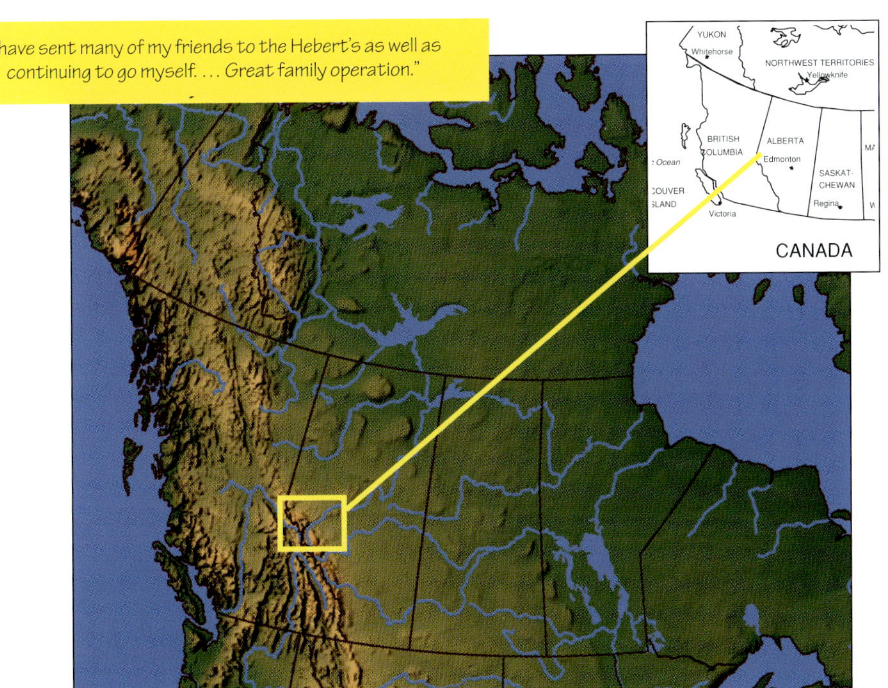

"I have sent many of my friends to the Hebert's as well as continuing to go myself. ... Great family operation."

Stricker Outfitting, Ltd.

Charlie Stricker
Box 5963 • Whitehorse, Yukon., Canada, Y1A 5L7
phone/fax: (403) 633-3366

We offer mighty bucks from the mighty Peace River Country of Alberta.

This is the most remote whitetail deer area available with nil or minimal hunting pressure. Hunters are positioned in prime tree stands in early morning before daylight and again in late evening. The stands are heated and positioned over active scrapes and rubs. During the day, we do drives or pushes. The guide will walk through the bush and drive the deer past the hunter. There is also an opportunity to take a coyote or wolf on these hunts.

We offer a bow and arrow bighorn sheep hunt out of Canmore, Alberta. On this hunt, when you step out of your tent, you're hunting.

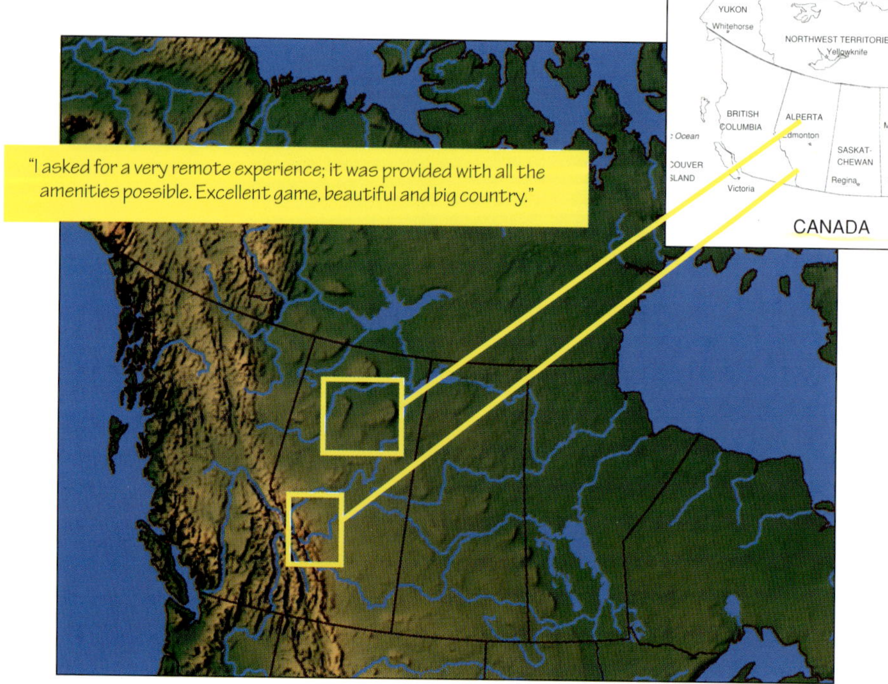

Tom Scott Outfitting

Tom Scott
Box 1122 • Westlock, Alberta, Canada T0G 2L0
phone/fax: (403) 349-3931

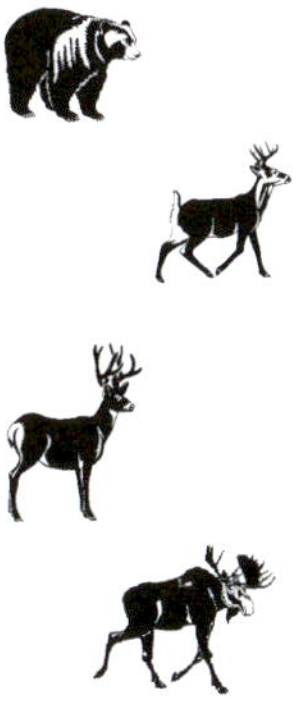

Tom Scott Outfitting is a small, very personalized operation with the outfitter on site and a maximum of four clients per six-day hunt.

We access fairly remote areas of Northern Alberta for moose, mule deer and bear, mainly by ATV. Camp accommodations consist of tents with heaters, cots with mattresses and good home cooked meals.

Whitetail deer are hunted from my home in farming country in North Central Alberta.

Highly experienced guides (whitetail, one-on-one, others two-on-one) work hard to show clients good animals with excellent success rates.

Come as a client, go home as a friend.

"The weather made it impossible to get in the area by land and Tom arranged to fly us in and out. Did not even ask us for monetary consideration even though I know that it cost him a great deal more than originally expected."

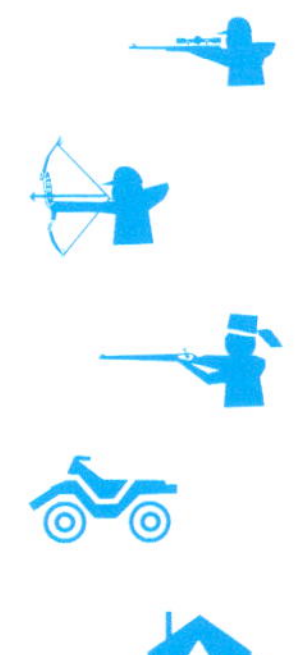

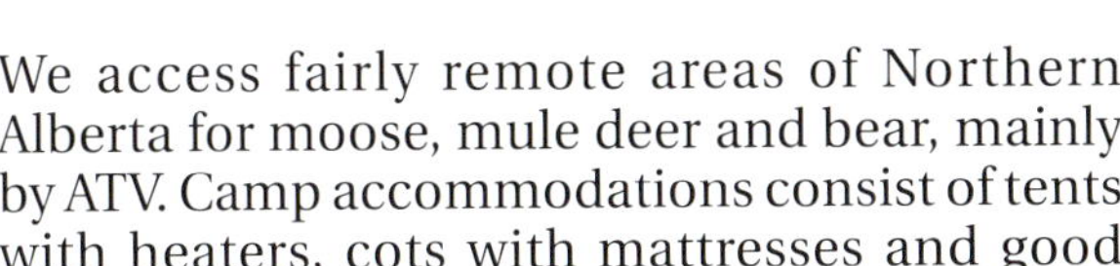

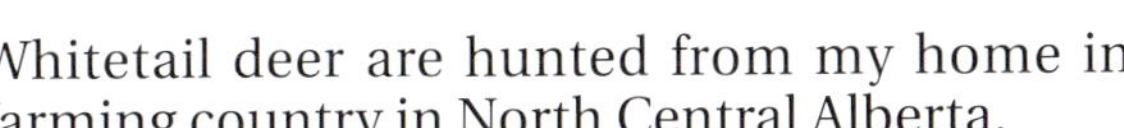

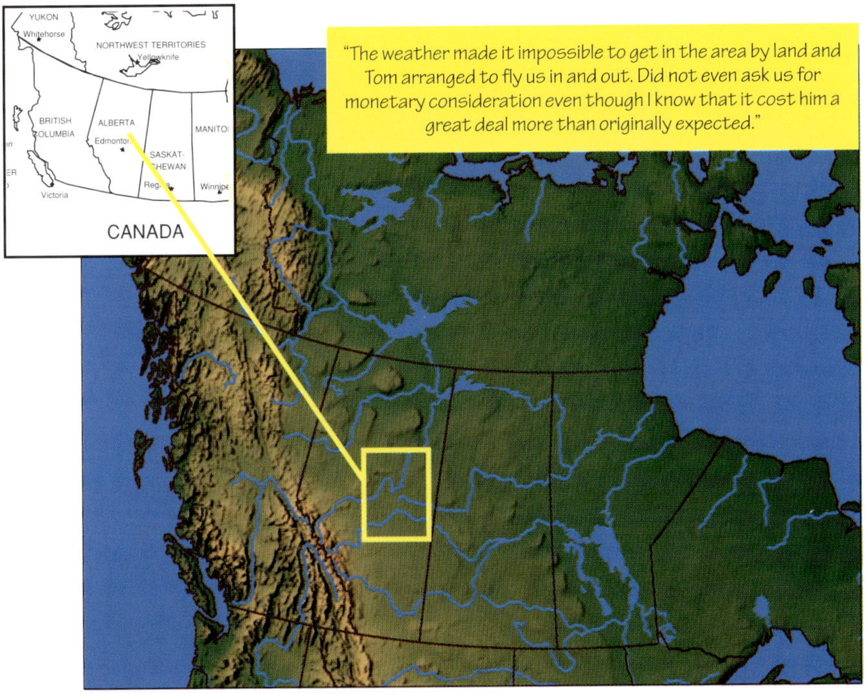

Western Guiding Service

Greg, Dave and Betty Molloy

Box 191 • Empress, Alberta, Canada T0J 1E0
phone: (403) 565-3775 • (403) 676-3300

Western Guiding Service is a family-run business specializing in trophy mule deer hunts for rifle and bow in Southeastern Alberta in four wildlife management units, which have been on resident draw since 1989.

This unique area has repeatedly provided clients with world-class mule deer each year.

Bow hunts are conducted on both the South Saskatchewan and Red Deer Rivers by jet and conventional boats.

Dave or Greg would like to talk to you about a mule deer hunt. Please call and get on our list for a hunt to remember.

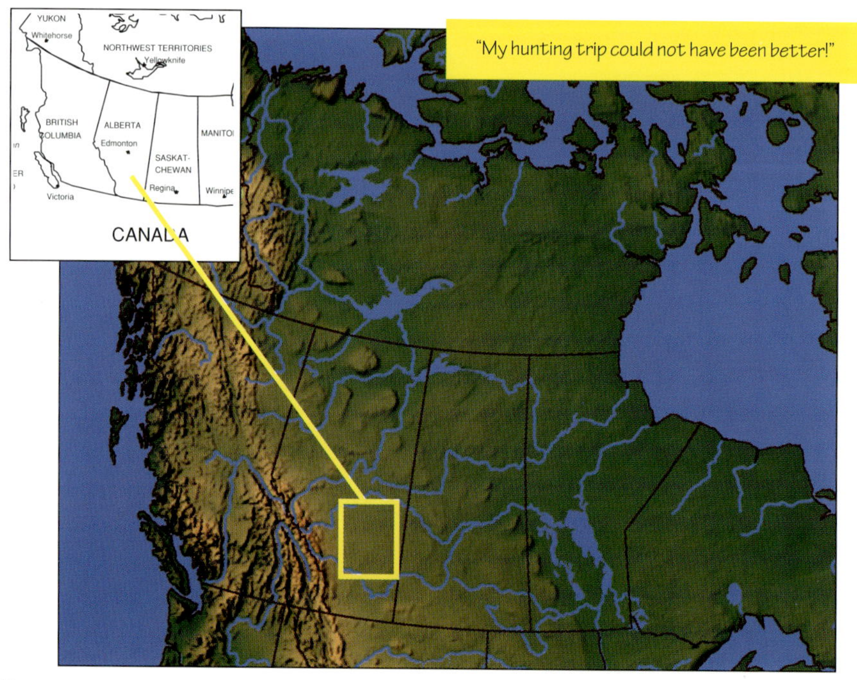

A/Z Outfitters, Ltd.

Bill DuBois

Box 86 • Windermere, B.C., Canada V0B 2L0
phone: (604) 342-3935

We offer un-roaded wilderness horse hunts in Southeast British Columbia. Beautiful country, log cabin camps, excellent guides and trophy wildlife. Specializing in elk, mountain goat, grizzly and black bear. Also offering hunts for the Shiras moose, mule deer and cougar.

We have 18 years' experience in the same area with the bulk of our clients being either repeats or referrals. Our hunts are ten days with one experienced guide for each hunter and seldom more than three hunters in the same camp.

We offer a total hunting and wilderness experience which will give you the opportunity to forget the pressure of business, to relax, and at the same time, enjoy a highly successful hunt.

Cariboo Mountain Outfitters

Bradley Bowden

Box 4010 • Quesnel, B.C., Canada V2J 3J2
phone: (604) 747-3334 • fax: (604) 747-3020

Cariboo Mountain base camp is 31 miles east of Quesnel, situated on a 3,000-foot meadow along Victoria Creek. It consists of log cabins with wood stoves, propane lights, running water and bath facilities. The guide area covers 700 square miles between Quesnel and the historic town of Bakerville. Hunts are conducted by horse, four-wheel-drive, and jet boat.

This is a family-run operation; I personally guide every client for part of their hunt. I limit my clients to a maximum of four per hunt to ensure the best success.

I have been guiding in this area for 29 years. Please call for further information.

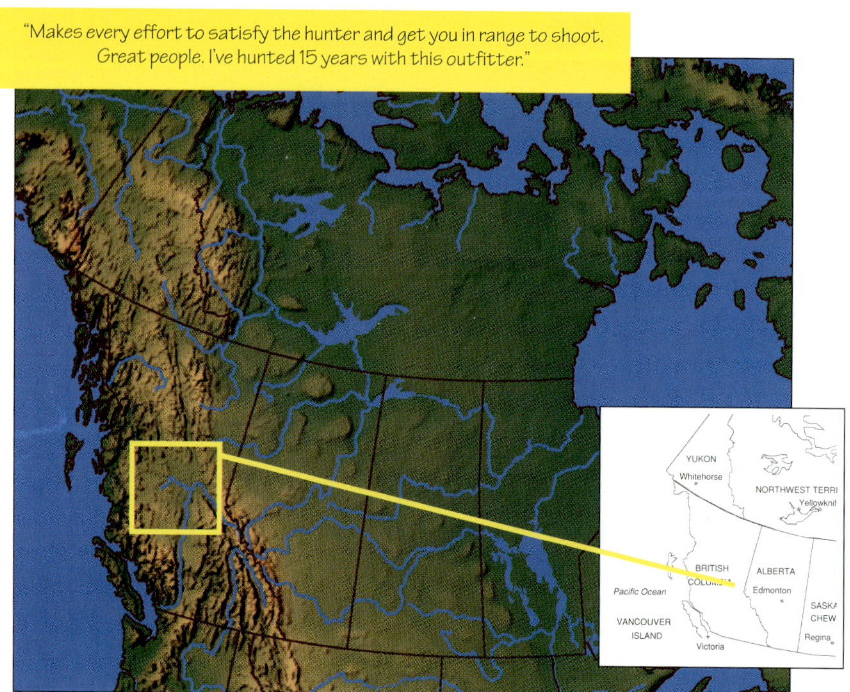

Love Bros. & Lee, Ltd.

Ron Fleming

R.R. #1 Kispiox Road, Site N • Hazelton, B.C., Canada V0J 1Y0
phone: (250) 842-6350

We specialize in combination hunts for mountain goat, mountain caribou, moose, grizzly, black bear and wolf — with bow or rifle. With five camps on lakes and rivers in 2,500-square miles of pristine wilderness, we have exclusive guiding rights to some of the best hunting and fishing in Northern British Columbia.

We provide guides, food, cooks, boats, motor, cabins, charter floatplanes trips and complete field care of trophies. Catering to small groups of four guests at a time, we offer excellent homecooked meals and professional guide service with a personal touch.

Our commitment to excellence and hunting ethics assures each guest a memorable trip.

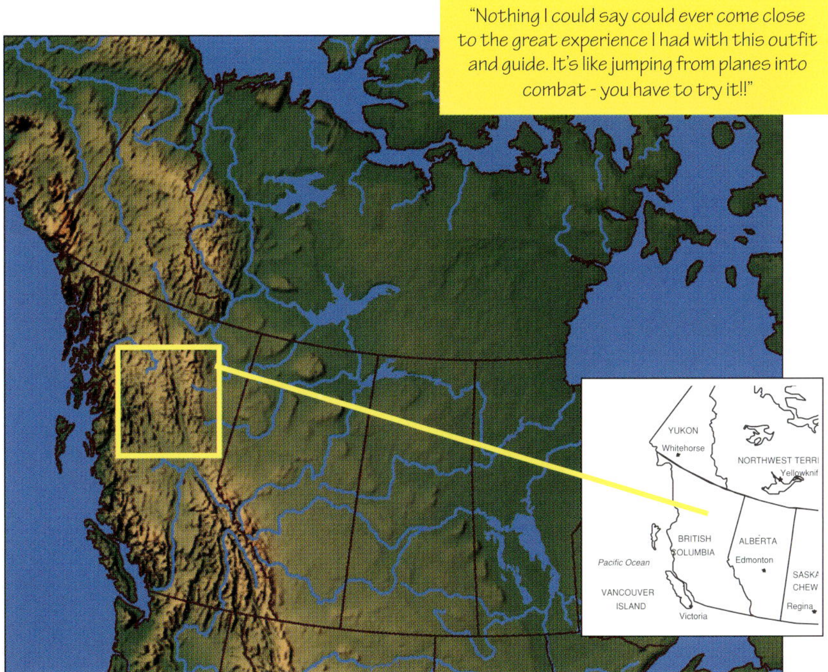

Moose Valley Outfitters

Ronald Steffey
General Delivery • Germansen Landing, B.C., Canada V0J 1T0
Radio phone: Vancouver Operator N50052, Channel 8

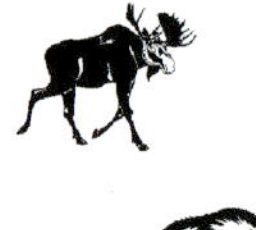

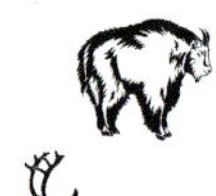

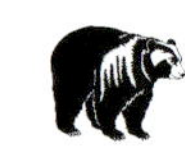

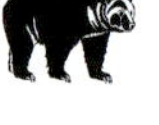

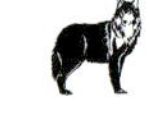

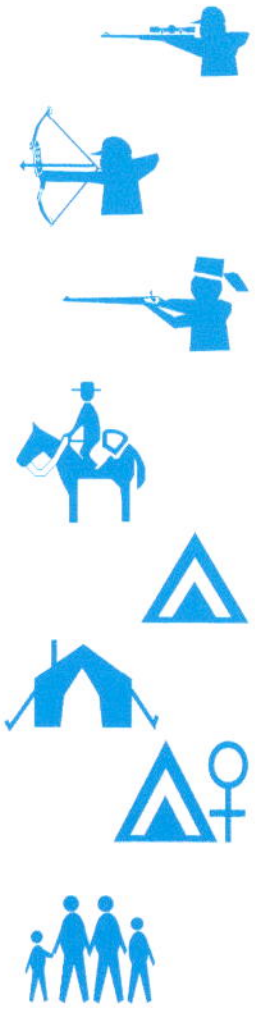

Our guiding territory is located in the rugged mountains of Northern British Columbia and is extremely remote with spectacular, breathtaking scenery, and trophy-class game.

We live in our guiding area year-round and recently completed an octagon log lodge. All of our hunting camps have comfortable log cabins. In order to maintain the wilderness atmosphere and assure your privacy, we specialize in small groups or families. Surround yourself in the majestic beauty of snowcapped mountains, meadows blanketed with wildflowers, beautiful glacier-fed lakes, and crystal-clear streams.

Hunt trophy-class game in their natural habitat in pristine wilderness.

"I feel that Ron puts together 'A once in a lifetime hunt,' and every hunter should have the chance to experience the effort that he puts in his hunts."

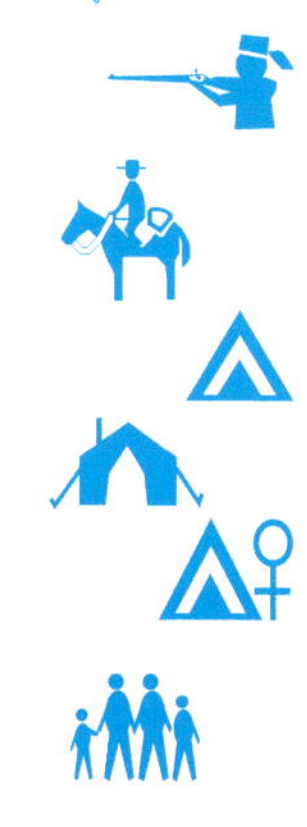

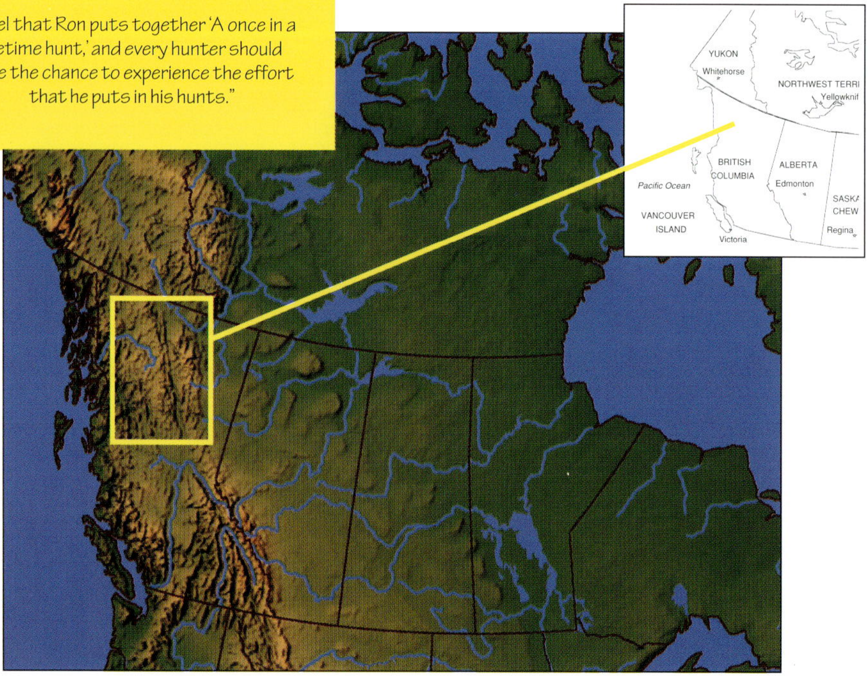

Blind Creek Outfitters

Walter and Diana Dmyterko

PO Box 469 • Fisher Branch, Manitoba, Canada R0C 0Z0
phone: (204) 372-6892 • fax: (204) 372-6661

We conduct our hunts in a semi-wilderness, non-pressure area with a good population of game in Manitoba Inter Lake areas G.H.A. #21 and #25.

Whitetail deer in the 180+ Boone & Crockett, black bears in 19-21 Boone & Crockett. Plenty of geese and upland birds.

Meals are home-cooked, and we always provide lots to eat in a good atmosphere.

Accommodations are provided in wood-framed, roomy and warm wall tents with bunk beds.
We accept four to six hunters per week.
For information, call or write.

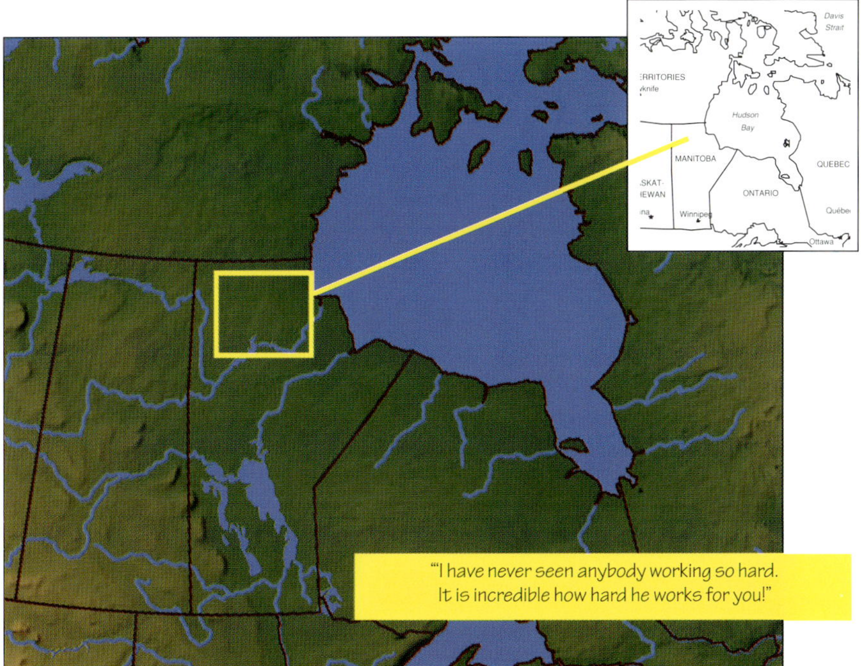

E&D Outfitters

Ed Balan

General Delivery • Olha, Manitoba, Canada R0J 1K0
phone: (204) 234-5531

E&D Outfitters has been in business since 1979. We are located on the south side of Riding Mountain National Park. We have both spring and fall bear season, and whitetail deer (rifle) in November.

Our success varies from 75-100%. Hunting is done from 14-foot tree stands. We have four color phases of bears to choose from. Sizes range from 150 to 800 pounds and most skulls score greater than 18 inches; we've taken a couple over 22. We bait daily, and provide skinning and game care.

Hunters stay in a four-bedroom cabin with shower but no indoor bathroom. Meals are cooked and eaten in our home.

Contact us for further information.

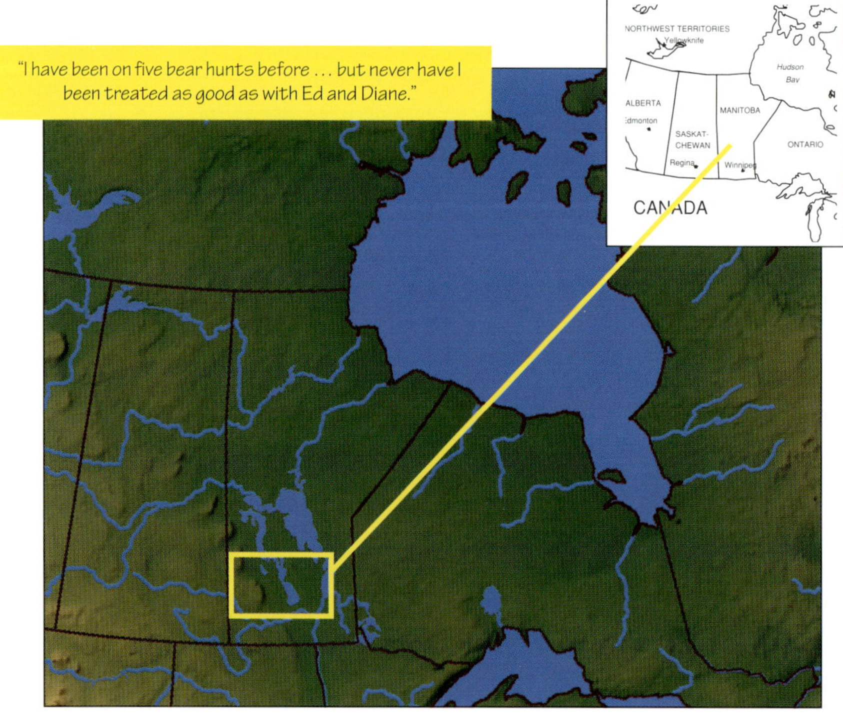

Ida Patey and Sons

Eric and Ida Patey

River of Ponds • St. Barbe District, Newfoundland, Canada A0K 4M0
phone: (709) 225-3221• fax: (709) 225-5591

The Patey family has been involved with big game hunting for more than 11 years with a combination of family members running the operation.

We use local guides, who are very professional at their work.

We also have our own aircraft to service our cabins. Each site is equipped with high frequency radio, thus keeping everyone in communication.

We have seven hunting cabins but we choose not to operate them all at one time.

We like to keep a reserve.

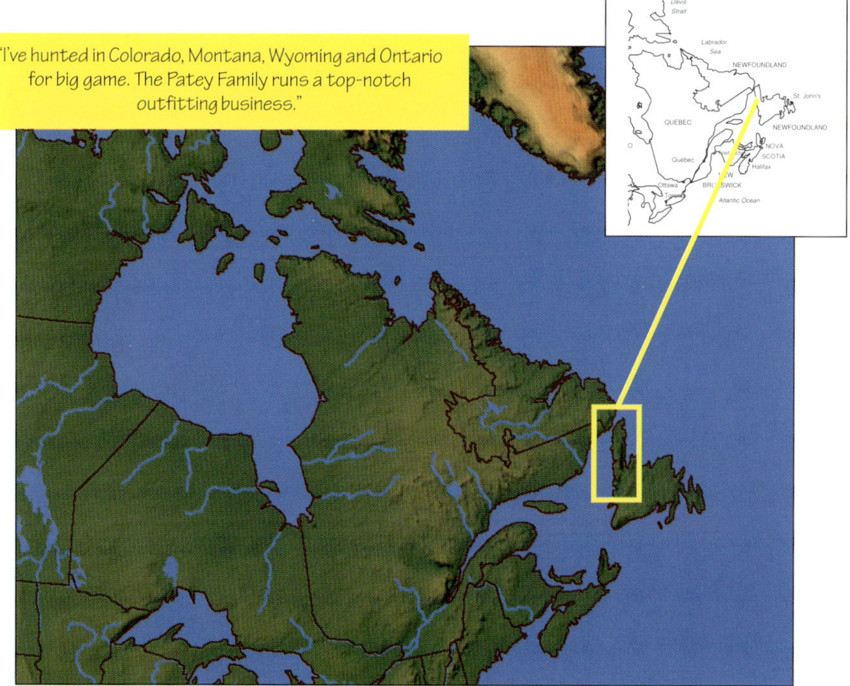

Portland Creek Outfitters

Leonard Payne and Aster Caines
General Delivery • Portland Creek, Newfoundland, Canada A0K 4G0
L. Payne: phone: (709) 898-2328 • fax: (709) 898-2558 • A. Caines: phone: (709) 898-2329

Come and enjoy our "Home Comfort Log Cabins," featuring mobile phones, friendly atmosphere, home- cooked meals, hot and cold water, and showers. We use one licensed guide per hunt and limit four hunters per camp unless requested.

You have a choice of six camps, and single or combination hunts. A $500 refund is guaranteed if you do not spot a moose or caribou. Hunts run from Sunday to Sunday (weather permitting). We fly in to all camps. Different types of private hunting terrain. Accommodations are a short distance from departure area. In the five years of our established business, our outstanding success has been proven by the large number of repeat hunters.

We specialize in making your trip "one you'll always remember."

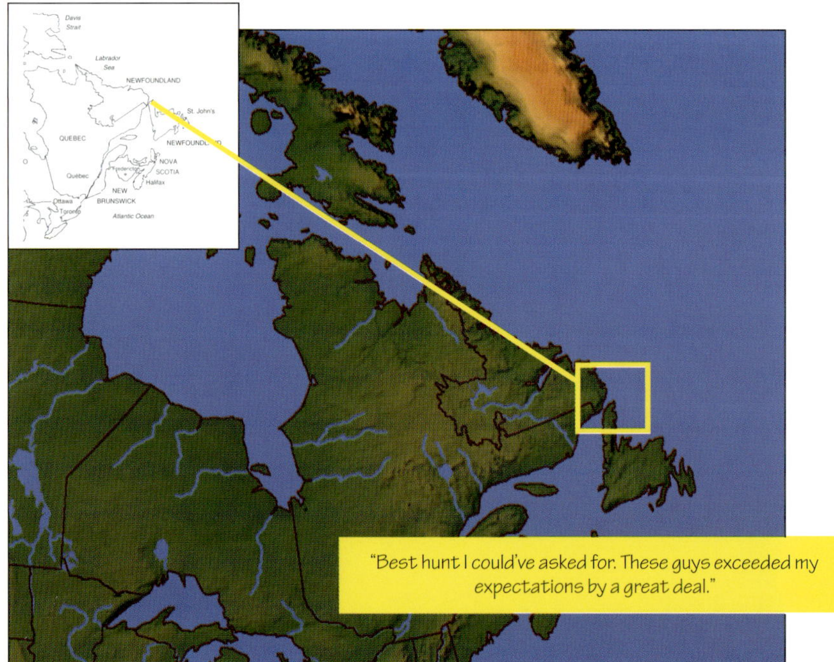

Sam's Hunting & Fishing Camps

Sam Caines
Portland Creek • St. Barbe South, Newfoundland, Canada A0K 4G0
phone: (709) 898-2535 • fax: (709) 898-2515

Sam has been operating as an outfitter in this area since 1970. The camps are wooden construction with indoor toilets and shower facilities. Two-way radios for daily contact or emergencies.

Each camp is equipped to accommodate four hunters per week, four guides and a full time cook. Hunting is mostly done by walking or glassing from the high country. All guides are registered and they are some of the best you can find in Newfoundland. They work hard to see that all guests get their game and enjoy their stay in camp. These camps have produced 95% success on moose and 100% on caribou.

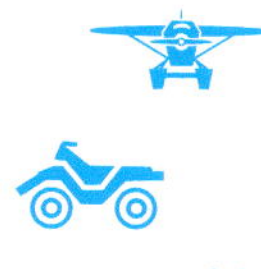

Most of our business comes from repeat clients and word of mouth advertising. We welcome all your calls for information or reservations.

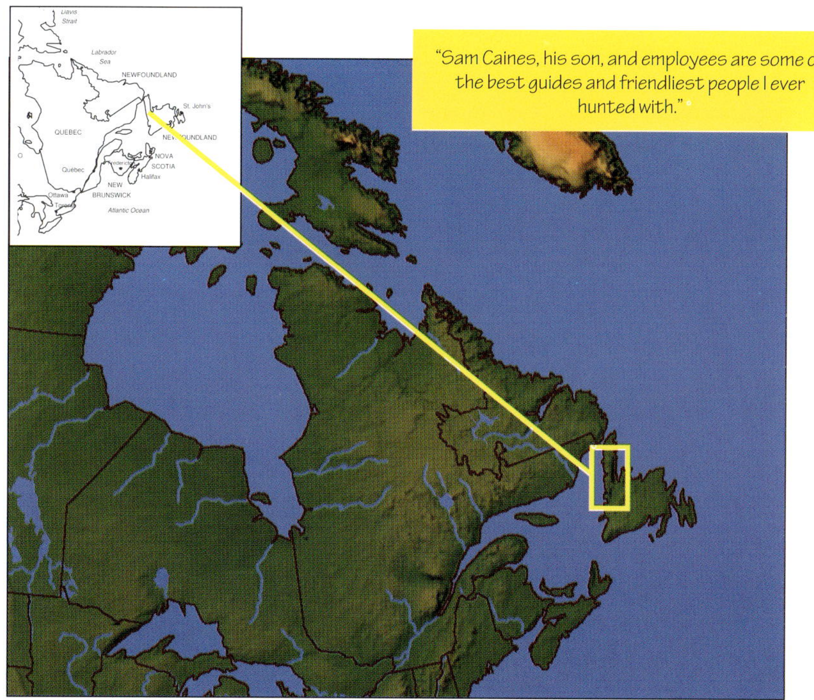

N.W.T. Outfitters, Ltd.

Darrell and Duane Nelson
Box 29 • Babb, MT 59411 or Box 1154 • Glenwood, Alberta, Canada T0K 2R0
phone: (403) 626-3279 • fax: (403) 626-3036

N.W.T. Outfitters, Ltd. is owned and operated by Darrell and Duane Nelson. We have been guiding and outfitting in the Mackenzie Mountains since 1975. We offer mixed bag hunts for Dall's sheep, mountain goat, caribou, moose, wolf and wolverine.

Each hunter has his own experienced guide and, in most cases, all hunting is done from spike camps with two hunters per party. We use horses to get where we hunt.

With N.W.T. Outfitters, Ltd. you get more than just a hunt. We stress personalized service and client satisfaction. You will be hunting in North America's last stronghold of untouched wilderness.

Our best advertisement is our clients' success.

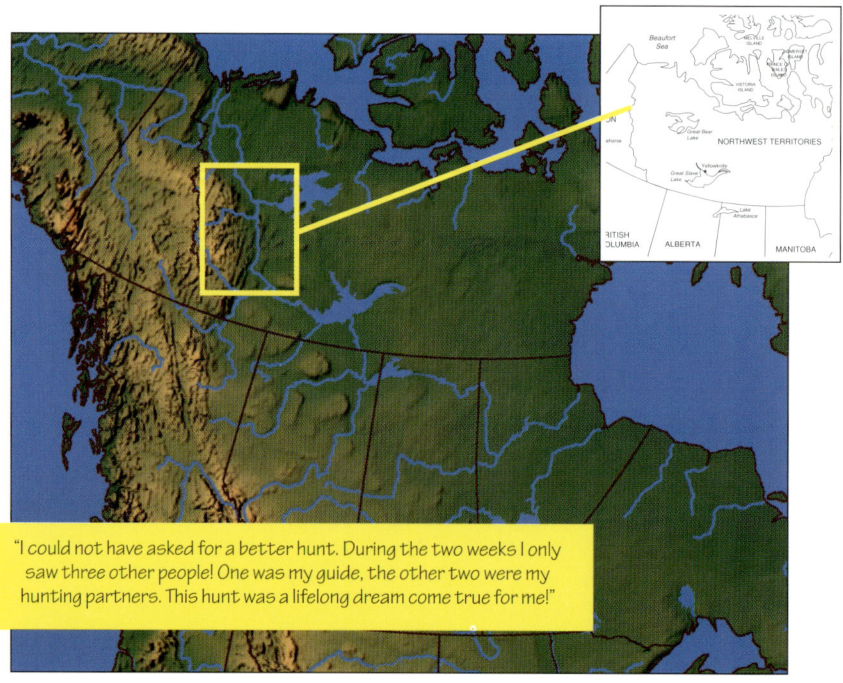

Camp Michi Wawa

Ken and Luanne Brezenski

Hwy. 17 North, P.O. Box 245 • Wawa, Ontario, Canada P0S 1K0
phone: (705) 856-7270

Drive right to your cabin door, just 2-1/2 hours north of Ste. Saulte Marie, Canada, via Hwy. 17 North. Nothing is impossible.

We specialize in customized bear and moose hunts. We do our best to fulfill our hunter's requests. Stay in one of our eight, newly-renovated cabins on Catfish Lake. We are the only camp in Wawa, situated with the lake right at your doorstep.

Our two-bedroom, HK cabins come fully-equipped with electricity, stove, fridge, hot and cold running water, electric furnace, linens, towels, and cooking utensils.

Also available, small game hunting, fishing, guiding service, boat, and motor rentals, hunter licenses, and much more.

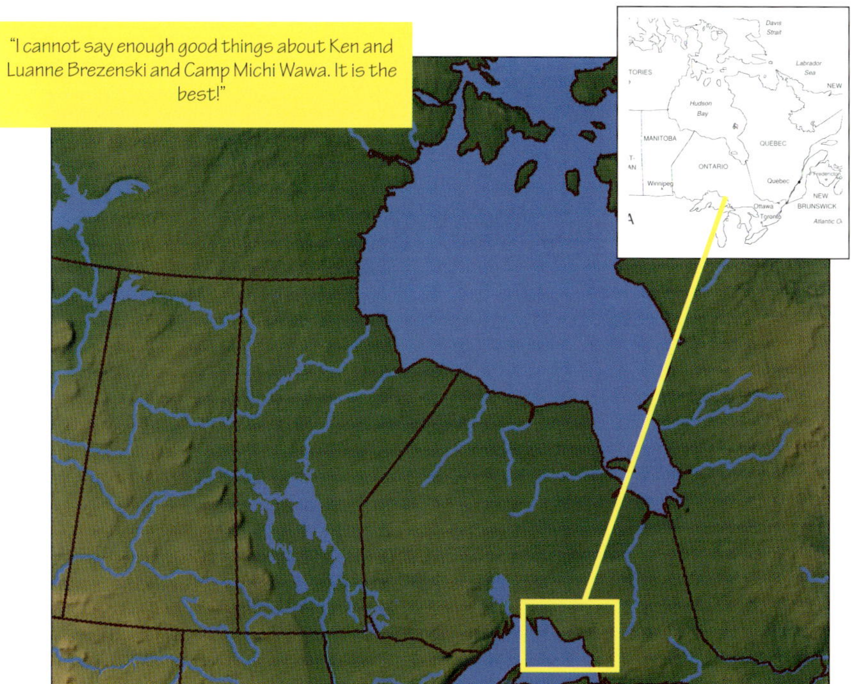

George River Lodge, Inc.

Pierre and Jean Paquet

C.P. 88 • Saint-Augustin, Québec, Canada G3A 1V9
October to May, reservations: (800) 473-4650 • (418) 877-4650 • fax: (418) 877-4652
June to September: phone: (418) 585-3477 • fax: (418) 585-2267

Established on the shores of the George River more than 30 years ago, our organization now controls 15 immense territories in different parts of Northern Québec.

We offer to our clients a very wide variety of specialized trips: first-class and very productive "mobile" caribou hunts, black bear and ptarmigan hunting, stream fishing for big brookies, Atlantic salmon fishing on the George, canoeing, adventure, and photography.

All these activities are under the American or the Housekeeping plan, in a lodge or in a drop camp. All our trips are organized from Montréal and our fees include transportation from Montréal to camp by private charter planes.

For more information, contact: Pierre or Jean Paquet.

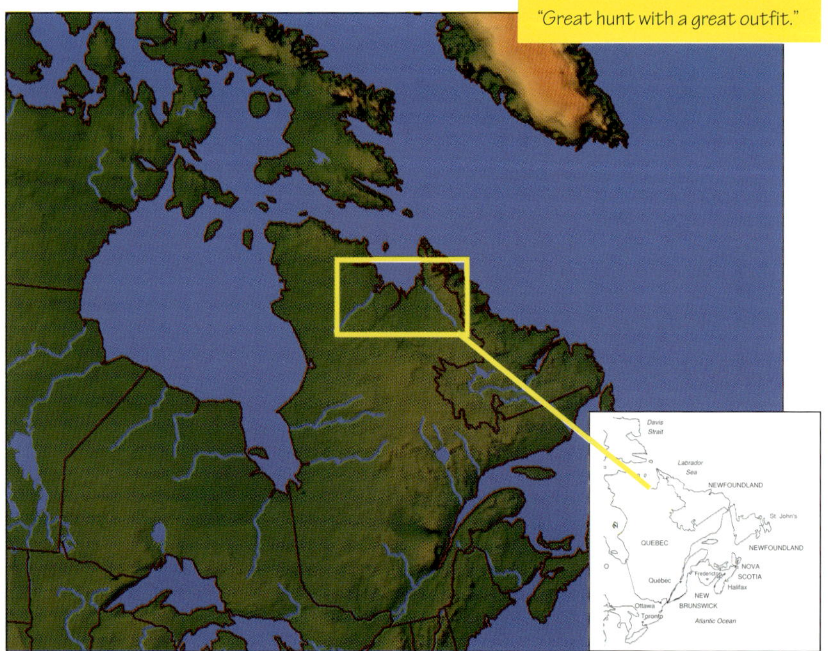

Jack Hume Adventures, Inc.

Jack and Richard Hume

250 Dunany Road • Lachute, Québec, Canada J8H 3W8
phone: (514) 562-3832 • fax: (514) 562-1413
www.roblyn.com/pourvoirie/hume/hume.htm

A hunting trip in the Ungava region of Northern Québec provides the sportsman with thrilling action in a true wilderness setting. For some, this is a "once in a lifetime" trip which requires a great deal of planning.

We will do everything possible on our part so that you have a wonderful and successful hunting trip. Should you have any complaints we will do our best to find a solution to the problem. We are certain that your trip with us will not only be a rewarding experience, but also one which you will always remember. If you require any further information, do not hesitate to get in touch with us.

We wish you the very best hunting season and we hope to see you in camp.

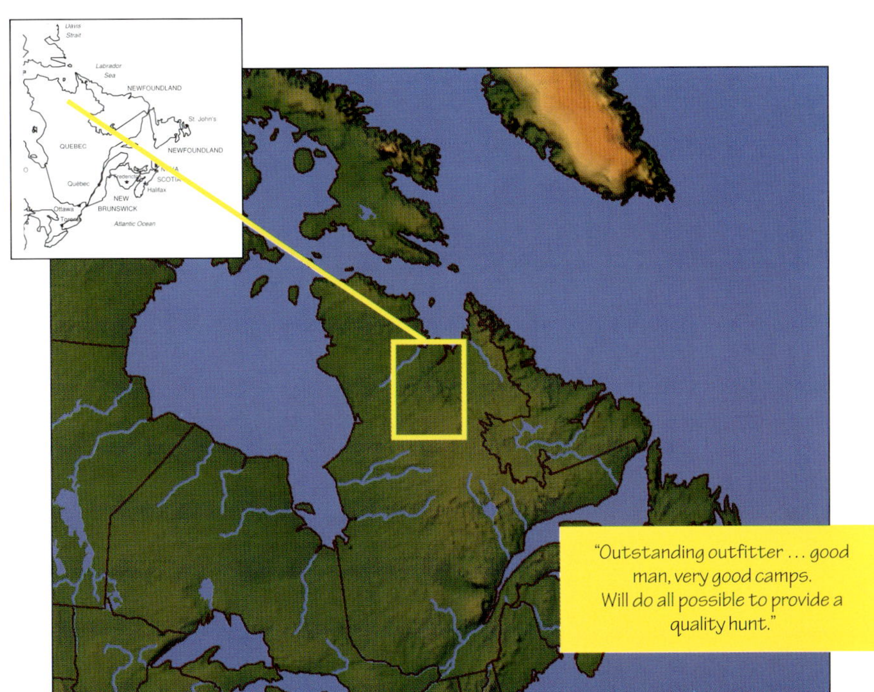

Safari Caribou du Nouveau Québec

Roch St. Laurent

45, av.du Collège nord, C.P. 88 • Robertsonville, Québec, Canada GON 1LO
phone: (418) 335-5557 • fax: (418) 335-0901

Schefferville is the top choice for the safest trophy hunt at the most affordable price. The majority of Boone and Crockett, Pope and Young, and Safari Club scores come from Schafferville guided and semi-guided hunts, undivided hunts and special drop camps.

All packages include return air fare from Montréal/Schafferville (round-trip, free parking in Montréal, transportation between Schafferville and your camp, free lodging in Schafferville), and caribou hunting license with two tags and two caribou. We book hunters in our camps only during the most productive weeks.

We also offer a "Protec-o-plan" that gives you a credit toward your next hunt of $500 or $ 1,000 (if you only kill one caribou or none). For more information, give us a call.

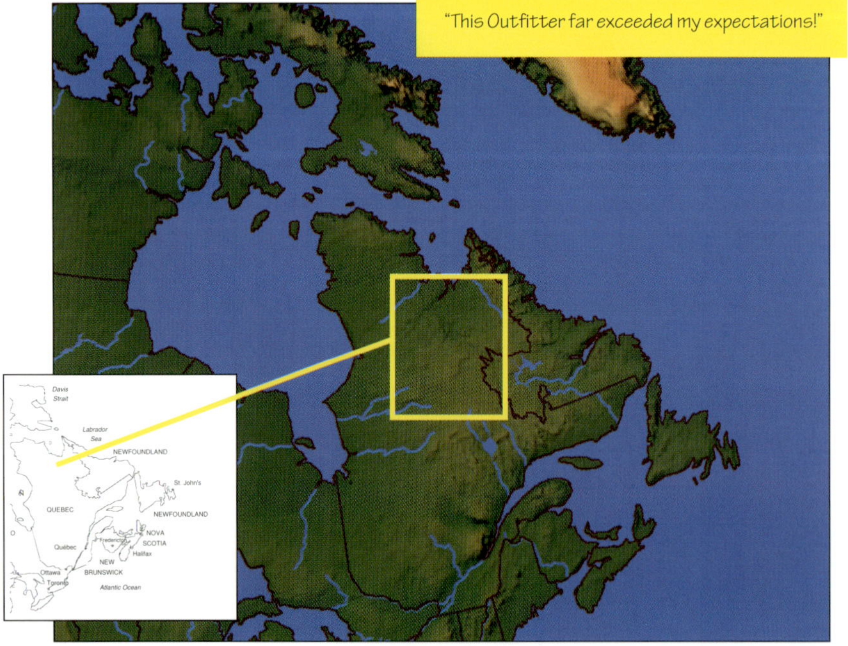

Bonnet Plume Outfitters, Ltd.

Charlie Stricker

P.O. Box 5963 • Whitehorse, Yukon Territories, Canada Y1A 5L7
phone/fax: (403) 633-3366

Located in the northeast portion of the Yukon against the Northwest Territories border, in Outfitting Area #5 and Game Management Zone 2. The area is noted as a good producer of good-quality game in horns and antlers for Dall's sheep, moose, Barrenground and mountain caribou. Also grizzly, black bear, wolf, and wolverine.

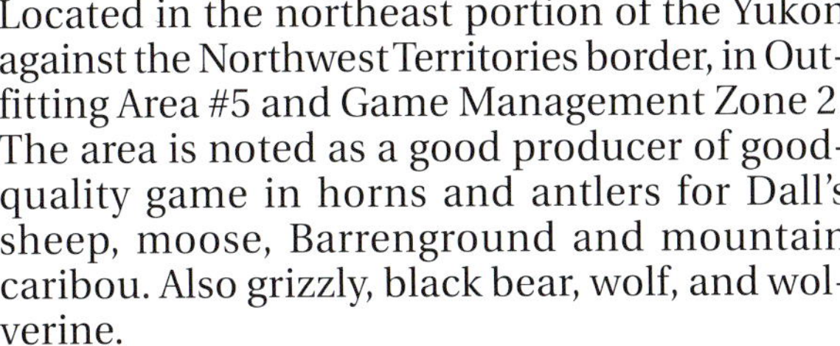
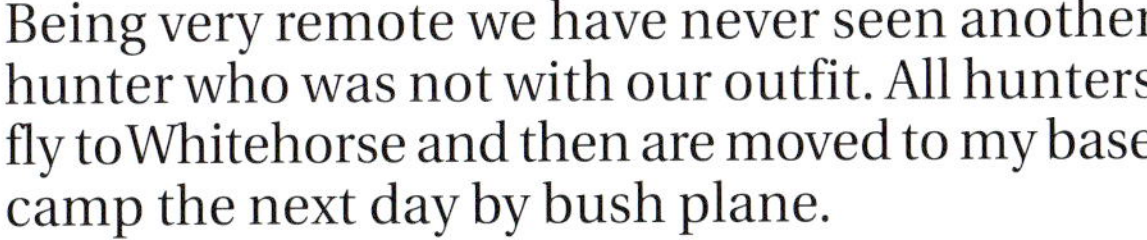

Being very remote we have never seen another hunter who was not with our outfit. All hunters fly to Whitehorse and then are moved to my base camp the next day by bush plane.

I have six base camps in a 100-mile stretch of wilderness. Plus, there are six different hunts for you to choose and experience the Yukon wilderness.

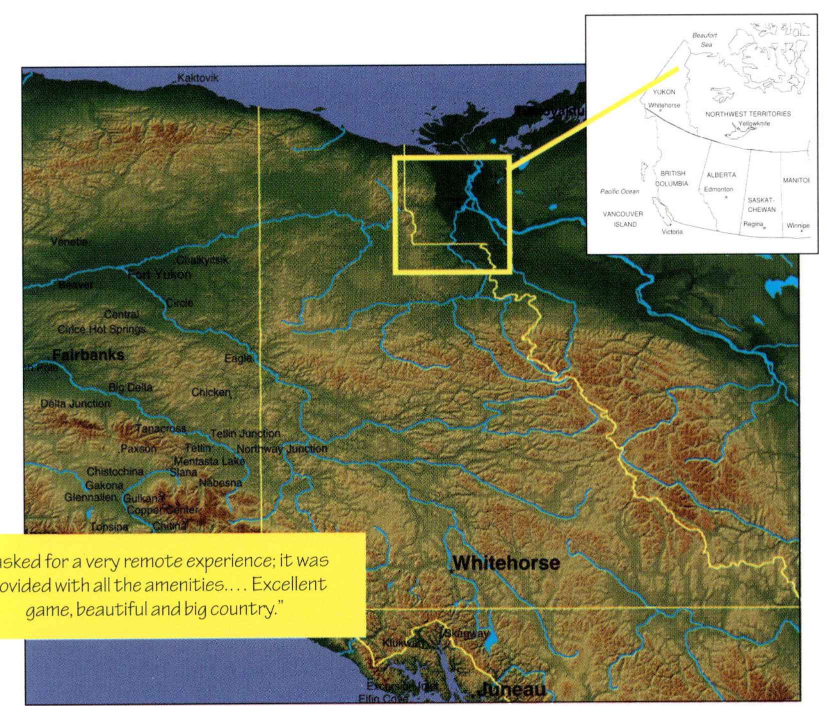

"I asked for a very remote experience; it was provided with all the amenities.… Excellent game, beautiful and big country."

Appendix

This is the complete list of *ALL* Registered Big Game Hunting Guides and Outfitters that we contacted during the compilation of our book.

We invited them to participate in our survey by simply sending us their complete list of clients. Some Outfitters did not respond.

Some replied prizing our idea, but still decided non to participate in our survey. Their main concern was the confidentiality of their client list. We truly respect their position, but we hope to have proven our honest and serious effort to them. We are sure they will join us in the next edition.

Others participated by sending their client list, but did not qualify for publication. In some cases because of a low score, and in other instances because of an insufficient number of questionnaires returned by their clients.

The names of the Guides and Outfitters who have received an A rating form their clients are **bolded** in the Appendix.

ALABAMA
Blueridge Hunting Lodge
  Robinson, John
Echo Canyon Outfitters, Ltd.
  Perry, Graham
Hamilton Hills Plantation, Inc.
  Smith, Lyle
Hawkins Ridge Lodge
  The Hawkins Family
Logging Camp Ranch
  Hanson, John
Macon County Guide Service
  Thomas, Brian
Rockfence Stations
  Hudmon, Ray
SE Whitetails of Mtn. View.
  Abramson, David

ALASKA
AAA Alaskan Outfitters Inc.
  Dan Schwarzer
Aasmudstad, Barry Herman
Acord, Gregory L.
Adams Alaskan Safaris
  Dale Leverett Adams
Afognak Wilderness Lodge
  Roy C. Randall
Air/Justin Tyme Guide
  Bill Woodin Services
Alaska Adventures
  Hugh Leslie Krank
Alaska Bush Adventure
Alaska Guide Service
  Ken Fanning, ,Master Guide
Alaska Hunting Co.
  Gary Thompson
Alaska Hunting & Fishing
  Meryl W. Wolford
Alaska Magnum Outfitters
  Keith Mattison
Alaska Outfitters
  Bill Stevenson
Alaska Remote Guide Service
  Wayne Kubat
Alaska Trophy Hunting & Fishing
  Melvin B. Gillis
Alaska Trophy Safaris
  Dennis Harms, Master Guide
Alaska Ultima Thule Outfitters
  Paul & Donna Claus
Alaska Wilderness Trophies
  James L. Baum
Alaska Wilderness Venture
  Len Mackler
Alaskan Mountain Safaris
  Kenny Lake & Robert Fithian
Aldridge, Ronnie L.
Almasy, Theodore J.
Alsworth Sr., Glen R.
Alsworth III, Leon R.
Arneson,Eric J.
Arno, Rodney M.
Atkins Guiding & Flying Service
  Ray Atkins, Master Guide
Atkins, James A.
Austin, Jerry R.
Averly, Deborah A.
Bara, Jeffry B.
Beardown Adventures
  Neil Webster
Beeman, Edward E.
Beier, Lavern R.
Bennett, Layton A.
Bergeron, Steven R.
Bickman, Jim W.
Big River Hunting & Trapping
  Harry Robert Hannon

Bill Slemp's Wild Alaska
  William M. Slemp
Bissell, Gordon Lee
Booch, Timothy L.
Booher, Benjamin R.
Bowden, Michael "Buck"-Master
  Guide
Boyd, Gregory J.
Braendel, Karl G.
Branham Adventures
  Dennis & Chris Branham
Bristol Bay Outfitters
  John A. Peterson
Brooks Range Adventures
  Arthur J. Andreis, Master
  Guide
Browning, E. Lee
Brunner, Eberhard George
Bryant, Larry Ray
Buist, Pete-Master Guide
Bullard, Billy F.
Burnett, Ralph C.
Burton, William E.
Burwell, Jeffery S.
Butler, Roger W.
Cameron, James Taylor
Carlson, Richard L.
Carney, Douglas Kent
Cerami, Mario
Chadd, Jeffery L.
Chandler, Charles L.
Chandler, Darrell D.
Chervenak, Paul A.
Chiappone, Robert B.
Clark, Winfield Yates
Cobb, Lawrence B.
Coleman, Edward A.
Collins, Mark F.
Cook Jr., Fred M.
Cox, Dennis Dean
Daigger, Dennis P.
Dam Sr., William E.
Davis, Carey G.
Davis, Russell T.
Decker, Eric G
Denali Wilderness Outfitters
  Kirk Martakis.
DeNeut, Michael C.
Dennison, Bradford A.
Deoudes, Demitrios Nicholas
Dick Gunlogson Master Guide
  & Outfitter–Dick Gunlogson
Dinello, Frank A.
Dobson, Michael W.
Dodge III,, Harry B., Master Guide
Don, Fred
Doyon, David Paul
Driskell, Clifford H.
Duncan, Donald C.
Durning, William C.
Ehrhart, James E.
Eide, Sterling H.
Elliott II, Daniel B.
Elliott, Robert
Ellis, Bill-Master Guide
Ellis, Kirk W.
Ellis, Lorene E.
Ellis, Lynn D.
Ellis, William Cole, Master Guide
Elmore, Jonh W.
Erickson, John E., Master Guide
Eubank, David Paul
Everett, Sharon McLeod
Faerber, Gerge L.
Fair Chase Hunts

Joe Hendricks, Master Guide
Farmen, Darrell L
Fassbender, Steven R.
Felmlee, Dwight S.
Fields Sr., Arthur R.
Fisher, Tom
Fitzgerald, Kevin B.
Fitzgerald, William James
Flynn, David H.
Flynn, Howard D.
Footloose Alaska Trophy Hunts
Forbes, Ben H.
Freel, Tracy Ray
Forsi, Ted J.
Fritts Jr., Robert T.
Gale, Michael Joe
Galla, Mark Alan
Gavin, William F.
Gay, Kirk Downing
George, Guy D.,Master Guide
Gerlach, Robert
Gilbert, Tad K.
Gilliam, Albert C.
Gilson,Ronald V.
Globis, Keith P.
Gratias, David Roy
Gray, Allen J.
Gray, Gary C.
Greenblatt, Andy D.
Gregg, Christopher J.
Grishkowsky, Vance
Grizzly Skins of Alaska
  Phil Shoemaker
Guthrie, Richard A.
Haeg, David Scott
Hagar, William Lee
Halford, Richard W.
Halladay, Joseph R.
Hammack, Roland D.
Hankerd, Mark Joseph
Hankerd, W. J. "Hank"
Hanson, Charles "Doug"
Happy Trails
  Andrew F. Paule
Hautanen Enterprise
  Butch Hautanen
Hedlund, Thomas A.
Heinz, Thomas A.
Heller, Frank J.
Helmericks, James W.
Henriksen, Burr
High Adventure Air Charter
  Gregory A. Bell
High Safaris Hunting Co.
  Tom Rigden
Hirsch,Jeffrey Ray
Hodge, James S. H.
Hooton, Larry C.
Horstman, Michael Paul
Hostetler, Charles D.
Hudson, Charles Brent
Humble, C. Vernon
Hutcheson, Calvin W.
Hyce, Richard Allen
Jack Sr., Peter
Jacobson, Patricia Ann
Jacques Adventure Company
  Jerry Jacques
Jake's Alaska Wilderness
  John J. GaudetOutfitters
Jamieson, David Y. "Sandy"
Johnson, Warren E.
Jones, Cecil R.
Jones, Harold "Brent"

Jones, Paul E.
Jones, Troy Allen
Jonhson, Paul E.
Kahn, Donald A.
Kahn, Steven H.
Katmai Guide Service
  Joe Klutsch, Master Guide
Katzeek, Leslie B.
Katzmarek, Clay M.
Kauer, Robert Lorin
Keeler, Larry D.
Kempf, Chris J.
Kempson, Bobby L.
Kennedy, Patrick R.
Kichatna Guide Service
  Harold "Zeke" Schetzle,
  Master Guide
King, Jay M.
Kinnear, Leslie William
Kirstein, Thomas J.
Kittoe, Daniel D.
Knighton, Donald E.
Kniktuk Adventures
  Bob Wener
Knutson, Howard J.,Master Guide
Kobuk Guide and Outfitters
  Henry C. Clark
Kodiak Discoveries
  Tom Stick
Kodiak Safaris
  Steven Perins & Buckey Windley
Koontz, Keith C.,Master Guide
Koskoavich, Richard J.
Kulas, Aaron R.
Lahndt, Laine W.
Lair, Johnnie R.
Lake Country Lodge, Inc.
  John C. Davis
Lambert, Ronald K.
Lamoure, Gus
Lamoureux, Gus, Master Guide
Lancaster, Jerry L.
Lanni, Joseph D.
Lanphier, Steven W.
Lapointe, Hal A.
LaRose Guide Service
  Gary LaRose, Master Guide
Last Frontier Guiding & Outfitting
  Rocky Keen, Master Guide
Latham, John H.
Lattery, Dennis L.
Lazer, David L.
Lee, Alfred M.
Lee, Anthony B.
Leeping, Kurt M.
Leonard, David J., Master Guide
Lindgren, Darrell Allen
List, Martinus R.
Litzen, Michael J.
Logan, Vernon D.
Lounsbury, Dick Lovin, Lloyd K.
Luster, John Eston, Master Guide
Lynch, Daniel T.
Madrid, Samuel Michael
Mark's Guide Service
Mark Sandland, Master Guide
Massey, Jay
May, Robert P.
Darrell,
McDonald, Kenneth
McDaneld, Michael E.
McMahan, Charles B.
McMahan, Harley B
Meekin, Austin F.
Meekin, Michael J.

Meredith, Jerry
Merry, Peter E.
Midnight Sun Adventures
 Philip Driver, Master Guide
Midnight Sun Wilderness Safaris
 Coke W. Wallace
Miller, Mark E.
Miller, Ralph D.
Miller, William Lynn
Montana Trout Lodge
 David H. Couch
Montgomery, Daniel George
Moore, Mark R.
Morgan, Robert A.
Morris, David Scott
Morris Hunting Company
 Steven Morris
Morris, Roger D.
Mulchatna Lodge
Muno, Gary Stephen
Munse, Robert A.
Munsey's Bear Camp
 Mike Munsey
Mystic Lake Lodge
 George Palmer, Master Guide
Navarro, Littlejohn
Nee, David
Nelson, C. Pierce
Ness, Stanley E.
Newcomer, Hiram J.
Northward Bound
 Jim Harrower, Master Guide
Oman, Scott
Osprey Island Lodge
 Gary C. Pogany
Owen, Matthew L.
Owens, Dennis C.
O'Brien, Stephen F.
O'Hearn, Frederick R.
Pahl, Gerald "Gary" A.
Palmer, Martin H.
Panorama Mountain Outfitters
 R. L. "Butch" Loper
Parker/Boyce Guide Service, Inc
 Bruce Parker & James Boyce
Pedersen, Alec S.
Perkins, Kenneth D.
Perrins, Steven Hall
Petersen, Richard Garth
Peterson, Brian L.
Peterson, William W.
Pettijohn, Elbert T.
Pinard, Gary A.
Pioneer Outfitters
 Terry L. Overly, Master Guide
Pollard, Dennis
Pollard, George R., Master Guide
Poor, Jeffrey L.
Powers, Kenneth T.
Pralle, Jeffory K.
R & R Guide Service
 Rod Schuh & Rob Jones
Rahoi, Urban E.
Rainbow River Lodge
 Chris F. Goll, Master Guide
Reiner, Dennis E.
Richards, Tod A.
Richmond, P. Michael
RiteOFF
 President Michael D. Justice
Rivers, Larry R.
Rob Holt Reg. Guide/Outfitter
 Robert N. Holt
Robertson, Ralph R.
Robertson, Randall A.
Rohrer, Richard A., Master Guide
Rosenbruch, Jimmie C., Master Guide
Rosenbruch, Mary Ann
Rothenbuhler, James A.
Rowe Jr., Walter,
Runkle, John R.
Runyan, Andy R., Master Guide
Ruttum, Scott Lee
Sable Expeditions, Ltd.
 Bob Hodson
Sailors, Daniel L.
Schoonover, Kenneth E.
Schwab, Max C.
Scott Mileur's Fair Chase Hunts
 Scott Mileur
See Alaska
 Jim H. Keeline, Master Guide
Seidl, Mark R.
Selby, Jerome M.

Sheep River Hunting Camps
 Ed (Master Guide) and
 Deb Stevenson
Shepherd, Peter E. K.
Siavelis, George
Simmons, John E.
Simpson, Brian L.
Sisson, Donald G.
Skaflestad, Wendell W.
Smith, Donald F.
Smith, Oliver J.
Smith, Ray S.
Smith, Ronald E.
Sofoulis, Michael C.
Sousa, Gerald L.
Southeast Alaska Guiding
 Hans Baertle
Southeast Guide Service
 Scott Newman
Spiridon CampLeon
 J. Francisco, Master Guide
Stanley, Barry
Stanton, Joseph D.
Stephan Lake Lodge & Kodiak
 Guides– Jim Bailey, Master Guide
Stewart, William L.
Stoney River Lodge
 Mark "Curly" J. Warren
Sullivan, P. David
Swanson, Eric R.
Swartzlender, Richard Dale
Swiss, Jack Stanley, Master Guide
T C Lewis Lodge
 Joseph M. Caraway
Tamse, Richard D.
Tarnai, Sandor Alex
Taylor, C. Wayne
Taylor, John A.
The Lodge at Hidden Basin
Thiele Sr., George F.
Thiele, Reinhold Max
Thometz, Kraig Steven
Tiffany IV, Henry Dyer
Tinker, Michael L.
Todd, Leland D.
Toennessen, Dennis
Tom Hundley Master Guide &
 Outfitter–Tom Hundley
Townsend, Richard
Tracker Guide Service Ltd.
 James M. Fejes
Tsiu River Lodge
 Samuel T. Fejes, Jr.
Twardowski, John S.
Umphenour, Virgil L.
Upriver Outfitters
 Rick Sylvester
Vaden, Henrietta Roberts
VanNest Jr., Timothy J.
Vienna, David J.
Vrem, Kelly Lee
Vrem, Tracy J.
Waitman, Bradley J.
Want, Joseph William
Webber, Michael D.
Welch, Jeffery S.
Wells, Stephen F.
Whitney Jr., Clark G.
Whitney, Clark
Wildman Lake Lodge
 Gary "Butch" King Jr.
Wildman Lake Lodge
 Keith N. Johnson, Master Guide
Willard, F. Bruce
Willard, Gerald L.
Williams, Raymond L.
Williamson, Eric
Winkley, Buckey
Witt, Eugene M.
Witt, Patton G.
Wolf Creek Outfitters
 Thomas W. Hillis
Wolfe, Matthew C.
Wolford, Sidney M.
Woods, Wayne Williams
Worker, Timothy M.
Wrangell R. Ranch
 Ray McNutt, Master Guide
Zabielski, John Stanley
Zeznock, Terence M.
Zimmerman Jr., Thomas V.
Zwolinski, Chris J.

ARIZONA
Aalbers, Carl
Adams, Jeff
Alexander, Gary
Allen, Paul
Allison, Frank
Alpine Adventures
 Ernest Fay
Amadei, George
Anderson, John
Anderson, M
Anderson, Ralph
Arizona Big Game Hunts
 Robert Adams
Arizona Mature Bulls & Trophy
 Mule Deer–Myrl Mineer
Arizona Outfitters
 Pete Davis
Arocho, Angelo
Ashley, Ken
Baker, Otis
Barkley, William
Barnes, Randall
Barrett, Jim
Barrios, Arthur
Beamer, Charles
Bechtel, Robin
Bedlion, James
Bennett, Vance
Bishop, William H.
Bishop, William W.
Black River Guide & Outfitting
 Steve Clonts
Blair, Jeffrey
Boggess, Tom
Boido, Bobby
Bowdoin, Deab
Bradley, Loren
Brandt, Layne
Bravo, Torivio
Brooks, Cole
Brush Busters Trophy Hunts
 Scott Brush
Bryant, Randy
Bunnell, Bill
Burruel, Eduardo
Byfield, Ted
Callahan, Robert
Campbell, Fred
Carlson, David
Carpenter, Ross
Carr, Dale
Castleberry, Olin
Chaparral Guides & Outfitters
 Bill Marshall
Chavez, David
Clapson, Douglas
Clark, Ronnie
Columbia, James
Cook, Randy
Copley, Darius
Coppedge, Daniel
Coppedge, James
Corbett, Robert
Crawford, Norman
Crilley, Anthony
Crockett, David
Damron, Gary
Dees, Curtis
Deponte, John
Dillman, Robert
Dodd, Dennis
Dodd, Jerry
Dodson, Larry
Dominy, Matt
Donnelly, Dennis
Dorulla Outfitters
 Ronald Dorulla
Double J Outfitters
 Jimmy & Jenny Heap
Dryden, Newell
Dunn, Chris
Earl, Ervin
Earven, Bert
Ellison, Nathan
Elmer, Jeff
Elmer, Randy
Emerald, Darin
Epperson, Randy
Estes, Corwin
Evans, Robb
Exline, Mark
Felker, Bruce
Finch, Shaun

Finstad, Daniel
Fleming, Leon
Francis, Richard
Frazier, Jack
Frost, Clinton
Garard, Kenneth
Garard, Randy
Gassaway, Henry
Gates, John
George, Steven
George, Thomas
George, Todd
Getzen's Outfitting
 David Getzen
Giordano, Gary
Glanzer, Monte
Glenn, Larry
Glenn, Tommy
Glenn, Warner
Glenn-Kimbro, Kelly
Good, Alva
Goswick, Mark
Graf, Stan
Grand Slam Outfitters
 Todd Rice
Green, Floyd
Griffith, Robert
Grimes, James
Grimmett, Charles
Grombly, Stephen
Grounds, Hub
Guaraldi, Luke
Gunn, Terry
Gutherless, Rick
Hamblin, Ryan
Hansen, William
Haralson, Jon
Harlow, Chris
Harris, Tim
Hartman Outfitters Corp.
 Roger Hartman
Haught, Desty
Haws, Allen
Heckler, Gary
Henne, Edward
Henry, Kent
Henry, Richard
Henry, Robert
Herrera, Randy
Hicks, Daniel
Higgs, James
Hines, Greg
Hobel, Paul
Hodge, Nathan
Hoffman, Michael
Hogan, Joey
Holmes, Cary
Holmes, Wayne
Hopkins, John
Hopkins, Steve
Hovis, David
Howell, Dave
Howell, Larry
Hualapai Wildlife Conservation
 Monroe Beecher
Hughes, Robert
Hulsey, Michael
Ivanoff, Igor
James, Marvin
Jaramillo, Jerry
Johnson, Danny
Johnson, Douglas
Johnson, Jack
Johnson, John
Johnson, Royce
Johnson, Sandy
Jones, Richard
Joy, Jimmy
Joy, John
Kane, Grover
Kane, Ross
Kannapel, Mike
Keener, James
Kellner, Walter
Kester, Alan
King's Guide Service
 Daniel King
Knight, Daniel
Koons, Greg
Kostelnik, Walter
Krank, Floyd
Kridelbaugh, Doyle
Lackner, Dan

Lackner, Wayne
Lafuze, Terry
Lange, Charles
Larson, Mark
Larson, Theodore
Lawson, Tom
Ledin, Jerry
Lening, George
Levy, John
Lewis, Marion
Liljenquist, Vaughn
Lippert, Dean
Lopez, Alfonso
Mark Upshaw Guide Service
Marshall, Brian
Martin, Drayton
Martin, William D.
Martin, William G.
Massey, Winston
Mast, Jerry
Maxwell, Riney
May, David
McCasland, James
McClendon, Clarence
McClure, Roy
McCracken, Michael
McGee, Ray
McNeeley, Michael
McNeeley, Tony
Meeske, Ernie
Mendenhall, Gary
Miller, Gary
Milligan, Ernerst
Mitchell, Joe
Mitchell, Richard
Mogollon Rim Outfitters & Guide
  Gregory Krogh
Moss, Richard
Moulton, Timothy
Moya, George
Musser, Paul
Myers, David
Nathews, Blaine
Neshem, Stephen
Neshem, Stuart
Nichols, Branden
Nichols Guiding Service
  Jared Nichols
Nikolaus, Gerry
Noland, Albert
O'Connor, Gilbert
Ohaco, Michael
Orona, Greg
Orona, Herbert
Ortega, Eleodoro
Owens, Richard
Outfitters Guide Service
  John McClendon
Padilla, David
Palmer, Billy
Paul, Nick
Pawlicki, Richard
Penrod, David
Penrod, William
Perez, Louis
Peters, Charles
Phillips, James
Pierce, James
Pishkur, Gregory
Ponderosa Outfitters & Guide
Service–Ron Eichelberger
Preder, Kenneth
Priest, Dan
Priest, Dean
Prock, Curtis
Pulsifer, David
Pusch Ridge Outfitters
Dale Kelso
Ralls, Todd
Ram Riders Guides & Outfitters
  Michael Mell
Rawlinson, Steve
Reece, David
Reece, James
Reed, Dan
Reidhead, Ernest
Richardson, Duane
Richins, Clark
Riddle, Michael
Ridgeway, Charles
Riggs, Jeff
Rincon Outfitters
  Robert Dryden

Ritchie, Howard
Robbins, Luther
Rodriguez, Larry
Rogers, Robert
Rosania, Joe
Rossi, Thomas
Roth, Mike
Rough Country Outfitters
  Wayne Curtis
Ruehle, Jerry
Saathoff, Bill
Salazar, Tim
San Carlos Apache Tribe
Sanders, Gary
Schoppmann, John
Shaff, James
Sheep Ltd.
  Larry Heathington
Shelton, Les
Silva, Noah
Smith, Frederick
Smith, Jerry
Smith, Lloyd
Snead, Lawrence
Soderberg, Roger
Sonora Outfitters
  Leon Hoeffer
Sorrells, Cliff
Spear, Johnny
Spielman, Richard
Starr, Douglas
Stephens, Harold
Stevens, Scott
Stewart, David
Sullivan, Billy
Sullivan, Lee
Swindle, Gerald
Tapia, Sonny
Taylor, Dennis
Taylor, Troy
Thomas, Brian
Timberline Outfitters
Perry Hunsaker
Tinnin, Glenn
Todd, Chris
Todd, Tommie
Trophy Outfitters/US Outfitters
  Cougar Unltd.–Van Hale
Urban, Daniel
Valenzuela, Luis
Vancas, Mark
Vicente, John
Wantland, Patrick
Warren, Dean
Weems, Randy
Weidman, Robert
Weigel, Marshall
Weinhold, Dale
Weisser, Stephen
Wells, Richard
Weminuche Wilderness
  Adventures   Dan Shupe
Whelan, Mike
White, Jimmy
White, Nathan
White, Richard
Whited, Glen
Whitlow, John
Whitmore, Dale
Wickham, Myron
Williams, Thomas
Willsey, John
Workman, Bill
Wyckoff, Donald
Wyckoff, Jeffrey
Yellowhorn Outfitters/Sand Tank
  Outfitters–Peter Cimellaro
Yount, Dana
Youtz, Robert

ARKANSAS
Beaver Creek Outfitters I
  Arnold, Lawrence
Cache River Outfitters
  Haralson, Bert
Hunting & Fishing World, Inc.
  Elder, Willima

CALIFORNIA
Arrow Five Outfitters
Jim Schaafsma
Burrows Ranch Hunting Club
  Bill Burrows
Colorado Wild Sports
  Pat Flaherty

Curtis Guide Service
  Curtis Fletscher
Fair Chase Outfitters/River S Ent.
Mike and Debbie Schwiebert
Flournoy, George
Gober, Wallace
H & S Trophy Hunts Inc.
  Steve Hodges
Hunt, Robert
Jerry Penland Guide Service
  Jerry Penland
MSA Outfitters
  Mark Ashcraft
O'Rourke's Outdoor
Adventures—Richard O'Rourke
Prophet Muskwa Outfitters
  Kevin Olmstead
Slack's Wilderness Adventures
  Mark Slack
Tom Willoughby Outfitter/Guide
  Service–Thomas Willoughby
Triangle C Outfitters
  Bruce Cahill
Wildlife Wilderness Retreat
  Robert Todd

COLORADO
2V Outfitters
  Stephen Greenway
4 UR Ranch
  Rock Swenson
4 + 2 T Ranch
*Craig T. Tomk*e
7W Guest Ranch
  Russ Papke
7-M Guide Service
  Seven Mazzone
Action Adventures
Adams Lodge
  Ron Hilkey
Adventure Experiences Inc.
  Tim Kempfe
Alameno Outfitting & Guide
Service Frank Alameno
Alexander Outfitters
  Dave & Kerry Alexander
All Seasons Ranch
  M. Bruce Cottrell
Allens Guide Service
  Don Allen
Almont Outfitters, Inc.
Matthew Outfitters
Alpine Outfitters
  Jack Cassidy
Altenbern Hunting
  Clay A. Altenbern
Al's Outfitting
  Allen J. Roberts
American West Safaris & Flying
Eagle Outfitters
  Mark Anderson
Anderson, Bob
Anderson's Guide Service
  Daniel J. Anderson
Anderson, Gregory John
Archery Unlimited Outfitters
  Marshall Ledford
Aspen Canyon Ranch
  David Lewis & Steven Roderick
Aspen Outfitting Co. Inc.
  John Hollinger
Astraddle A Saddle Inc.
  Gary Bramwell
Atwood Hunts
  Hollis Atwood
Avalanche Outfitters
  Mike Schilling
B 4 J Outfitters
  Robert Jeffreys Jr.
B & J Hunting Camp
  Robert W. Wells
B & W Guide Service
  Lawrence Beagley
Backcountry Outfitters
  Bill Yeagher
Backcountry Outfitters Inc.
  David Guilliams Sr.
Badger Basin Outfitters
  Randy E. Tinlge
Badger Creek Guide & Outfitter
  Tim Hamilton
Bar Diamond Ranch
  Dellis Ferrier
Bar X Bar
  Arnold Watson
Bar Z X Ranch & Lodge
  Dean Lampton
Basin Outfitters
  Kenneth E. Wissel
Bear Creek Ranch
  Edward Wintz
Bearcat Outfitters
  Seth Peters
Beaver Mountain Outfitters
  Duain Morton
Beaver Valley Ranch
  Michael Cosby
Behrman, Russell

Belleville, Lynn Robert
Best Guide and Outfitters
  Donald L. Ankrum
Big Cimarron Outfitters
  Matt or Ken Munyon
Big Creek Reserve
  John E. Sandelin
Big Horn Outfitters
  Lester Dean Hawkins
Big Mountain Outfitters
  Sam Potter
Big Rack Outfitters
  Eric Lee Hamilton
Big Timbers Guest Ranch Inc.
  Brad Nothnagel & Dean Wagner
Bighorn Outfitting
  Dan Cooper & Dan Moyer
Bill Law Guide Service
  Bill Law
Black Elk Guides & Outfitters
Black Elk Outfitters Ltd.
  Dell H. Bean
Black Mesa Lodge
  Tom McLeod
Blackshere Jr., Frank
Black Timber Outfitters
  Kent Fischer & Carroll Johnson
Blanco River Outfitters
  Carl Bentley
Blays Western Colorado Outfitters
                Gordon Blay
Blue Creek Outfitters
  Scott Dillon
Bookcliff Outfitters
  Bruce Nay
Breckenridge Outfitters Inc.
  Paul H. Brooks
Broadacres Guest Ranch
Broken Spoke Ranch
  Clifford Davis
Brush Creek Outfitters Inc.
  Dennis Russell Grieve
Brushbusters Inc/B & B Outfitters
  of Durango–Robert Fertsch
Bryce Outfitting
  Jim Bryce
BSL Enterprises
  Scott Taylor
Buck Ridge Outfitters
  Ed Ilhareguy
Buck's Livery Inc.
  Ben & Mindy Breed
Bud Flowers Guide & Outfitters
  Bud Flowers
Buford Guide Service
  Tom Tucker
Buglin Bill Outfitters
  Bill Allen
Bull Basin Guides & Outfitters
  Dean Billington
Bull Mountain Outfitters Inc.
  Vicki Hale
Bull's Eye Outfitters Inc.
  Warren R. Allmon
Burton's Guide Service
  Clyde Warren Bruton
C & D Outdoors
  Don Polzin
C & M Outfitters
  Marcus Walker
Cabin Creek Outfitters
  Tony Tingle
Cache Creek Outfitters
  Jim DeKam
Cache Creek Outfitters
  Andrew Harris
Cadwell Outfitters
  Curtis Cadwell
Calhoun Guide & Outfitting
  Jay Jefferson & Bob Stokes
Camilletti, Darrell W.
Camilletti and Son's Inc.
  Edward Camilletti
Canyon Creek Outfitter
  Frank Fraser
Capitol Peak Outfitters
  Steve & Sandy Rieser
Cedar Mountain Guide Service
  Daniel L. Weber
Chair Mountain Stables
  Tom Mainer III
Challenge Outfitters
  David Eider
Champion Outfitters
  Dale V. Sundblom
Chaparral Park General Store
  Karen Johnston
Cherokee Outfitters
  Chuck Baker
Chris Loncarich Guide Service
  Chris Loncarich
Chuck Davies Guide Service, Inc.
  Chuck & Mark Davies
Circle Bar Outfitting
  Larry Allen
Circle K Ranch Outfitters
  Al & John Cannon
Cirrus Corporation
  Gary White
Coal Basin Partners

Coal Creek Outfitting
  Rod Black
Collegiate Peaks Outfitters
  David Douty
Colorado Back Country Outfitters
  Alan Bishop
Colorado Big Game Outfitter
  Kenneth Osborn
Colorado Diamond D Outfitters
  Thomas Dunn
Colorado Elite
  John D. Verzuh
Colorado Guest Ranch
  Larry & Elaine Mautz
Colorado High Country Outfitters
  Steven Weaver
Colorado High County Outfitters
  The Hatlees
Colorado High Guide Service
  Dennis Bergstad & Cade Benson
Colorado Hunting Adventures
  Brad & Terry Knotts
Colorado Mule Deer
  Linda L. Strong
Colorado Outfitters Inc.
  Jerome Bradley
Colorado Trail Riders &
  Outfitters–Doug Flowers
Colorado Trophies
  Jay Scott
Colorado Trophy Guides
  John & Jim Stehle
Colorado's Mountain West
Outfitting   Co–Wllly Pete
Georgiou
Columbine Outfitters
  Dan Bell
Columbine Outfitters LLC
  Greg Ward
Comanche Wilderness Outfitters
  Scott Limmer
Conejos River Outfitters
  Walter Heady Jr.
Conkey, Ralph W.
Cook, Rodney S.
Cooper's Outfitting & Guide Service
  Paul Cooper & Mark Chiono
Cougar Mountain Inc.
  Si H. Woodruff
Coulter Lake Guest Ranch Inc.
  C. Norman Benzinger
Cowboy Camp Outfitters Inc.
  Robert Port
Craig Outfitting Service
  Philip Craig
Culbreath Cattle Co.
  Grady Culbreath
D & G Horses
  Dale Boombs
DAL Outfitters Inc.
  David Lowry
Dale Haskins Hunting
  Dale Haskins
Dan Hughes Outfitting & Guides
  Dan Hughes
Daniel J. Humphrey Guides
  Daniel J. Humphrey
Dashing Through The Snow
  Mancel Griggs
Dave Parri's Outfitters
  David Parri
Dave Yost Outfittters
  Merrilee Yost
Deer Valley Ranch
  Harold DeWalt
Del's Triangle 3 Ranch
  Ray Heid
Devils Thumb Ranch Resort Inc.
  Barry John Gordon
Diamond D Bar Ranch
  Obbie & Willa Lee Dickey
Diamond Hitch Stables & Outfitting
  Joe Fahrion
Diamond M Outfitters
  Bob Martin
Diamond S Ranch
  Mike Walck
Diamond X Bar Outfitting
  Robert Campbell
Dick Pennington Guide Service
  Dick & Alan Pennington
Dilley's Guide Service
  Dale Dilley
Dog Gone Outfitters
  Perry Williamson
Dooley, Theordore
Double B Ranch Outfitters Inc.
  William D. Harmon
Double Diamond Outfitters
  Jack Wheeler
Double Dollar Cattle LLC
  Wayne Lacovetto
Double H Bar Outfitting
  Rick Hummel
Double LJ Outfitters Inc.
  Layne K. Wing
Drowsy Water Ranch
  Kenneth Fosha
DTD Outfitters
  Jack Lowe
Duarte Outfitters

Elmer Duarte
Eagle Mountain Ranch and
Outfitters   Jerry Broadfoot
Eagle Spirit Outfitters
  Carl Spina
Eagle's Nest Outfitting
  Billy Howard
East Divide Outfitters Inc.
  DennisYost
Echo Canyon Outfitters
  David & Kathleen Hampton
Elite Outfitters
  Brian Newell
Elk County Outfitters
  David Butterfield
Elk Mountain Guides & Outfitter
  John Pickering
Elk Ridge Adventures
  Stephen F. Watwood
Elk River Guest Ranch
  Patrick Barrett & William Hinder
Elkhorn Outfitters Inc.
  Richard & Cheryl Dodds
Elkstream Outfitters Inc.
  Jon T. Van Ingen
Engine Creek Outfitters
  Jim Houghton
Fantasy Ranch Outfitters
  James R. Talbot
Farmer, Bobby Ray
Farris Outfitters
  Paul Farris
Fawn Gulch Outfitters
  Dave Hemauer
Ferro's Blue Mesa Outfitters
  John Ferro
Field, Gerald
Finlay River Outfitters
Flynn & Sons Outfitters
  Delnor Flynn
Fossil Ridge Guide Service
  Rudy & Deb Rudibaugh
Fotopulos, Bruce
Four Corners Expeditions Inc.
  Reed Dils
Foutz Outfitting Service
  Charles Foutz
Fox Creek Adventures Inc.
  Cal Junker
Frazier Outfitting
  Sammy Frazier '
Freberg, Pauline "PS"
Fredrickson, Dennis
Fritzlan's Guest Ranch
  Calvin Fritzlan Outfitter
Frosty Acres Ranch
  Doug & Janet Camilletti
Fyvie, Joseph
Gafford Outfitters
  Jackie Gafford
Garvey Bros. Outfitters
  Doylene & Stan Garvey
Geneva Park Outfitters
  Terry Sandmeier
Gent, L. Dean
Gerald Field Outfitters
  Glen Eden Stables
Marie E. Wolf
Goode, Albert
Gorsuch Outfitters
  Scott Gorsuch
Grand Wapiti Outfitters
  Lyle Horn
Granite Mountain Lodge Inc.
  Susan Glittenberg
Great Divide Outfitters
  Dan Newman
Great Western Hunting Camps
  Darrell Gilks
Green Acres Ranch
  Terry Green
Green, Ivan
Groundhog Outfitters
  James J. Wagoner
Gurule, Art
Gypsum Creek Outfitters
  John Jodrie
H & H Hunting Camp Inc.
Halandras, Gus
Hammer Packing & Meat
  Processing–James Hammer
Hanging Horse Ranch Outfitter
  Colby Olford
Happy Trails Outfitters
  Gary Calhoun
Hardagine, David & Russell
Hartong, Ronald
Hatlem, John
Hawk Creek Outfitting
  Billy Jackson
Hawk Creek Outfitting Co.
  Wesley T. Gore
Hawkins, Melvin
Hermosa Creek Outfitters
  Frank Moringstar
Herrera, Thomas
Hesselman, John
Hi Country Outfitters
  Dick Cooper
High Country Guide & Outfitter
  Paul Irwin

High Country Outfitters Inc.
  Conrad A. Wygant
High Country Outfitters, LLC
  Van Johnson
High Lonesome Outfitter
  Tom Bowers
High Lonesome Outfitters
  Mark T. Lumpkins
High Meadow Outfitters
High Mountain Drifter Guide
Service   Michael Wilson
High Plains Outfitters
  Donny E. Talton II
High Plateau Outfitters Ltd.
  Angela Vannucci
High Trail Outfitters Inc.
  Bill Hopp
High West Outfitters
  Robert Knowlton & Kim Miller
Highlands Unlimited Inc.
  Geoff Burby
Hillview Outfitters
  Willard Forman
Hill's Guide Service
  Clifford & Jancice Hill
Hobby Horse Ranch
  Dorothy Hatterman-Smith
Holman's High Country Outfitters
  Buddy Holman
Honaker Guides & Packers
  Pat Honaker
Horn Fork Guides
  Joe Boucher
Horsethief Adventures
Hot "T" Camp
  Jack Flowers
Hoza Guide & Outfitting
  Tony Hoza
Hyatt Guides & Outfitters
  Bruce Hyatt
Imperial Expeditions
  Micheal John Jones
Indian Peak Outfitters
  Ardis M. Wright
Indian Summer Outfitters
  Rick House
Iron Nipple Fishing & Hunting Co.
  Bob Huffman
J M L Outfitters
  Maggie & Marie Haskett
J & B Outfitters
  Brad Gray
J & J Guides & Outfitters
  John Markham
J & J Guides & Outfitters
  Jerry Woolsey
J & Ray Colorado High Country
  Ronald Franks
J & V Guides & Outfitters
  Glenn Jones & Lonny Vanatta
Jackson's Guide & Outfitter Service
  Robert Jackson
Jake's Rio Grande Outfitting
Service   David J. Powell
Jeffcoat Outfitters
  Danny Jeffcoat
Jerry Craig Guide Service
  Jerry Craig
JML Outfitters
John's Outfitter and Guide Service
  John Harmon
Jolley Jr., Malcolm Carter
Jones, James
JT Outfitters
  Jeff Burtard
Judd Cooney Outfitting & Guiding
  Judd Cooney
J.C. Trujillo Guide & Outfitter
  J.C. Trujillo
K & K Outfitters
  Marion Bricker
K & W Outifitters
  Drew & Billie Kissire
Kings Guide Service
  Douglas King
Koo-Sto Wilderness Outfitters
  Phillip L. Foster
Kuhns' Guide & Outfitters
  Douglas Kuhns
K.E. Schultz Guide & Outfitting
Service–Kurt E. Schultz
L & B Hunting & Guide Service
  Larry Herod
Lakeview Resort & Outfitters
  Dan Murphy
Lakota Guides & Outfitters
  Bob Littlejohn
Lamicq Guides & Outfitters Inc
  John & Diane Lamicq
Latigo Ranch
  James Yost
Lazy F Bar Outfitters
  Bill Guerrieri
Lazy FF Outfitters
  Kirk Ellison
Little Big Horn Lodge
  Harry Ergott, Jr.
Little Cone Outfitters
  Roy Hutt
Little Creek Ranch

Alan Baier
Little Grizzly Creek Ranch Inc.
  Leo Douglas Sysel
Lobo Outfitters
  Dick Ray & Mike Ray
Lodgepole Outfitters
  Don Pinnt
Lone Tom Outfitting
  Paul Janke
Lost Creek Guides
  Lance Edinger
Lost Solar Outfitters Inc.
  Thomas Marucco & Gary Stoaks
Louisiana Purchase Ranch
Outfitters   M. Lee Tingle
Lunney Mountain Outfitters/
Marvine   Outfitters–Brett
J. Harvey
M & M Outfitters
  Tom and Susan Mikesell
Mamm Peak Outfitters
  Jeff & Dea Mead
Manhattan Creek Outfitters, Inc.
  Linda Wright-Winterfeld
Mark Justin Inc.
  Mark Justin Halderman
Marvine Ranch LLC & Elk Creek
  Lodge–William Wheeler
Matt Bridges Guide & Outfitting
  Matt Bridges
Mc Callister & Carroll
Adventures–Norm McCallister &
  David Carroll
Meadows Vega
  Tom Cox
Medano Pass Guide & Outfitter
  Donny Carr
Medicine Bow Outfitters
  Jared Florell
Mega Buck Outfitters
  Michael Gillis
Mike Murphy Wilderness Exp.
Mill Creek Outfitters
  Chuck Wisecup
Mineral Mountain Guide &
Outfitters   John Martin
Mountain Enterprises
  Gary & Robin Edwards
Mountain Man Tours
  Greg Coln
Mule Creek Outfitters
  Randy & Brenda Myers
Mule Shoe Guide Servie
  Billy Joe Dilley
Natural Adventures Inc.
  Thomas E. Tietz
Needle Rock Ranch
  Steven Duffy
Noah's Ark Adventure Program Ltd
  Chuck Cichowitz
Norm Harder Outfitter
  Norm Harder
North Park Outfitters
  Bob Martin
Northwest Colorado Ranching for
  Wildlife–Jarrell Massey
OFC Outfitting
OK Ranch Outfitters
  John Carelli
Old West Outfitters
  Randy Messick
Over the Hill Outfitters
  John R. Neely
Oxbow Outfitting Company
  William Hayes
Oxbow Outfitting Co.
  Donald DeLise
Pack Country Outfitters
  Mike Reid
Pass Creek Outfitters
  Lee Sinclair
Peak T Outfitting Inc.
  Anthony Benkoski
Peregrine Guides & Outfitters Inc.
Peters Hunting Service
  Harley & Bonnie
Phil's Bowhunting Adventures
  Phil Phillips
Piedra Packing & Outfitting
  Roger Kleckner
Pierce Brothers Outfitters
  William "Leon" Pierce
Pike's Peak Outfitters
  Gary Jordan
Piney River Ranch
Platte River Outfitters
  Richard Aldrich
Pollard's Ute Lodge
  Troy Pollard
Pomotawh Naantam Ranch
  Jon & Dori Lee
Powderhorn Outfitters
  Vincent Woodrow Tanko
Powderhorn Primative Outfitters
  Cletus Bissell
Prime Time Hunts
  William Malizia
Proline Excursions Inc.
  Paul Howard
Purcell Brothers Outfitting Inc.
  Duane & Dale Purcell

Purgatoire Outfitters
Jay Waring
Pyramid Outfitters
Steve Whiteside
Quaking Aspen Outfitters Inc.
Dave Mapes
Quarter Circle Circle Ranch
John Judson
R & R Ranch
Ralph Royster
Ram's Horn Guides & Outfitters
Alan Vallejo
Rapp Guides Service Inc.
Anne & Jerry Rapp
Razor Creek Outfitters
Ron Brink
Red Feather Guides & Outfitters
Todd Peterson
Red Mountain Outfitters
Jim Flynn
Red Saddle Outfitting
Don Taylor
Redd Ranches Guides & Outfitters
Inc.–David Redd
Rendezvous Outfitters & Guides
Russ & Cheri Eby
Rick Edinger & Sons
Rick Edinger
Rick Warren Guide & Outfitting
Ricky Warren
Rim Rock Outfitters
Monty Elder
Rimrock Guide & Outfitting
Charles Harrington
Ripple Creek Lodge
Ken Jett
Rocky Mountain Adventures Inc.
G. David Costlow
Rocky Mountain High Tours Inc.
Chet Bevilacqua
Rocky Mountain Outfitters
Gary Bohochik
Rocky Mountain Outfitters
Colt Ross
Rocky Mountain Ranches
Lawrence Bishop
Rocky Mountain Safaris
Denzel Hartshorn
Rocky Pappas Guides & Outfitters
Rocky Top Outfitters
Jimmy (Buck) Ward
Rod Wintz Guide Service
Rod Wintz
Ron-D-View Ranch & Outfitting
Ron Pfeffer
Royal Gorge Outfitters
Bill Edrington & Bill Carson
Rudy Steele Guides & Outfitters
Inc.   Rudy Steele
R.J.'s Greystone Guide & Outfitting
Ronald Tull Jones
S & K Outfitting & Guide Servie
Skeeter Gingery
Saddle Action
Pam Green
Saddle Mountain Guide Service
Lawrence Zeldenthuis
Saddle Tramp Outfitters
Thomas Bullock
Samuelson Outfitters
Richard & Cathy Samuelson
San Juan Outfitting
Tom & Cheri Van Soelen
San Pahgre Outdoor Adventures
Stuart Chappell
Sangre De Cristo Outfitters
Tom & Bill Schulze
Schmittel Packing & Outfitting
David Schmittel
Scoop Lake Outfitters Ltd.
David Suitts
Scott Fly Rod Co.
John Duncan
Seely Hunting
Bruce Seely
Seven Lakes Inc.
Steve Cobb
Shamrock Ranch Outfitters
Bruce Wilson
Shankster, Thomas G.
Shavano Outfitters
Jim James
Silver Peaks Outfitters
Scott E. Williams
Sky Corral Guest Ranch
David Vannice
Skyline Guest Ranch & Lazy 3X
Ranch–David Farny
Slater Creek Cattle Co.
Larry Lyster
Sly Creek Guide & Outfitters
Gary Baysinger
Snowmass Falls Outfitters
Mat Turnbull
Snowmass Stables Inc.
Marlene Christopher
Solomon Creek Outfitter
Nancy Solomon
Southfork Stables Inc.
Kimberly Kay Baird
Southwest Adventures

Corey Veach
Southwest Adventures Ltd.
Charles Hughes
Spadafora Ranch Lodge
Roger Cesario
Sperry's
Joe Sperry
Spike's Outfitters
Perry Alspaugh
Stajduhar Ranches & Outfitting
John & Steven Stajduha
Stalbach, Tony
Star Outfitters
Jeffry Corriveau & Dennis Craig
Steamboat Stables/Sombrero
Ranches Inc.–Rex Walker
Stetson Ranches LLC
Franklin L. Stetson
Steward Ranch Outfitter
Laverne Gwaltney & John Brennan
Stillwater Gun Club Inc.
Mark Bean
Stockstill, Charlie
Stone Creek Outfitters
Bob Helmer & Clay Bassett
Story Creek Outfitters
Frank Menegatti
Summit Guides
Dale Fields
Sundown Outfitters
David Cordray
Sunrise Outfitters
Leroy & Paul Schroeder
Sunset Ranch Inc.
Patsy Wilhelm
T Lazy 7 Ranch
Rick Deane
T & J Outfitters
Walter Tycksen & Sue Jameson
Tageguache
Richard Hansen
Taylor Creek Inc.
William Fitzsimmons
Taylor Guide & Outfitters
Lance & Terri Taylor
Telluride Outside
William C. White
Templeton, Jay
Tenderfoot Outfitter & Guide
Services   Inc.–Paul & Steve
& Jim Pike and   Brent Carlson
Teocalli Outfitters
Al & Laura Van Dyke
Texas Creek Outfitters
David Butcher
The Gunnison Country Guide
Service   John C. Nelson
The Outfitter
Jack Childs
Thompson's High County Guides
& Outfitters–Greg Thompson
Three Rivers Outfitting
Mark Schumacher
Three String Outfitting & Guiding
Dennis Clendenning
Timber Basin Outfitters
Gregory Geelhoed
Timberline Outfitters
Perry B. Abbott
Timberline Outfitters
Douglas Frank Jr.
Timmer Jr., Jack E.
Tom Fritzlan & Family
Tom Fritzlan
Toneda Outfitters
Ed Wiseman
Track'em Outfitters
Rob't Pedretti & Tracy
Grzeskowiak
Trail Ridge Outdoors
Thomas Clinkenbeard
Trail Skills Inc.
Robert Getz
Trapper Creek Outfitters
Lloyd C. Thompson
Trappers Lake Lodge
Ross Wheeler
Triple G Outfitter & Guides Inc.
Daniel Eckert & Alan Echtler
Triple-O-Outfitters
Larry & Reta Osborn
Twin Buttes Ranch Outfitters
Steve Titus
Two Rivers Guest Ranch
Uncompahgre Outfitters Inc.
Chris Hutchison
Ute Trail Guide Service
Glenn Everett
Valley Hunting Service
Cliff Bankston
Vic Taylor Outfitter
Vic Taylor
Vickers Enterprises, Inc.
Larry Vickers
Vision Quest – Guided Hunts
Chris Furia
W3 Outfitters
Dale & Sheri Hopwood
Wallace Guides & Outfitters
Fred & Bill Wallace

Walz Guide Service
Jimmie Walz Sr.
Wapiti Outfitter & Guides
Jon Garfall
Wardell's Guide Service
Layne Wardell
Waterfall Ranch Outfitters
Edwin A. Zink
Watkins San Juan Outfitting
Thomas F. Watkin
Watson Ranches Ltd.
James L. Watson
Waunita Hot Springs Ranch
Ryan Pringle
Weimer Hunting Camp
Jody C. Weimer
Welder Outfitting Service
Brian & Shawn Welder
West Elk Outfitters
John Hatlem
West Fork Outfitters
G. Eugene Story
Western Horizon's Guides &
Outfitters–Myron Morrow
Western Sports
Robert O. Woods
Western Ways Ltd.
Eric Glade
Western Wildlife Inc.
Rob Raley
Wetherill Ranch
George Hughes
Whinnery, Steve
Whistling Elk Outfitters Inc.
John Ziegman
White, Bruce
White Pine Ranch
Dennis & Cindy Hall
White River Resort
Jack Harrison
Wilcox, James T.
Wild West Outfitters
Allen Kennon
Wilderness Adventures Inc.
Larry Ehardt
Wilderness Aware Inc.
Joe Greiner
Wilderness West
Gordon Kent & Scott Garber
Williams Guide Service
Patrick C. Williams
Willmarth, Lyle
Willow Creek Outfitters
Don Hawkins
Wilton Earle & Sons
Leon Earle
Winding Stair Mountain Outfitters
Sam Smith
Winterhawk Outfitter Inc.
Larry L. Amos
Wit's End Guest Ranch & Resort Inc.
Brad Custer
Wolf Creek Outfitters
Jason Ward
Yampa River Outfitters
Randall Baird
Yampa Valley Outfitters LLC
Mack & Boyd Tallen
Yeager, Ronny
Younger Bros. Guiding & Outfitting
Glen Younger
Ziegler, Gary

CONNECTICUT
Sportsmans Pride Outfitters
Keith Cote

FLORIDA
Airboat Guide Service
Tim Spaulding
Barker, David
Big Cypress Guide Service
Jim Curwood
Bryant, Jerry
Camp Wanikewin Lodge
Ken Baker
Doug's Guide Service
Douglas Burbella
Eagle's Nest Hunt Club Inc.
Ed's Firearms Consultant
Ed Shumate
Elkhorn Guide Outfitters
Wayne Zorn
Everglades Guide
Tom Glaze
Fin & Feather Guide Service
Steve Ambrose
Hammond, Dennis
Fisheating Creek Hunting Camp
D. Williams
J & R Outfitters
Floyd O'Bannon
Malone, Kevin
Neal's Wilderness Outfitters, Inc.
Neal Atkinson
Outdoor Adventures Ltd.
Jim Conley
Razorback Camp

John J. And Buck Mclin
Reilly Lake Camps/Reindeer Lake
Lodge–Wayne Gangler
R. McAlister's Guide Services Unltd.
Royce McAlister
Seymour, Jim
The Wildlife Safaris & Taxidermy
Mike Acreman
Trek International Safaris
Mike Cloaninger
West Fork Outfitters
David Walker
Williams, Chris

GEORGIA
Lone Cone Outfitters Inc.
Ron Clements
Mountain Wilderness Outfitters
Jim Garmon
Sheep Creek Outfitters
Johnny Campbell
Silver Bullets Outfitters Inc.
Robert May
Williams, Debbie

IDAHO
4 x 4 Outfitters, Inc.
Gary Madsen
62 Ridge Outfitter and Guide
Kenneth L. Smith
Action Hunts
Charles Loeschen
American Adrenaline Co. Inc.
Deb Wood & Steven E. Zettel
Anderson Outfitting
Robert and Mary Anderson
Antelope Valley Outfitters, Inc.
Harold E. Smith Jr.
A-W Wilderness Outfitters
Sandy Podsaid
B Bar C Outfitters
Mike & Belinda Stockton
B & K Outfitters
Brian E. Butz
Barker Trophy Hunts
Jon Barker
Beamer's Landing
F. James & Jill Koch
Bear Creek Outfitters
Lyle Phelps
Bear River Outfitters
Marriner R. Jensen
Big Creek Lodge & Outfitters Inc.
Donald E. Manly
Big Track Outfitters
Johannsen & Johannsen
Bigfoot Outfitters
Harvey Whitten & Tom Fliss
Bigfoot Outfitters Ray Rall
Bighorn Outfitters
George Butcher & Dave Melton
Birch Creek & Clearwater Driftr.
David L. Peterson
Boulder Creek Outfitters Inc.
Tim Craig & Allen D. Jones
Bugling Bull Archery Outfitters
Rocky Jacobsen
C Bar D Outfitters
Darrell Meddle
Castle Creek Outfitters
Shane McAfee
Cat Track Outfitters
Todd Molitor
Cayuse Outfitters
Patti & Rich Armiger & Steve
Ayers
Central Idaho Outfitters
Stephen A. Kaschmitter
Chamberlain Basin Outfitters Inc.
Edward A. McCallum
Chuckar Chasers
Rick Schultsmeier
Clearwater Outfitters
Thomas J. Rucker
Clifford Cummings Outfitter
Clifford Cummings Jr.
Coeur d'Alene Outfitters
Murray "Bat" Masterson
Coeur D'Alene River Big Game
Outfitters–Gary & Jan Sylte
Cook's Idaho & Wind River
Outfitters–Rick & Judy Cook
Cross Outfitters
Larry W. Cross
Diamond D Ranch Inc.
Thomas & Linda Demorest
Dixie Outfitters Inc.
W. Emmett Smith
Eakin Ridge Outfitters
Lesley & Lamont Anderson
Edwards, Bruce A. & Donna
Fall Creek Outfitters
Dalbert Allmon
Flying B Ranch Inc.
Robert Burlingame
Flying Resort Ranches Inc.
Wm. R Guth & David E Williams
George E. Duncan Outfitter & Guide

George E. Duncan
Gilmore Ranch Outfitters & Guides
  Charles D. Neill Jr.
Gospel Mountain Outfitters
  Jim Daude
Green Feather Adventures Inc.
  Billy Wayne Hampton
Guth (Norman H) Inc.
  Norman H Guth & Mel Reingold
Happy Hollow Vacations
  Martin Capps
Hat Point Outfitters Inc.
  Marlin Kennedy
Heart Mountain Outfitters
  Timothy N. Thomas
Heinrich & Smith Outfitters
  Wm. Heinrich & Robt. Smith
Hidden Creek Ranch
  Iris Behr
High Country Outfitters
  Ray Seal
High Desert Enterprises
  Andrede & Chris Maisel
High Desert Expeditions
  Rodger Tiffany
Hincks Palisades Creek Ranch
  Bret Hincks
Horse Creek Outfitters
  Rick Trusnovec & Jim Thomas
Idaho Whitetail Guides
  Jack M. Skille
Indian Creek Ranch Inc.
  Jack W. Briggs
Indian Meadows Outpost & Pack
  Station–Dave Stucker
Jarbidge Wilderness Guide &
  Packing–Lowell & Diane Prunty
Jarvis, Tom L.
Juniper Mountain Outfitters Inc.
  Stanley Paul Meholchick
Keating Outfitters
  Earl Keating
Kootenai River Outfitters & Guides
  Victor Frederickson
Kuykendall, Herman C.
Lazy J Outfitters Inc.
  Larry A. Jarrett
Lemburg's Priest Lake Outfitters
  Randall Lemburg
Little Wood River Outfitters
  Robert L. Hennefer
Lochsa River Outfitters
  Sherry & Jacey Nygaard
Loomis, Chris Paul
Loon Creek Ranch Inc.
  Lyle M. Thomas
Lost Lakes Outfitters Inc.
  Albert & Diane Latch
Mackay Bar Corporation
  Vince Ivanoff
Middle Fork Lodge Inc.
  Mary Ossenkop & Larry
  WhiteheadMiddlefork Ranch Inc.
  Ben Grammar
Middlefork Ranch Inc.
  Jimm Sullivan & Bill Widgren
Mile Hi Outfitters Inc.
  Jerry Jeppson & Cliff Zielke
Moose Creek Outfitters
  Darrell Norris
Moyie River Outfitters
  Stanley A. Sweet
Mystic Saddle Ranch
  Jeff & Deb Bitton
N ID Border Ranch Oftr. & Guide
  Serv.–Ardella E. Book
North Star Outfitters
  Kenneth Wolfinbarger & Les Udy
Ospry Adventures
  Cheryl Bransford
Oswold Pack Camp
  Ralph Oswold
Outlaw Outfitters
  Douglas A. Sayer
Pioneer Mountain Outfitters
  Tom & Deb Proctor
Quarter Circle A Outfitters
  Rick Hussey
Rawhide Outfitters
  Kathy John Cranney
Red River Corrals Guest Ranch
  Archie George
Renshaw Outfitting, Inc.
  Jim Renshaw
Ridgerunner Outfitters
  Marlene West
River Mountain Wildlife
  Experiences–Shannon Lindsey
Robson, Dale R.
Rudeen Ranches
  Kent A. Rudeen
S D Outfitters Inc.
  Raymond R. Hamell
S & S Outfitters
  David J. Bream
Salmon River Lodge Inc.
  Jim Dartt
Sawtooth Wilderness Outfitters
  Darl & Kari Allred
Shattuck Creek Ranch & Outfitters
  Andres Molsee

Shepp Ranch Idaho
  Jinny Hopfenbeck & Paul Resnick
Shoup Trophy Outfitters
  Garry L. Pedrow
Sleeping Deer Outfitters Inc.
  Ronald J. Clark
Smoky Mountain Outfitters
  Bruce T. Butler
Snake River Outfitters
  Norman Riddle
South Fork Expeditions Ltd.
  John Hill Jr.
South Fork Outfitters
  Ralph L. Hatter
Spring Creek Outfitters & Guides
  Lawrence E. & Lillian Joy Hill
Stanley Potts Outfitters
  Stan & Joy Potts
Steel Mountain Outfitters
  Ronald L. Sherer
St. Joe Hunting & Fishing Camp Inc.
  Will Judge
Sulphur Creek Ranch
  Tom T. Allegrezza
Taylor Ranch Outfitters
  Steve Zettel
Teton Ridge Ranch
  Albert Tilt III
Trail Creek Outfitters
  Layne Davis
Triangle C Ranch
  Ron Gillett
Triple O Outfitters Inc.
  Harlan Opdahl
Trout Creek Outfitters
  Ray & Barbie Cox
Twin Peaks Ranch Inc.
  Dave Giles
Valley Ranch Outfitters
  Randall G. Baugh
Wally York & Sons Inc.
  Bev York Travis
Wapiti Meadow Ranch & Outfitters
  M. Barry Bryant & Diane Haynes
Wapiti River Guides
  Gary Lane
War Eagle Outfitter & Guides
  Ken & Dolly Jafek
Warm Springs Outfitters
  Gordon E. Frost
Warren Outfitters & Steelhead
  Outfitters–James R. Thrash
Weitas Creek Outfitters
  Steve Jones
Whiskey Mountain Outfitters
  James I. Bass
White Cloud Outfitters
  Mike Scott & Louise Stark
Whitewater Outfitters
  Zeke & Erlene West
Wild Horse Creek Ranch William R.
  "Bill" Shields
Wilderness Outfitters
  Podsaid & Hart
Willey Ranch Outfitters/ B & B Davis,
  Buzz Davis
Williams, David E.
Wolf Fang Outfitters
  Scott A Minter
Yellow Wolf Ranch
  Edd S. Woslum
Youren, Dusty

ILLINOIS
Blyth's Canyon Lake Lodge
  Bruce & Joan Blyth
Lac Seul Airways Ltd.
  John & Pat Renfro
Northern Illinois Outfitters
  Jerry DeVries
Smooth Rock Camp
  Don & Lynn Leavens

INDIANA
Global Outfitters
John & Diosa's Wabaskang Camp
  John & Diosa Record
Oak Lake Lodge
  Jerry & Wanetah Helgason

IOWA
Eva Lake Resort Airway Ltd.
  David Cunning
Gold Arrow Camp
  Don Moore
Golden Fawn Chalet
  Barb & Al Wiegert
Hawley Mountain Guest Ranch
  Ronald T. Jarrett
Iowa Trophy Hunting
  John Hambleton
Lac Seul Evergreen Lodge &
  Golden Eagle Resort–Gary & Pat
  Beardsley

KANSAS
Big K Hunting
  George E. Savage
Chautauqua Hills Guide Service
  Mark D. Jones
Daniels, Robert L.
Diamond V Ranch
  Thomas P. Sollner
Elliott's Son's Guide Service
  Terry L. Grubbs
Five Double Bar Farms
  Thomas J. Beckman
Flint Hills Guide Service
  Brian L. Wheeler
Golden Prairie Outfitters
  Keith A. Horney
Goose Creek Guide Service
  Bruce S. Shultz
Kalivoda Hunting Guide Service
  Roland L. Kalivoda
L & L Lodge
  James M. Larsen
Midwest Outfitters
  Scott A. Wilkins
Milligan Brand Outfitters
  Carl A. Morgan
Mortensen Buck Buster
  Steven V. Mortensen
North Central Kansas Guide
  Service Brian D. Blackwood
Oak Valley Guide Service
  William F. Shank
Paradise Adventure
  Kurtis A. Nunnenkamp
Pheasant Creek
  Douglas L. Kysar
Pike Island Lodge & Outposts
  Ron McKenzie
Quail Lodge
  Pierson S. Morrill
R L Guide Services
  Robert E. Landrum
R M F Guide Service
  Ronald M. Ford
Rollow, Kenneth H.
Servant Guiding
  Larry D. Thatcher
Shadow Oaks
  Terry Daniels
Sugar Creek Trophies
  Gerald & Marc Gilliland
Thunder Prairie Guide Service
  Timothy R. Larson
Triple J. Hunt Club of Kansas
  John C. Gable
Uhlik Hunting Grounds
  Mark G. Uhlik
Verdigris Valley Outfitters
  Douglas C. Arnold
Verdigris Valley Outfitters
  Michael D. Collins
Walkers Guide Service
  Everett H. Walker
Wolf River Outfitter
  Jim P. Aller

KENTUCKY
Beals, Robert
Boitnott Guide Service
  Billy Joe Boitnott
Campisano, Tony
Carter, Thomas
Cone, Keith
Eller, Virgil Rankin
Grant, C.A. (Tony)
Hight, Kevin
Hitchcock Jr., Robert E.
Houchens, Bobby & Sandra
Johnson, Ronnie
Kentucky Whitetail Hunting
  David & Sandy Woosley
Keown, Jerry
Leech's Guide Service
  Jim Leech
Ludwig, Dale
Pool, James
Silver Creek Outfitters
  Steve Bostick
Sportsman's Quest
  Henry Joe Lyon
Vanvactor, Darrell
Wethington, Harold
Wynn, E.D.

LOUISIANA
Big Burns Hunting Lodge
  Roger G. Vincent Jr.
Hoover, Lloyd G.
Joanen, Gene
O'Connor, George
Tall Timbers Lodge
  Judy Davis

MAINE
9 Lake Outfitters
  Edward Richard
Ashland Bear Camps
  Boyd Ward
Baker Brook Sporting Camps
  Scott Clark
Bear Creek Guide Service & Lodge
  John Schmidt
Beaver Creek Guide Service
  Paul Behring
Beech Nut Sporting Camps
  Dan & Margaret LaPointe
Beech Ridge Guide Service
  Glenn Ricker
Big Country Guide Service
  Russell Cummings
Birch Hill Guide Service
  Steven Botelho
Buck Stop Sporting Camps
  Richard Streeter
Camp Wapiti
  Anita & Frank Ramelli
Cedar Ridge Outfitters
  Hal Blood
Conklin's Lodge & Camps
  Lester Conklin
Corson, Gary
Crooked Tree Lodge & Camps
  Nick Curtis
Crooked-Eye Camp
  Kenneth Robinson
Dave Tobey Guide & Outfitter
  Dave Tobey
Dean's Den
  Dean Paisley
Driftwood Lodge & Camps
  Harold Schmidt
Dri-Ki Lodge
  Robert & Carrie Keim
Flint River Camp
  The Goodman Family
Foggy Mountain Guide Service
  Wayne Bosowicz
Geno's Guide Service
  Gene Rossignol
Gentle Ben's Lodge
  Bruce Pelletier
God's Country Guide Service
  Leonard Coover
Hardtime Big Game Guide Service
  Jason McDonald
Harry's Lodge
  Ed Harris
Hillside Guide Service & Game
  Ranch–Scott Beede
Katahdin View Lodge & Camps
  Jack Downing
King & Bartlett Fish and Game
  Club–Todd Wallace
Maine Outdoors
  Don Kleiner
Matagamon Wilderness
  Campground   Donald Dudley
Meadow Mountain Guide Service
  Robert Sanborn
Mount Chase Lodge
  Richard Hill
Mt. Henry Guide Service
  Rick Lausier
Nelson Cole & Son
  Nelson Cole
North Country Lodge
  Dale Goodman
North Ridge Outfitters
  Maynard Pierce Jr.
Northern Outdoors
  Wayne Hockmeyer & Chris Russell
PB Guide Service
  Paul Beauregard
Red Buck Sporting Camps
  Sandra & Thomas Doughty
Remote Maine Tent Hunts
  Dan Legere
Rivers Bend Camps
  Sheldon Lyons
Rocky Ridge Guide Service
  Carl Bois
Rowe Jr., Andy
Sebago Lake Cottages
  Ray & Fran Nelson
Secret Pond Camps & Guide Service
  Mark Carver
Skunk Hill Guide Service
  John Robinson
Snowy River Adventures
  Claude Rounds
So. Maine Guide Service Stony
  Brook Outfitters–Robert Parker
Sundown Cabins
  Patrick & Shirley Dubord
The Enchanted Sporting Camps
  Don Burnham
The Last Resort Hunting & Fishing
  Ellen & Tim Casey
Tim Pond Wilderness Camps
  Harvey & Betty Calden
Track Down Kennel & Lodge
  Joel Guimond
Tuckaway Shores
  Phil & Paulette Thomas

Turnpike Ridge Outfitters
  Don Helstrom Jr.
Umc'olc'us
  Al & Audrey Currier
Umiakovik Fishing & Hunting
  Ltd.–Harvey Calden
Western Mountain Hunter's Service
  Ronald Rackliff
White Birch Guide Service
  Paul R. Bois
Wilderness Sports
  Clark Wormell
Wilds of Maine Guide Service
  Michael Patterson
Wilsons
  Shan & Wayne Snell
Woody's
  Woody & Elsie Martin

MARYLAND
Buck "N" Bears Guide Service
  Robert Bandy
F & M Ranch Outfitting
  Floyd W. Price
Running Creek Ranch
  David Les Udy
Suder, Omar Dale

MASSACHUSETTS
Barrett, William F.
Duke's Butternut Cabin & Guide
  Service–Lee Duke
Gammon River East Outcamps
  Bob Crockett
High Island Ranch
  George Nelson Jr.
Ridge Runners & River Runners
  William E. Davis Jr.
Rol-Yat Guide Service
  George Taylor

MICHIGAN
Anderson, Anton F.
Bowler, Ernest W.
Como Lake Resort
  Ken Woodard & Lee Burk
Paquette's Camp
  Wayne Blocher & Lewis Scheid
Trail Creek Lodge
  Ralph Mersdorf
Wildcat Creek Outfitters
  Russell L. Newton III

MINNESOTA
Aili, Keith
Andrews, Allen
Ashambie Outpost Ltd.
  Scott & Lynda Marvin
Baker, Michael R.
Baker, Robert
Beans, Donald
Bending Lake & Raleigh Lake Lodge
  Mike Muelken
Bissonette, Michael J.
Blakesley, Glade
Boes Jr., James
Brattrud, Andy
Burandt, Ivan
Dreher, Phil
Edwards, Emery A.
Fleming, Paul T.
Garvick, Greg
Goble, Daniel
Goble, Rodney W.
Gotchnik, Gary
Green, Bill
Gross, Terry
Hanson, Russell
Hazelton, Bernard
Hebl, Lona
Herr, Dale
Himes, Dale
Hoeschen, Mike
Holm, Merrill
House, Frank
Householder, Loy
Hughley, Joshua
John, Douglas
Jourdan, Jon
KaBeeLo Lodge
  Harold & Ann Lohn
Klos, Dana
Krech, Richard
Krienke, Kenneth
Kuduk, Chris
Laegeler, Jonathan
Larson, Randy
Lavalla, Al
Leonard, Bruce
Liard River Outfitters
  Bob Johnson
Lindley, Tom & Chad
Manz, Burt

Martinson, Gary
McDowell, Shawn
McNurlin, Mark
Meyers, Thomas
Misaw Lake Lodge
  Bob & Shar Johnson
Moose Creek Outfitters
  Rodney Paulson
Nelson, Frank E.
Nikula, Jeff
Norstebon, Darrell
Pearson, Richard T.
Petersen, Dale
Pfremmer, Ray
Pope, Gale
Powis, Joseph R.
Ramsey, Darrell
Reese, Richard G.
Reiling, Philip
Ross, Tom
Schaefer, Charles J.
Schultz, Orville
Schumacher, Kurt V.
Schuster, Tom
Scott, Rodney
Shepard, Kelly L.
Sherrill, Robert
Skogrand, Wayne
Strand, Keith
Streiff, Fred H.
Sundberg, Wade
Swanstrom, Steven G.
Swenson, Gordon G.
Tate Island Fishing Lodge
  Richard Chrysler
Thunderbird Resort
  Paul & Nancy Vollmar
Toriseva, Albert
Troumbly, Darren J.
Udovich Guide Service
  Dennis Udovich
Ullrich, Peter
Viall, David
Waage, Roger J.
Wenz, David W.

MISSISSIPPI
Deep South Wilderness Outfitters
  James Goss
Delta National Guide Service
  Jim Wilson
Mississippi Delta Hunts
  Steve Prather
Tara Hunt Club & Willow Point
  Islands–Sidney Montgomery

MISSOURI
Fraley Ranch
  Tom Fraley
Herefordale Ranch
  Curtis Sidwell
Show-Me Safaris
  Mark Hampton
Trophies Plus Outfitters
  Richard M. Watkins
Walker Outfitters
  Larry Walker

MONTANA
5/S Outfitting & Guide Service
  Glenn E. Smith
63 Ranch
  Sandra M. Cahill
7 Devils Outfitters
  William R. Briggs
7C Quarter Circle Outfitters
  Dennis P. Chatlain
7W Guest Ranch
  Glenda S. Reynolds
A Lazy H Outfitters
  Allen J. Haas
Absaroka Outfitters
  Vernon T. Smith
Allaman's Montana Adventure
  Kenneth C. Allaman
American Hunting Services
  Guy Shanks
Anchor Outfitting
  Charles M. Rein
Antelope Creek Outfitters
  Paul C. Cornwell
Antlers Guide Service
  George H. Athas
Atcheson Outfitting
  John D. "Jack" Atcheson
Avalanche Basin Outfitters
  Douglas Caltrider
Babcock Creek Outfitters
  LeRoy Books
Back Country Outfitter
  Elbert Loomis
Badland Buck & Bull Outfitters

Lee A. Zeller
Bales Hunts
  Keith Bales
Bar Six Outfitters
  Terry D. Throckmorton
Bar Y Seven Ranch
  Claude Saylor
Barlett Creek Outfitters
  Mike Smith
Bear Creek Ranch & Outfitters
  William E. Beck
Bear Paw Mountain Outfitters
  Eric M. Olson
Bear Paw Outfitters
  Tim Bowers
Bear Trap Outfitters
  Kenneth R. Whitman
Beardsley Outfit. & Guide
  Service–Tim Beardsley
Beartooth Plateau Outfitters
  Ronnie L. Wright
Beartooth Ranch & JLX
  Outfitters–James Langston
Bear's Den Outfitters
  Bruce C. Delorey
Beaver Creek Outfitters
  Clayton A. Barkhoff
Benchmark Wilderness Ranch
  Darwin C. Heckman
Big Cir Outfitters & Lodge
  Stanley A. Cirspinski
Big Hole River Outfitters
  Craig Fellin
Big Salmon Outfitters
  Richard Kehoe Wayman
Big Sky Expeditions
  Joel S. Wiemer
Big Sky Guide & Outfitters
  Tom D. Brogan
Big Sky Outfitters
  Richard F Kountz
Big Sky Trophy Outfitters
  Sam C. Borla
Big Timber Guides
  Robert J. Bovee
Big "M" Outfitters
  Robert E. Hogue
Bighorn Country Outfitters
  George Kelly
Bill Mitchell Outfitters
  William H. Mitchell
Billingsley Ranch Outfitters
  Jack Billingsley
Birch Creek Outfitters
  William W. Galt
Black Butte Outfitters
  J.O. Hash
Black Mountain Outfitters
  Glen Scott Sallee
Black Otter Guide Service
  Duane Neal
Blacktail Ranch
  Tag Rittel
Blizzard Mountain Outfitters
  Nicholas Smetana
Blue Nugget Outfitters
  Eugene R. Knight
Blue Ribbon Flies
  Craig R. Mathews
Blue Ridge Outfitters
  Earl Ray Shores
Blue Rock Outfitters
  O. Kurt Hughes
Bob Marshall Wilderness Ranch
  Virgil B. Burns
Borderline Outfitters
  Miles G. Hutton
Bridger Mountain Guide Service
  James R. Brogan
Bridger Outfitters
  David B. Warwood
Broken Hart Ranch
  Lee I. Hart
Broken Heart Guest Ranch
  Bernard C. Nieslanik
Buck Creek Ranch Guide Service
  Thomas W. Parker
Buckhorn Ranch Outfitters
  Harry T. Workman
Buffalo Creek Outfitters
  John & DruAnn Robidou
Buffalo Horn Outfitters
  James H. Walma
Bugle Ridge Outfitters
Bull Mountain Outfitters
  M.J. "Mike" Murphy
Bull River Outfitters
  Doug Peterson
Bull Run Outfitters
  Bud Heckman

Bull Run Outfitters & Guest Ranch
  Joe Tripp
Bullseye Outfitting
  Jeff Smith
Bunky Ranch Outfitters
  DeVon "Smut" Warren
Burke Ranch
  Don J. Burke
Burns Creek Outfitters
  Alan R. Klempel
Burwell, Bill
Cabin Creek Outfitters
  Kenneth W. Phillips
Cabinet Divide Outfitters
  Terry N. Kayser
Cabinet Mtn. Outfitters
  Gerald Carr
Cameron Outfitters
  Del Cameron
Camp Baker Outfitters
  Donald W. Johnston
Canyon Creek Guest Ranch
  David L. Duncan
Canyon & Creek Outfitters
  Lyle S. Bainbridge
Cargill Outfitting
  John C. Cargill
Castle Creek Outfitters
  John D. Graham
Castle Lodge
  D. Castle Smith
Cat Track Outfitters
  Cal Thornberg
Cayuse Outfitters
  Larry A. Lahren
Cedar Breaks Outfitters
  John A. Stuver
Centennial Outfitters
  Mel W. Montgomery
Central Montana Outfitters
  Chad S. Schearer
Centre Island Resort
  David Ballinger & Laura St. John
Chase Hill Outfitters
  William L. Brown
Cheff Guest Ranch
  Edward "Mick" Cheff
Chris Branger, Outfitter
  Chris W. Branger
Circle Bar Guest Ranch
  Sarah Hollatz
Circle KBL Outfitters & Guides
  Robert A. Lamberson
Clearwater Outfitters
  Larry J. Kenney
Clearwater Outfitters
  Tom Ziberman
Climbing Arrow Outfitters
  Frank Bartow Anderson
Coman's Guide Service
  Stan Coman
Continental Divide Outfitters
  Walter D. Easley
Copenhaver Outfitter
  Steven D. Copenhaver
Cottonwood Outfitters
  John A. Wilkinson
Cougar Ranch Outfitters
  Buck Wood
Cougar Ridge Outdoors
  William Richard Briggs
Covered Wagon Outfitters
  Edward L Hake
Cow Creek Outfitters
  John R. Fritz
Cowboys Outfitters
  Gib Lloyd
Coyote Outfitters
  Donald E. Mawyer
Crane Mountain Guide Service
  Fred W. Buchanan
Crazy Mountain Outfitter & Guide
  Phillip Ray Keefer
Crow Creek Outfitters & Guides
  Michael E. Parsons
Curry Comb Outfitters
  William L Knox
Curtiss Outfitters
  Ronald L Curtiss
DC Outfitting
  Richard L. Cox
Davis, William L.
Deep Creek Outfitters
  Gary L. Anderson
Diamond Hitch Outfitters
  Robert I. McNeil
Diamond N Outfitters
  Brian D. Nelson
Diamond R Expeditions
  Peter Rothing

Diamond R Guest Ranch
James A. Slack
Dick Lyman Outfitters
Dick P. Lyman
DL Elk Outfitters
Dennis A. LeVeque
DN & -3 Outfitters
Eldon H. Snyder
Don Carvey Outfitting
Donald R. Carvey
Donohoe Outfitting
Paul T. Donohoe
Doonan Gulch Outfitters
Russell E. Greenwood
Double Arrow Outfitters
Jack C. Rich
Double R Outfitting & Guide
Service   Glen Nepil
Douglas Fir & Furs
Douglas H. Gauf
Eagle Outfitters
Gerald W. Good
East Fork Outfitters
Mark McKee
East Slope Outfitters
James R. Laughery
Eastslope Outfitters
Anthony John Fowler
Elk Creek Outfitters
Thomas J. Francis
Elk Creek Outfitters
Gerald K. Olson
Elk Creek Outfitting
Brent Fitchett
Elk Horn Enterprises
Pete Clark
Elk Horn Hot Springs
Ralph Mersdorf
Elk Range Outfitters
William J. Montanye
Elk Ridge Outfitters
Doug & Michelle Landers
Elkhorn Outfitters
Henry T. Barron
Esper's Under Wild Skies Lodge
& Outfitters–Vaughn Esper
Espy Ranch
Jim Espy
EW Watson & Sons Outfitting
Ed & Wanda Watson
Faber Ranch
Leo M. Faber
Fallon Creek Outfitters
Monte J. Berzel
Five Bears Outfitters
Gary Peters
Flat Iron Outfitting
Jerry C. Shively
Flying D Ranch
Rob Arnaud
Flying Diamond Guide Service
Jack W.P. Davis
Flying Eagle Ranch
Wayne H. Mackie
Flying S Outfitting
Duane L Nollmeyer
Flying W Outfitters
Sherry Ann Ward
Ford Creek Outfitters
Elizabeth Barker
Four Six Outfitters
Fred Ennist
Ft. Musselshell Outfitters
Bill Harris
Gadoury, Allan W.
Gary Webb Guide & Outfitters
Gary Webb
George Klemens Outfitting
George C. Klemens
Glacier Fishing Charters
James P. Landwehr
Glacier Outfitters
Gary Abbey
Golden Bear Outfitters
Walter C. Earl
Great Basin Hunters
Gerald Nyman
Great Bear Outfitters
H.J. Gilchrist
Great Divide Guiding/Outfitters
Richard T. Jackson
Great Divide Outfitters
Albert F. Lefor
Great Northern Outfitters
Ken Mitchell
Great Waters Outfitting
John Keeble
Greyson Creek Meadows Rec.
Ted Flynn
Hailstone Ranch Co.
Samuel Langhus

Hanging "J" Ranch
Joyce G Rehms
Hargrave Cattle & Guest Ranch
Ellen White Hargrave
Hawkins Outfitters
Steve Hawkins
Hawley Mountain Guest Ranch
Sadako W. Jarret
Hell Creek Guest Ranch
John E. Trumbo
Hell's A Roarin' Outfitters
Warren H. Johnson
Hibbard, Scott G.
Hidden Hollow Hideaway
Kelly & Jill Flynn
High Country Connection
Dave Lindquist
High Country Connection
Larry C. Timber
High Plains Outfitters
Mike Bay
Hill Country Expeditions
John F. Hill
Hill's Professional Outfitters
Edna V. Hill
Hole In the Wall Outfitters
Todd Earp
Homestead Ranch
Edward F. Arnott
Horse Creek Outfitters
Robert Bruce Malcolm
Horseshoe Guide Service
Ted Dinsdale
Howard Zehntner Hunting
Howard Zehntner
Hubbard's Yellowstone Outfitters
James L. Hubbard
Hunters Montana
Keith J. Atcheson
Iron Horse Outfitters
Art Griffith
I.C.R. Outfitters
Wade Warren Durham
J & J Guide Service
Jamie J. Byrne
Jacklin's Inc.
Robert V. Jacklin
Jerry Malson Outfitting
Jerry R. Malson
Jess Jones Outfitting Service
Jess D. Jones
Jim McBee Outfitter
James L. McBee
JJJ Outfitters
Max D. Barker
JM Bar Outfitters
Jeffery & Maria Freeman
Joe Heimer Outfitting
Joseph A. Heimer
John Maki Outfitters
John C. Maki
Johns, Justin
Johnson Outfitters
Kathryn M. Johnson
Johnson, Richard
Jorgenson, Tony E.
Josephson Outfitting
Edward & Elisa Josephson
JR Outfitters
Paul E. Hedrick
JR/Buffalo Creek Outfitters
John W. Robidou
J-L Outfitters
Arthur J. Stevens
K Lazy Three Ranch
Mary Faith Hoeffner
K & D Outfitting
Kenneth L. Torgerson
K & N Outfitting
Wade D. Nixon
KB Outfitters
Gerald "Bo" Kezar
Kavanagh, Dennis G.
Grimm, Kent D. "Jake"
KG Guides & Outfitters
Ken D. Graber
Kibler Outfitting
Myron & Mary Beth Kibler
Kincheloe Outfitting
Robert B. Kincheloe
Klick's K Bar L Ranch
Dick Klick
Koocanusa Outfitters
E. Neven Zugg
Kootenai Angler
David Blackburn
Kootenai High Country Hunting
David Lee Hayward
Krogedal, David M.
L Diamond E Ranch
Dan J. Ekstrom

Lakeview Resort & Outfitters
Dan Murphy
LaMarche Creek Outfitting Co.
Russell B. Smith
Lapham Outfitters
Max & Debbie Lapham
Larson Outfitters
William G. Larson
Lazy Heart Outfitters
Linda M. Budeski
Lazy JR Outfitters
William S. Crismore
Lazy T4 Outfitters
Spencer G. Trogdon
Lepley Creek Ranch
Matthew Holmes
Limestone Kamp
Raymond O. Hill
Lion Creek Outfitters
Cecil L Noble
Little Rockies Outfitting
David L. Rummel
Lone Tree Outfitting & Guide
Service–Larry A. Pendleton
Lone Willow Creek Guide Service
Jim M. Schell
Lone Wolf Guide Service
Mark A. Baumeister
Lost Coulee Outfitters
Thomas J. Fisher
Lost Creek Outfitters
Don O. Wright
Lost Creek Outfitting
James Leslie Haynie
Lost Fork Ranch
Merritt G. Pride
LS Adventures
Larry M. Surber
Lucky Day Outfitters
Ed. F. Skillman
M Hanging Cross Outfitters &
Guide–Michael "Chip" Gollehon
M & E Outfitter's
Keith Meckling
M & M Outfitters
Monty D. Hankinson
Mark Kayser Outfitting
Mark D. Kayser
Mark Young's Hunting Services
Mark E. Young
McCormick's Sunset Guest Ranch
Mike C. McCormick
McDonough Outfitters
Robert McDonough
McFarland & White Ranch
Gilbert White
Medicine Lake Outfitters
Thomas M. Heintz
Milller Outfitters
Robert E. Miller
Ming Coulee Outfitters
James M. Gasvoda
Mission Mountain Outfitters
Richard R. Bishop
Missouri Breaks Adventures
John E. Vaia
Mitchell Outfitting
Floyd W. Mitchell
Montana Breaks Outfitting
Donald B. Lynn
Montana Experience Outfitter
Carl A. Mann
Montana Guide Service
Edwin L. Johnson
Montana High Country Outfitter
Timothy R. Reishus
Montana High Country Tours
Russell D. Kipp
Montana Outdoor Expeditions
Robert James Griffith
Montana Outfitter
Alfred S. Bassett
Montana Ranchers Hunts
Lester M. Morgan
Montana River Guides
Gregory G. Mentzer
Montana River Outfitters
R. Craig Madsen
Montana River Ranch
Wagner D. Harmon
Montana Riverbend Outfitters
Robert J. Zikan
Montana Safaris
Rocky J. Heckman
Montana Trail Trophy Outfitter
Michael J. Clark
Montana Wilderness Outfitters
David H. Kozub
Monte's Guiding & Mtn. Outfit.
LaMonte J. Schnur
Monture Face Outfitters

Tom Ide
Monture Outfitters
James L. Anderson
Mossy Horn Outfitters
Gordon W. Sampson
Mountain Trail Outfitters
David B. Gamble
Mountain Trails Outfitters
A. Lee Bridges
Mule Shoe Outfitters
Jack Howser
Musselshell Outfitters
Randy D. Higgins
M.B.K. Outfitters
Michael B. Krueger
Neal Outfitter's
Danielle Neal
New West Outfitters
David B. Moore
North Star Outfitters
Everett "EB" Morris
North Yellowstone Outfitters
William H. Hoppe
Northern High Plains Outfitter
Edwin R. Anderson
Northern Plains Outfitters
Douglas M. Dreeszen
N-Bar Land & Cattle Co.
Thomas E. Elliott
Otter Creek Outfitters
James W. Wilkins
Paintbrush Trails
Thomas Michael Wolfe
Painted Rock Outfitters
Mike & Debbie Rodgers
Painted Rock Outfitters
Larry D. Rogers
Paradise Outfitters
Jim H. Cooper
Parson's Outfitting
Jean Parsons
Paul Ross Outfitters
Paul S. Ross
Pelly Lake Wilderness Outfitters
Dennis LeVeque
Peterson's Fairmont Corral
William H. Peterson
Pig Eye Outfitters
Peter B. Rogers
Pine Hills Outfitters
Robert "Mike" Barthelmess
Pine Ridge/Bartlett Creek
Outfitters Robert M. Labert
Pintler Wilderness Outfitting
Jim Sperry
Pionier Outfitter
Charles A. Page
Point of Rocks Guest Ranch
Irvin "Max" Chase
Powder River Outfitters
Kenneth F. Greslin
Quarter Circle E.M. Outfitters
Ernest E. McCollum
Rach Outfitters/Flathead Chtrs.
Jeff E. Rach
Rainbow Outfitters
Jim L. Becker
Ram Mountain Outfitters
Robert L Neal
Ramshom Outfitters
Audie & Vivianne Anderson
Randy Petrich Big Game Hunts
Randy Petrich
Rawhide Guide Service
Leroy A. Fatouros
Ray Perkins Outfitter
J. Ray Perkins
Red Mountain Outfitters
Les G. Nader
Redbone Outfitting
Carl "Bud" Martin
Rendezvous Outfitters
Herbert A. Moore
Reynolds Hollowtop Hideaway
Harvey D. Reynolds
Rick Wemple Outfitting/Wildlife
Adv.–Richard J. Wemple
Rimrock Ridge Outfitters
Roy L. Coneen
River Breaks Outfitting
Rick R. Wood
River Road Outfitters
Herbert Weiss
RL Outfitters
Dwain Rennaker
R. L. Sourbrine Outfitters & Sons
Richard Sourbrine
Robert Butler Outfitting
Robert G. Butler
Robert Dolatta Outfitters
Robert Dolatta
Robert Dupea Outfitters
Robert L. Dupea
Rock Creek Outfitters
Dean Armbrister

Rocky Mountain Adventures
  Daniel J. Shoemaker
Rocky Outfitters
  Rocky L. Niles
Rocky Point Outfitters
  Orvall Kuester
Ron Mills Outfitting
  Ronald E. Mills
Ross Childers
  Ross Childers
Royal Outfitters
  Tyrone L. Throop
Rugg's Outfitting
  Raymond Rugg
Rumph Ranch Outfitters
  Richard N. Rumph
Running M Outfitters
  Monte McLane
Running Waters Ranch
  Bruce E. Funk
Rus Willis Outfitting
  Richard K. Willis
Rush's Lake View Ranch
  Keith S. Rush
Rush's Lake View Ranch
  Kevin Rush
R.L. Sourbrine Outfit. & Sons
  Richard L. Sourbrine
R.W. Outfitters
  Robert M. Wetzel
S&W Outfitters
  Brad D. Hanzel
Sage & Sun Outfitting
  David J. Patts
Salmon Forks Outfitters
  William H. Tidwell
Scapegoat Wilderness Outfitter
  William M. Plante
Scoffield Ranch Outfitters
  George B. Scoffield
Selway Bitterroot Outfitters
  Dave Hettinger
Selway-Magruder Outfitters
  Ken Wells
Seven Bar Cross Ranch
  Dale W. Williams
Seven Lazy P Guest Ranch
  Charles C. Blixrud
Shadow Basin Outfitters
  Troy Ginn
Sherwood Outfitting
  John Sherwood
Shields Valley Outfitters
  Gregory L. Cissel
Shining Mountain Outfitters
  Paul K. Johnson
Shining Times Outfitting
  Richard Steve Vetsch
Shiplet Ranch Outfitters
  Bob Shiplet
Silver Bow Outfitters
  Leonard Howells
Simpson Outfitters
  Mike W. Simpson
Skalkaho Ldge. Outftr. & Guides
  John V. Rose
Skyline Guest Ranch & Guide
  Victor Jackson
Skyline Outfitters & Wilderness
Lodge   Cameron E. Lee
Slack, James & Pattie
Slip & Slide Guide Service
  Franklin J. Rigler
Slough Creek Outfitters
  Perry Handyside
Snowline Outfitters
  Patrick G. Sinclair
Snowy Range Ranch Outfitters
  Patrick R. Landers
Snowy Springs Outfitters
  Shawn Little
Sphinx Mountain Outfitting
  Gregory J. Doud
Spotted Bear Ranch
  H. William Armstrong
Spotted Bear Ranch
  Kirk & Cathy Gentry
Spring Creek Outfitters
  Rodney Allen Heier
Stan Fisher Outfitter & Guide
  Stanley Fisher
Steve Fillinger Outfitters
  Steve Fillinger
Stillwater Outfitting
  Brian Paul Tutvedt
Stockton Outfitters
  Billy D. Stockton
Story Cattle Co & Outfitting
  Michael Story
Sugarloaf Mountain Outfitters
  William Ray Flanagan
Sun Canyon Lodge
  Lee Carlbom
Sun Trek Outfitters
  John J. Humble
Sunburst Adventures
  Terry C. Johnson
Sundown Outfitters
  Lyle G. Reynolds

Tamarack Lodge
  William A. McAfee
Tate's Upper Canyon Ranch
  Donna & Jake McDonald
The Tom Miner Lodge
  John A. Keenan
Think Wild Enterprises
  Eugene G. Clark
Thompson Outfitters
  Teddy Thompson
Thunder Bow Outfitters
  Mike Robinson
Timberline Outfitters
  Willis L. Newman
Track Outfitters & Guide Service
  Johnny C. McGee
Treasure State Outfitting
  Michael J. Canavan
TriMountain Outfitters
  Andy Celander
Triple Creek Outfitters
  Roy G. Ereaux
Triple Creek/Thunder Bow
  Charlotte A. Zikan
Triple M Outfitters
  Mark J. Faroni
Triple Tree Ranch
  William L. Myers
Triple "B" Outfitters
  David L. Gill
Twin Buttes Outfitters
  Paul V. Mobley
Twitchell Brothers
  Judd Twitchell
Two Leggins Outfitters
  David C. Schaff
Tyler, James K.
Upper Canyon Outfitters
  Donna Tate MacDonald
Valley View Ranch
  Richard Gondeiro
Vikings Mountain Ranch
  Douglas K. Knutson
Wayne Hill Outfitting
  Wayne Hill
Wellborn Bros.
  David A. Wellborn
Wellborn Bros.
  Joseph R. Wellborn
West Fork Outfitters
  Ronald M. Corr
West Fork Outfitters
  David & Janet Walker
Western Guide Services
  Randy L. Walker
Western Rivers
  Fred J. Tedesco
Western Timberline Outfitters
  Jammin Krebs
Whiskey Ridge Outfitter's
  Steven R. Knox
White Tail Ranch/WTR Outfitters
  Jack E. Hooker
Wild Country Outfitters
  Jerry E. Strong
Wild West Outfitters
  Michael A. Goyins
Wilderness Connection
  Charles G. Duffy
Wilderness Lodge
  Rick A. Vandermeyde
Wilderness Lodge, Ltd.
  Gregory C. Grabacki
Wilderness Outfitters
  Arnold D. Elser
Wilderness Riders Outfitting
  Bruce J. Duffalo
Williams, Don A.
Williams Outfitters
  Harry L. Williams
Willow Ranch
  Storrs M. Bishop
Willow Springs Outfitters
  Gordon L. Patton
Wolfpack Outfitters
  Jeffrey Wingard
Wolverine Guide Service
  Richard A. Labert
World Class Outfitting Adv.
  Jason & Carolyn Clinkenbeard
WW Outfitters
  William A. White
X-A Ranch
  Boland Clark
Yaak River Outfitters
  Patrick "Clint" Mills
Yellowater Outfitters
  Roy G. Olsen
Yellowstone Mountain Guides
  Steven R. Gamble
Yellowstone River Hunting
  Scott Cornell
Z Bar J Outfitters
  Mark Story

NEBRASKA
Ron & Cindi Holmes
  Reindeer Lake Trout Camp

NEVADA
Big Smoky Valley Outfitters
  William A. Berg
Black Rock Outfitters
  Michael J. Hornbarger
Blackrock Outfitters
  Henry K. Arrien II
Burdick Guide Service
  Shaun A. Burdick
Cottonwood Ranch & Wilderness
  Exped.–E. Agee Smith
D/G Outfitters
  Eric Dalen
Daum, George A.
Elko Guide Service
  William S. Gibson
First Strike Sportfishing
  Jeffrey L. Vogl
George Flournoy Outfitting
  George Flournoy
Hall's Outfitting & Guide Service
  Keven M. Hall
Hidden Lake Outfitters
  Henry W. Krenka
High Desert Outfitters
  Steven J. DeRicco
Holcomb, Richard
Hudson, Bruce D.
Humboldt Outfitters
  Wilde F. Brough
McMillan, Andrew G.
Mustang Outfitters
  Jim Stahl
Nevada Desert Trophy Hunts
  Roy Lerg
Nevada Guide Service
  James R. Puryear
Nevada High Country Outfitters
  Paul D. Bottari
Nevada High Country Outfitters
  Chris & Todd Schwandt
Nevada High Desert Outfitters
  William B. Watega
Nevada Trophy Hunts
  Tony Diebold
Pine Forest Hunt Club & Guide
  Service–Laurence Montero
Prunty, Frank P.
Prunty, Gary A.
Sage-Pine Guide & Outfitter
  Paul L. Strasdin
Secret Pass Outfitters
  Stephen G. Wright
Silver State Guides & Outfitters
  Elvin W. Cronister
Silver State Guides & Outfitters
  Phillip E. Trousdale
Snake Mountain Guide Service
  Harvey Pete
Southern Nevada/Utah Outfitter
  Boyd J. Wittwer
Southern Nevada/Utah Outfitter
  Harold Wittwer
The Great Ripoff Guide Service
  James A. & Robert R. Combs
Timberline Outfitters
  Stanley R. Galvin Jr.
Timberline Outfitters
  Nicholas G. Perchetti
Virgil's Desert Bighorn Hunts
  John V. Zenz
White River Guide Service
  Mark A. Lane
Wildlife West Taxidermy & Guide
  Service–Ron W. Biggs

NEW HAMPSHIRE
Cairns, Bruce
Caron, Charles R.
Collins, Catherine
Collins, Layford
Courchesne, Karen & Steven
Daley, Brian F.
Dionne, Kenneth T.
Elkins, Duane Carlton
Fantasia, George
O'Neal, Latson B.
Piwarunas, Paul M.
Schanda, Richard
Starkey, John McMahon
Szurley, James F.
Untamed Wilderness
  Alex Cote
Untamed Wilderness
  Mark Stilkey
Varney, Roderick A.
Wilder, Gordon

NEW MEXICO
4C's Guides and Outfitters
  Chet Connor
5 M Outfitters
  Bruce Maker
Adventures in the Great Outdoors
Back Country Hunts
  Steve Jones
Bar X Bar Ranch
Bear Creek Outfitters
  Louis Probo
BeaverHead Outfitters
  Jack Diamond
Black Range Outfitters
  Sterling Carter
Blue Mountain Outfitter
  Bob Atwood
Butler - Moreno Ranch West
  Bobby & Ginni Butler
Cactus Hunting Service
  Jon Corn
Cecil Ralston Guide & Outfitters
  Cecil & Jodie Ralston
Circle J Guiding Service
  J R Rodella
Copper Country Outfitters
  Steve Harvill
Cougar Mountain Guide Service
  Doug Dobbs
CS Ranch Hunting & Outfitting
  Randy Davis
Derringer Outfitters
  David & Susan Derringer
Dirk Neal's Outfitting Service
  Dirk Neal
East Moreno Ranch
  Albert Murray & Ron Simmons
Elmer Nelson Trophy Outfitters
  Bill Elmer & William B. Nelson
Four Corners Guide & Outfitters
  Ted Stiffler
Garrison Guide & Outfitting
  Gary Garrison
Gila Hotspring Ranch
  Becky Campbell
Gila Wilderness Lodge
  Robert Rawlins
Gonzales, Jesse
Gonzales Outfitting Guiding
  Thomas Gilbert Gonzales
Green Gap Ranch
  Mike Hansen
Haggitt, Donald S.
Halfmoon Outfitters
  Dr. Mike Jones
Handrich Guide & Outrfitters
  Dave Handrich
Hi Valley Outfitters
  Bill Wright
High Country Connections
  Casey Veach
High Lonesome Outfitter
  Kerry Sebring
High Mountain Outfitters
  Pete Trujillo
Horizon Guide & Outfitters
  Kelly Dow
Jakalope Adventures
  J. Lance Andrew
Jicarilla Apache Tribe
  Jicarilla Game & Fish Dept.
Kennedy Hunting Services
  Kirk Kennedy
Kiowa Hunting Service
  Tim Barraclough Jr. & Al Cata
Kite, Cecil
Klumker, Tom K.
Lazy BW Outfitters
  Bob Ward
Lewis, Evan
Limestone Outfitters
  Chip Welty
Lonesome Dove
  H.R. & Brandi Tomlin
Mangas Outfitters
Mark Upshaw Guide Service
  Mark Upshaw
Michael Root's Guide Service
  Michael Root
Milligan Brand Outfitting
  Marvin N. Henry Jr.
Mimbres Outfitters
  Mark Miller
Moismann, Martin
Moreno Valley Outfitters
  Robert Reese
New Mexico Prof. Big Game Hunting
  Mike Chapel
North American Outfitters
Northern New Mexico Elk Hunts
  Mike Lopez
Ortiz, Robert M.
Oso Ranch & Lodge
  John & Pamela Adamson
Pusch Ridge Outfitters
  Kirk & Roxane Kelso
Redwing Outfitters
  Bob Daugherty
Reserve Outfitters & Guides
  Bill Jernigan

Ric Martin's Trophy Adventures
 Ric Martin
Rio Costilla Park
Rio Nutrias Cattle & Hunting
 Juan Montano
Rocky Mountain Big Game Hunts
 Jan M. Brown
Ross Johnson Prof. Big Game
 Outfitter–Ross Johnson
San Francisco River Outfitters
 Tom Klunker
Serna, Martin D.
Shelley, Terrell
Sibley Ranch
 Christine Freeman
Sierra Grande Outfitters
 Les Ezell
Sofia Outfitters
 Roger Manning
Terrero General Store and
 Riding Stable Inc.–Huie Ley
The American Elk Conservatory Inc.
 Frank Simms
The Pueblo of Laguna
Timberline Outfitters
 Perry Hunsaker
Trappers Trophy Hunting
T-N-T Adventures
 Joe M. Torrez Jr.
United States Outfitters Inc.
 George Taulman
Val's Trophy Outfitters
 Val DeHerrera
Valerio, Andy F.
Vermejo Park Ranch
 Jim Baker
Way West Outfitters
 Keith Reiley

NEW YORK
Algoma East Cottages & Outfitters
 Tom Lembke & Family
Breen, Tim
Blue Mountain Lake Guide Service
Coe Cummins
Bob Horowitz Guide Service
 Bob Horowitz
Callaghan, John
Call Of The Wild
 Boyce D. "Bud" Rawson Sr.
Catskill Outdoor Adventures
 Charles "Sonny" Somelofski
Chartrand, O.J.
Cold River Ranch
 John Fontana
Conook Charters & Hunting Guide
 Svc.–Gregory Harmych
C.P.'s Guiding Service
 Chirs Palumbo
Dixon, John
Don Brown Guide Service
 Don Brown
Drybrook Environmental
 Adventures–Martin C. Giuliano
East Wind
 Luke H. Evans
Empire Outfitters & Guide Service
 James M. Baker
Fox Den Guide Service
 Dennis M. Coulman
Gad-About Griz Charter & Guide
 Service–Capt. Paul Sents
Gaponiuk Jr., Daniel
Hemlock Cliff Bed & Breakfast
Lodge   William M. Nolis
Jr.
Hills-A-Vaille
 Charles Baldwin
Hogancamp's Guide Service
 Gregg Hogancamp
J & J Outdoors
 Judd V. Groff
Jay, Marty
Kidney Creek Farms & Preserve
 Gary Breski
Kilcher, Mike
Knudsen, Bruce
Le Billet D'or
 Ted Meskunas
Limbhanger Lodge
 Paul Paduano
Lincoln, David W.
Linda-Vue Charters
 Capt. Walt Boname
Linx Guide Services
 Larry E. Winslow
Mad Dragon Dynasty
 Guide Shihan & Pete Traina
Masters, Wayne
Meadow Brook Guiding
 Delbert Ryan
Middle Earth Expeditions
 Wayne Failing
Moose River Co.
 Mark H. Eddy
Mountain Man Guide Service
 Joe Eggleston
Newell's Guide Service

Gary K. Newell
North Country Outfitters
 Barney & Bob & Rick Mundy
North Star Guiding Service
 Michael F. Newell
Northwoods Wilderness Guide
 Service–John Huston
Outdoor Activities
 John C. Couser
Outlaw Charters
 R. Stephen Yaw
Pepperbox Outfitters
 Jack Finklea
Placid Bay Ventures Guide &
 Charter Svc.–Capt. Uwe Herb
Dramm
Plateau Guide Service
 Wayne Kwasniewski
Rainbow Lake Lodge & Outfitters
 Donald Wooster & Gary Eaton
Robinson, Tom
R. L. C. Services
 Roland (Rollie) Card
Sam Orne Adventures
 Sam Orne
Schwark, Cliff
Smokey's Bow Hunting Guide
 Service–Carroll Miller Jr.
Spring Valley Sportsman
 Mark Finne
Stillwaters Guide Service
 Terry Watson
Temagami Riverside Lodge
 Roger Watson & Tom Dorr
Thor's Trophy Outdoor Guide
Service   Thor S. Yarabek
Tightlines Guide Service
 Donald Kingsley
Tompkins, George F.
Torregrossa, Peter J.
Trailhead Lodge
 John & Michael Washburn
Turkey Trot Acres Hunting Lodge
 Peter M. Clare
Upper Delaware Outfitters
 Bill Fraser
VanSplinter, Neal
Vezzetti, Skip
Wharton's Adirondack Outfitters
 Bill Wharton
White Dog Trail Company
 Jeff Whittemore
Whiteface Guide Service
 G. L. Scott
Wilderness Adventures
 Joe Lombardi

NORTH CAROLINA
Buffalo Creek Guide Service
 Johnnie Dale
Chestnut Hunting Lodge
 Jerry Rushing
Northampton Lodge
 Gene Varnadoe

NORTH DAKOTA
Albright, Robert J.
Anderson, Jim
Badlands Taxidermy & Guide
 Blaine Dokart & Rick Froelich
Beam, Dave
Bieber, Harvey D.
Binstock, James
Blacktail Creek Ranch
 Kenneth Eberts
Blanchfield, Kyle
Chimney Butte Outfitters
 Allan T. Thompson
Dakota Fins, Feathers & Tails
Guide   Service–Jim
Nagel
Dakota Hunting Guide Service
 Terry Feist
Dakota Lodge & Trail Rides
 Loren V. Ross
Dakota Outfitters Unltd.
 Larry Brooks
Dewhirst, Lynn
Elkorn Outfitters
 Randall Mosser
Emerson, Betty & David
Folden, Richard
Freed, Larry
Freitag, Blane
Fritz, Joe
Hininger, Monte
Kautzman, Doug
Kelly Creek Outfitters
 Knokleberg, Jorgen & Tony
Kolstad, Greg

Kongslie, Lynn
Lahren, Norma
Lang, Scott
Lawrence Bay Lodge
 Randy Engen
Legg, George
Little Knife Outfitters
 Glendon Nelson
Little Missouri River Bowhunting
 Guide–Billy Freitag
Lund's Landing
Martel, Don
Meyer, Monica
Missouri Valley Guiding
 David Hoffman & Monte Hininger
Olson, Peter
Otterson, Walter
Peterson, Paddy
Plath, James
Red Willow Outfitters
 Jack Haines
Rohweder, Curtis
Schlecht, Sheldon
Schramm, Delmar
Schroeder, Brian
Schumacker, Tom
Swanke, Willard
Tailfeathers Guide Service
 Al Soderfelt
Tangedal, Rick & Shane
 Thvedt, Errol B.
Timm, Ronald
Tonneson, Dave
Turtle Mountain Adventures
 Larrett Peterson
Vossler, Todd
Wanner, Ronald P.
Wehrman, Jamie L.
Woltes, Steve
Zimbelman, Terry

OHIO
Chalets Newman-McKenzie Enr.
Houston Lake Camp
 Ken & Iona Kronk
James Bay Outfitters & Air Service
 Ltd.–Rob Lafleur
Little River Lodge
 Chuck & Pat Crone
Mountain Cove Lodge
 Grace & Michael Piano
Pourvoyeur Du Lac Des Quinze Enr
Shawnee Ridge Hunting Preserve
 Paul Richter
T & T Outfitters
 Thomas Belville

OKLAHOMA
Beaver Creek Outfitters
 Roger Franks
Bird-N Buck Outfitters
 Ronald D. Thompson
Crazy Horse
 M.L. Bill Swanda
Esper's Cedar Lake Camp
 Terry & Kim Schale

OREGON
Anderson Land & Livestock
 Terry Anderson
Antlers Inn
Arrow Five Outfitters
 Jim Schaafsma
Backcountry Outfitters
 John Moore
Berg, Matthew
Big K Guest Ranch & Guide Service
 Charles Kesterson
Black Tails Unlimited
 John Lehnherr
Blue Mountain Outfitters
 Mark Heuett
Boice, William
Brown, Robert
C Bar C Outfitters
 Rocky Campbell
Cascade Adventures
 Darian Corey
Centerfire Outfitters
 Robert Rodgers
Chewing, Brad
Cougar Creek Outfitter
 Foy Hopkins
Crazy Cayuse Ranch & Pack
 Ronald Adams
Cummins, Richard
Cyrus Happy Guide & Outfitter
 Cyrus Happy
Dave's Guide Service
 David Johnson
Deadwood Outfitters
 Thomas Carter
Don's Guide Service
 Donald Hamblin
Dusky Flyways
 Ronald Helgeson
Elkhorn Guide Service
 Jeff Givens
Flying M Ranch

Barbara & Bryce Mitchell
Game Getter Guide Service
 Stephen Lyon
Gamegetter Guide Service
 Ronald Hopkins
Gorham, Jeffrey
Great Bawls of Fire
 Steven Zabriskie
Hells Canyon Packers
 Butch Brown
High Country Outfitters
 Matthew McDowell
High Desert Outfitters
 Charles Messner
High Lonesome Hunts
 Mike Schaffeld
Hillsman, Raymond
Honker Hideout
 Kenneth McCol
Hunters Rendezvous
 John Cole
King Salmon Stalker
 Herbert Good
Lofton Creek Outfitters
 Brad Santucci
Lookout Outfitters
 Bill Zikmund
M & G Outfitters
 Michael Smith
Maverick Adventures
 Donald Dungey
Migliaccio Jr., Arnold (Dino)
Miranda Jr., Edward
Mountain Man Lodge & Marina
Northwest Outdoor Specialties
 Donald Richelderfer
Oregon Blacktails
 Randy Allen
Paulina Tours
 Todd Brown
Quimby, John
Real Eastern Oregon Tours
 Chary Mires
Ron's Guide Service
 Ronald Jones
Rouge River Guide Service
 Paul Lopes
Rushing, David
Sien's Guide Service
 Dale Siens
Simington, Ronald
Southern Oregon Game Buster
 Duglas Gattis
Spot Country Outfitters
 Elvin Hawkins
Steens Mountain Packers
 John Witzel
Steen's Wilderness Adventures
 James Steens
The Oregon Experience
 Arden Corey
Tom Phillips Guide Service
 Tom Phillips
Tri-State Outfitters
 Mark E. Moncrief
Trophy Blacktail's
 Bill Danielson
Up-A-Tree Guide Service
 Jason Gard
V & M Guide Service
 Vern Hayward
Wapiti Outfitters
 Barbara Seeger
Western Frontier Adv.
 Richard A. Hankins
Wick Outfitters
 Edward Millar
Wick Outfitters
 Jonathan Wick
Wick Outfitters
 Kenneth Wick
Wikander, Doug
Winema Outfitters
 Allan Vanzant
Wyatt, Kevin

PENNSYLVANIA
Debach, Robert J.
Eubank, Robert L.
Arctic Outfitters
 Fred A. Webb & Sons
Granite Creek Outfitters
 Jay King Jr.
High Ridge Hunting
 Fred Kamisnsky
Homestead Hunts
 Bill & Judy Dyroff
Starlight Lodge
 Patrick Schuler

RHODE ISLAND
Nahmakanta Lake Cabins
  Rene & Dorothy Cardon

SOUTH DAKOTA
Badlands Wildlife Preserve
  Grant Paterson
Biggins Hunting Service
  Gregg Biggins
Bob Stalley Outfitting & Guide
  Service–Bob Stalley
Byrum's Hunting Camp
  Laurence Byrum
Colony Outfitters
  J im J. Dacar
Cow Creek Ranch
  Glendon & Pam Shearer
Crow Creek Sioux Tribe
Crow Creek Wildlife Mgmt
  Service–Bob Speirs
Dakota Hunting Farms
  Tim & Julie Metz
Dakota Outfitters, Inc.
Dakota Safaris
  Kirk Cordes
Dakota Wild Bird Hunts
  Jack Campbell
Dakotaland Outfitting
  Larry Neugebauer
Flying T Sky Ranch
  Drew Tinaglia
Gunsel Horse Adventure
  Robert D. Lantis
Heartland Hunts
  Kern Otteson
Hidden Valley Hunting Club
  Robert Anderson
Hunters Haven
  Terry Marso
Ingalls Prairie Wildfowl Hunts
  Jim Ingalls
J B Outfitters
  Gil & Carol Wammen
John Gill Farm
  John Gill
Kirwan Hunting & Guide Service
  Jow Kirwan
Lake's Byron Lodge
  Doug Lake
Langeliers, Todd
Lewis & Clark Trail Guide Service
Lower Brule Wildlife Enterprise
Lubber's Farms Hunting Service
  Jim Lubbers
Mon Dak Outfitters
  Alvin Cordell
Outdoor Adventures of So. Dakota
  Tony Beckler
Oyster Mountain Outfitters
  Dan Hefner & Bob Parsons
P & R Hunting Lodge
  Ruth Taggart
Padden Outfitting
  Bryce H. Padden
Painter Ranch
  Joe & Cindy Painter
Prairie Bird Paradise
  Sue Herman & Tom Falencik
Real Ranch Living
  Terry & Laurie Goehring
Ringneck Roost
  David & Alice Jocobsen
Rooster Tales
  Brad Hutchison
S & S Hunting Service
  Gary & Mary Ann Shaffer
Saw-A-Buck
  Bill Huntington
Smith's Guide Service
  Jeff Smith
South Dakota Hunting Service
  Mike Moody & Bob Waterbury
State Line Resort
  Ken Mosser
Stone, Will
Stukel's Birds & Bucks
  Frank Stukel
Sully Flats Social Club
Sunset Lodge
  John Gilkerson
Sutton's Place
  Lyle Sutton
The 49'er
  Dennis Peterson
Willow Creek Wildlife Inc
  Steve & Bob Stoeser

TENNESSEE
Wilderness Hunting Lodge
  Alan Wilson

TEXAS
31 Ranch
  Joe Kyle Parker
4 Miles Ranch
  Tryon Fields
50/50 Ranch
  Charles R. Carr
AA Ranch
  Harry Wood
Action Outfitters
  Arvin Stroud
Adobe Lodge Hunting Camp
  Skipper Duncan
Alfred, Jerry
Ariola Catfish Farm
BACA Outfitters
Bajio Ranch
  Warren Uecker
Bakers Crossing Ranch
  Mary Hughey
Bar S
  Harry Simon
Baze, Ethl
Beaird, John K.
Bitter Creek Hunting Company
  J.T. Petrie
Black Top Mountain Ranch
  Eldon M. Berry
Bottlinger Ranch
  Milton & Jean Bottlinger
Bradley 3 Ranch
  Bill J. Bradley
Brandenberger 99 Ranch
  Raymond Brandenberger
Brnovak
  Frank Brnovak
Broken Arrow North Ranch
Burson, John True
B. E. Wilson Corp.
  Michael Morris
C Bar Land Cattle & Company
  Malcom Calaway
Caddo Pass Lodge
  Peshing & Marcille Hughes
Camp Stewart
Canyon Springs Ranch/Texas
  Exotic Safaris–Frank Pulkrabek
Carleton Ranches
  J. Preston Carleton
Carter, Larry D.
Caverhill Ranch
  John T. Fargason
Chambers, Boyd
Chapa, Joe E.
Chisholm Trail Ranch
  Mickey Cusack
Cinco de Mayo Ranch
  The Hodge Corp.
Circle "E" Ranch
Cochina Hunting Club
  John Austin
Cohen Ranch
  Opal & Bob Cohen
Collins, James
Connor, Mrs. A.S.
Cooper Properties
  Bryce & Jason Cooper
Cotton Mesa Trophy Elk
  Lester & Robert Gegenheimer
Crabtree, Bert
Crene Ranch Company
  E. J. or Jimmy Crane
Creswell, R. G.
Cuevas, Edwin G.
Cutbirth Cattle Company, LTD
  Treldon & Minnie Cutbirth
C.R. Baker Ranch Hazel E. Johnson
Darsey, Winifred
Davis Bros. Ranch
  Bros. Davis
Davis, G. D. & Grant, J.B.
  Davis, Mary M.
Davis Ranch
  Darrel Davis
Diamond Half Ranch
  Hilmar Blumberg
Diamond & A-Half
  Susan Dunmire
Dixon, Douglas & Carol
Dochada
  Charles E. Bearden
Dolan Creek Hunting
Double C
  Gary Covington
Double T Ranch
  Tim & Trudy Schmidt
Dove Ranch
  Levetta & Sandra May
Dunbar Ranch

Dayn Dunbar
Edgmon, Edgar D.
El Venado
  Richard Herdell
Emzy Barker Outfitters
Escondido Ranch
  Kurt Wiseman
Farmer, Mildred
Farmland
  Eddie Earl Shaw Jr.
Fennessey Ranch
Flores, Adolph
Flying M Ranch
  Johnnie W. Musgrove
Ford Ranch
Foster & Foster Ranch
  J. L. & M. K. Foster
Four Arrows Outfitters
  Jarred Peeples
Frantzen Ranch
  Henry Frantzen
Fuhrmann Ranch
  Walter O. Fuhrmann
Gafford Ranches
  Bill Gafford
Giestweidt, Kurt
Glass Mt. & Housetop
  Mike Bruce
Goorich Ranch
Grogan Hunting Club
  George D. Grogan
Guadalupe Ranch
  Gene Smith
Guerra Brothers
  A. R. "Felo" Guerra
Guffin, J. D.
Hagerman Ranch
  Kenneth Dolezalek
Harlow Ranch
  William L. Harlow
Harvester Hill Ranch
  Stephanie Burman
Henry, Clayton
Hicks, Vernon
High Sierra Outfitters
  John Kuenstler
Hill Ranch
  Tery Hill
Hillje Hunting Haven
  Kay & Jud Hillje
Hoff, Carol G.
Homer Martin Ranch
  Homer Martin Jr.
Hopf, David
Houston Clinton Co.
Hudspeth River Ranch
  Claudia Abbey Ball
Indian Springs Ranch
  Frank A. Stanush
Inks Ranch
  Jin Inks
Irvin Ranch
  Larry Irvin
J B Ranch
  Mark Balette
Jane Mudd Trust
Jarrett Juno Ranch
  Norman Farmer
Jennings Ranch
  Gary Jennings
Jim B. Cloudt Ranch
  Jim B. Cloudt
J. Lloyd Woods Game Leases
J.T. Maner Ranch
Kash Ranch
  Karl Kash
Kelly Creek Ranch
  Charles Domingues
Kiker, Yvonne (Snow)
Kothmann Ranch
  Billy Kothmann
Kuykendall Ranch
  Dale Perry
La Coma Ranch Redgate Corp.
Landon Ranch
  John I. Landon
Las Plumas de Aguila
Laurel, S.L.
Lazy J
  Mrs. D. Hunter
Lazy U Ranch
Lee Phillips Ranch
  Lee Phillips
Lewis, Billie C. & Son
  Lewis, E.D.
LH7 Bandera Ranch
Lintnicum Ranch
  Lad Lintnicum

Lone Star Trail Outfitters
  Trent Huckaby
Long Hollow Vista Ranch
  John H. Crow
Los Mendozas Ranch
  Jose A. Mendoza
L. G. Electronics
  Pat Waggoner
Marr's Farms
  Gary Marrs
Matapeak Ranch
  James H. Scott
Mauldins Place/Griswald Ranch
  Mr. & Mrs. C. W. Mauldin
McKinnon, J.Y.
Mesa Ranch
  E. G. Nava
Middle Concho Whitetail Lodge
  Larry & Glenn Jameson
Milam Bowhunting
  Mike Milam
Moseley, Robert
Mountain Home Hunting Service
  David Lee
Myrick, T.M.
N Ranch
  Calvin Jones
Nail Ranch
  Craig Winters
Newman Wildlife Managment
  John Newman
Nobles Ranch
  Earl H. Nobles
Old Slovacek Home Place
  Clyde M. Shaver
Open V Ranch
  Elmo King Jones
Operation Orphans
Otey III, Frank
Parker, Bob
Pecan Creek/Dutch Mountain
  Gene Hall Reagor
Pila Blanca Ranch
  Jesse M. Ruiz
Ponderosa R Ranch
  Orville & Rebecca Luedecke
Powell Ranch
  Jim T. Roche
Presa Vieja Ranch
  Jesus M. Garcia
Proffitt's Farm & Ranch
  Kenneth Proffitt
Quahadi Wildlife Refuge
  Lorin S. McDowell III
Quapaw
  Penelope Gregory
Rafter S Ranch
  John M. Sirman
Ranch Escondido
  Eduardo Guajardo
Rancho de Los Jefes
Randee Ranch
  Randee Fagan
Real Hunting
  Darrel York
Rech, Anna
Red Bluff Ranch
  Dalton L. Bowere
Reichenau, Dayton
Ricardo Ranch
  Bobby Hill
Rice Ranch
  Rosalie Grahmann
Riggs Ranch
  Teddy R. Riggs Jr.
Rio Paisano Ranch
  Casey Taub
Robby Robinson Ranches
  Robby Robinson
Robert J. Wells Ranch
Roche, Warren P.
Rock Eagle Ranch Corp.
  Richard E. Weinberg
Rockin' B Ranch
  Aubrey L. Brown
Rocky Top Outfitters
  Rudy Steele
Roitsch, Arnold
R.E. Jackson Ranch - Resort #1
Santa Catalina Ranch
  G. Sisco
Santa Rita Ranch Ruben Garza
Scheuer, C.B.
Schmidt Hereford Ranch
  James K. Schmidt
Shields, C.B.
Shipp, Randy
Silver Mesa Safari --Top of
  Texas Hunting–Gary Conner

Silver Spur Ranch
  Tex Tom Winchell
Sky Harbor Ranch
  Eli Kramer
Slator Ranch
  Smith, T.A.
Stone Ranch
  Ms. Sammye Stone
Stone Ridge Ranch
  Carl Brugger
Stone Ridge Ranch
  Richard Crisp
Stovall Ranch
  Eric Martin Stovall
Stovall Ranch
  Linda Joy Stovall
Swint, B.W.
Sycamore Ranch
  Wilson Hodge
Talisman Hunting
  Chuck Berg
Tamanet Ranch
  Tom Joseph
Texas Choice Hunting
  James Barnett
Thompson Temple's Texas
  Wildlife–Thompson Temple
Trammell, C.A.
Treadwell, Gary C.
Triangle T Outfitters
  Ed James Tibljas
Tule Ranch Hunts
  Kent Carpenter
Volz Ranch Encinal
  James Volz
Wallis, Ben A.
Wardlaw, Jack
Webb Shooting Preserve
  Wesley L. Webb
Wendel Ranch
  Lorenz or Jannabeth Wendel
West Outfitters
  Ronnie West
White, Larry
White, Tommy
Whitley
  J. C. Whitley
Wildlife Connection
  Nolan Fontenot
Wildlife Service
  Terry Fincher
Wildlife Systems
  Greg Simons
Williams Ranch Co.
  Rowdy McBride
Wilson Ranch
Witte Ranch
  Patrick J. Witte
Wolff Jr., Mr. & Mrs. Ernert
Worsham, James

UTAH
Allen's Outfitters
  Jeff Allen
Alpine Angler
  Rich & Kim Cropper
Blindforl Guide Service
  Ken & Cathy Church
Bucks & Bulls Guides & Outfitters
  Kim Bonnett
Bugle Creek Outfitters
  Jeff Jensen
Bugle Point Outfitters
CC Lodge & Outfitters
  Cass Casper
Cedar Mountain Outfitters
  Steve Sillitoe
Circle E Outfitters
  Randy Eames
Dry Creek Hunts
  Bryce Pilling
Flying "J" Outfitters
  Lawny Jackson
H & H Hunting
  Bruce & Robert Hubbard
K.A. Guides & Outfitters
  Kenneth A. Sorenson
Kohlbrecher, Ken F.
Lecount, Karen C.
Leeder Hunting
  Charles F. Leeder
Porcupine Adventures Inc.
  Roland Leishman
Red Creek Outfitters
Sagewood Outfitters

Justin Jones
Ute Indian Tribe
  Fish & Game/Outfoor Rec. Program
Wasatch Outfitters & Guides
Western Mountain Outfitters
  Dudley Henderson
Wilderness Tracks
  Harley Johnson
Willow Creek Kennels & Guide
  Service–Kelly Laier

VERMONT
Black Mountain Enterprises
  Milt Sherman
Green Mountain Long Beards
  Michael C. Senecal
Green Mtn. Outdoor Adv.
  James F. Casey Jr.
Green Mtn. Outdoor Adv./Rdg.
  Runner Bowhunts
  Jas. or Sharon Paige
Hot Pursuit Guide Service
  Vincent J. Ranucci
Hubbard Park Outfitters
  John Guilmette
Mr. O's Sporting Goods
  Michael Olden
North Country Guiding
  Al Morelli
Northeast Kingdom Guide Service
  Harry Burnham
Otter Creek Campground
  George Araskiewicz
Otter Creek Outfitters
  Daniel Barrows
Sears, Larry
Seymour Lake Lodge
  Dave or Sue Benware
Southern Vermont Guide Service
  Michael Schnaderbeck
The Outside Connection
  Bryce M. Towsley
The Vermont Sportsman
  Bob Beaupre
Thurston, Kurt
Thurston's Guide Service
  Sidney F. Thurston
Uncle Noel's Bait & Tackle
  Todd Sudol or Randy Savage
Willoughby Lodge Enterprises
  Malcolm Davidson Sr.

VIRGINIA
Boar-Walla Lodge
  Ken Martin
Virginia Upland Outfitters
  Tal McBride
Willis River Hunting Adv.
  Danny Henshaw

WASHINGTON
Back Country Wilderness Outfitters
  Dave Porter & Jim McWorter
Bear River Lodge Ltd.
  John Priebe
Bearpaw Outfitters
  Dale R. Denny
Bobcat Ranch
Cascade Wilderness Outfitters
  Steve Darwood
Cusack's Alaska Lodge
  Master Guide Bob Cusack
Early Winters Outfitting
  Aaron Lee & Judy Burkhart
Goodnights' Hunting Preserve &
  Sporting Clays
Granby Guides & Outfitters
  Barry Brandow
Gray Wolf Outfitters
  Glenn Cantwell
H & L Outfitters
  Rick A. Lane
Hancock, John K.
Hansen, David M.
High Country Hunting
  Mike Ehlis
Highland Stage Company
  Donald & Kristen Super
Icicle Outfitters & Guides
  Bruce & Sandy Wick
Indian Creek Corral
  Dan & Carleen Bleton
Last Chance Outfitters
  George & Carolyn Trice
North Cascades Safari
  Claude Miller
Panhandle Outfitters
  Tom Loder

Sawtooth Outfitters
  Brian Varrelman
Selkirk G&O/Priest Lk. Outdoor Adv.
  Patrick J. Prentice & Bruce Duncan
Susee's Skyline Packers
  Albert L. "Roy" Susee
Three Queens Outfitting
  D.L. "Cougar" & Janice Osmonovich

WEST VIRGINIA
Cheat Mtn. Outfitting & Guide
  Service   Treve Painter
Greenbrier River Company
  Virgil Hanshaw
McCabe, Kramer L.
Moore, Robin E.
Moutaineer Guides
  Richard T. Shepherd
White III, Byrd E.
Whitewater Travel
  Kyle Coon

WISCONSIN
Black Island Resort
  Mike & Barb Sergio
Blue Diamond Whitetail Ranch
  David Zirbel
Bridger Peak Outfitters LLC
  Robert Millar
*Chip's Call of the Wild Guide
  Service–Chip Mosser*
Pickerel Arm Camp
  The Edwardson's
Ridge Runner Outfitters
  Tom Haack
Sable Mountain Guides
  Jim Beaulieu
South Bay Lodge
  Bob Lammers
Sturgeon Lake Lodge
  Shannono & Don Utynek
Ten Mile Lake Camp
  Richard & Michelle Carpenter

WYOMING
46 Outfitters
  R. Lane Turner
7D Ranch
  Marshall Dominick
88 Ranch Outfitters
  William Henry III/Robert Henry
A Cross Ranch
  Chuck Sanger
AA Outfitters
  Ronald Ball
Absaroka Ranch
  Robert Betts Jr.
AJ Brink Outfitters
  Jim Brink
AJ Outfitters
  Jeffery HIll
Aladdin Outfitters
  Walter Marchant
All American Outfitters
  Forest Stearns
Allen's Diamonnd Four Ranch
  Jim Allen
Antelope Outfitters
  Steve Beilgard
Arizona Creek Outfitters
  Roy Bonner
*Arrowhead Outfitters
  Bobby Lowe*
Aspen Grove Ranch Outfittters
  Frederick Neuman
Autumn Meadows
  Gary Dean Buck
B & B Outfitters
  Brett Jones
Bald Mountain Outfitters
  Terry A. Pollard
Bare Tracks Trophies
  Major F. Miller
Barlow Outfitting
  Robert Barlow
BB Outfitters
  Brian Beishers
Bear Creek Hunting Camp
  Francis Fox
Bear Lodge Outfitters
  Kenneth Rathbun
Bear Track
  Peter J. Dube
Beard Outfitters
  Lyle Beard
Beartooth & Absaroka Wilderness
  Charles H. Smith

Beaver Creek Outfitters
  L.D.Gibertz
*Beaver Creek Outfitters
  Steve Kobold*
Beaver Creek Outfitters
  Keith Manning
Beaver Trap Outfitters
  Al Martin
Big Horn Basin Outfitters
  Ed R. Cormier
Big Horn Mountain Outfitters
  Toby Johnson
Big Horn Outfitters
  Bryce Antley
Big Horn Outfitters
  John Nation
Big Sandy Lodge
  Bernard Kelly
Billings Enterprises
  Ray Billings
Bitterroot Ranch
  Bayard Fox
BJ Outfitters
  William Hollingsworth
Bliss Creek Outfitters
  Tim Doud & Doris Roesch
Bolten Ranch Outfitters
  Robert Terrill
*Boulder Lake Lodge
  Kim Bright*
Box K Ranch
  Walter Korn
Boxelder Trophies
  Maurice Bush
Boysen Outfitters
  William M. Weaver
Bridger Teton Outfitters
  Randy Foster
Bridger Wilderness Outfitters
  Tim R. Singewald
Broken Horn Outfitters
  Rock Buckingham
Broken Horseshoe Outfitters
  William Carr
Buckhorn Mountain Outfitters
  Jerry Martin
Bud Nelson Outfitters
  Bud Nelson
Buffalo Bill Cody FFA
  Josh Stratman & Dan Benson
Buffalo Creek Outfitters
  Galen Bloom
Buffalo Creek Outfitters
  Otis Bloom
Butte Creek Outfitters
  Theresa Lineberger
B.J. Outfitters
  James Ellison
C Bar C Outfitters
  Clifford J. Clark
C K Hunting & Fishing Camp
  Darrell Copeland
Cabin Creek Outfitters
  Duane Wiltse
Cash Outfitters
  Douglas Cash
Central Wyoming Archery Outfitter
  Kim Cooper
Cherokee Outfitters
  Ivan L. Samson
Circle S Outfitters
  Don Smith
Clarendon, Dave
Cole Creek Outfitters
  Jon C. Nicolaysen
Coulter Creek Outfitters
  Robert Johnson
Cowpoke Outfitters
  Jack Risner
Coy's Yellow Creek Outfitting
  B. Joe Coy
Crandall Creek Outfitters
  Bruce Hillard
Cross C Ranch & Outfitting
  Willard M. Woods
Cross Milliron Ranch
  Larry Miller
Crossed Sabres Ranch
  Fred Norris
Crystal Creek Outfitters
  Gap Puchi
D & D Outfitters
Dampier Hunting Lodge
  James Dampier
Dan Kinneman Outfitter-Guide
  Daniel Kinneman
*Darby Mountain Outfitters
  Robert John Harper*
*Darwin Ranch
  Loring Woodman*

Dave Filtner Packing & Outfitting
David Filtner
Dave Hanna Outfitters
Dave Hanna
David Ranch
Melvin David
Deadman Creek Outfitters
Gregg Fischer
Deer Forks Ranch
Benny Middleton
Diamond D Ranch Outfitters
Rod Doty
Diamond J Outfitters
Elmer Joe Stuemke
Diamond Tail Outfitters
Stan Filtner
Dick Page
Richard L. Page
Dodge Creek Ranch
Jerry Kennedy
Don Scheer Outfitters
Don Scheer
Don (Tip) Tipton's Outfitting
Don K. Tipton
Double Diamond Outfitters
Craig Griffith
Double Diamond Outfitters
Reed "Rick" Miller
DT Outfitting
Ray Focht
Dull Knife Hunting
Kenneth Graves
Dunior Outfitters Corp.
George William Snodgrass
East Slope Outfitters
Steven A. Richards
East Table Creek Hunting Camp
Kerry Chadwick
Edwards, Dennis
Edwards Outfitting
Richard Edwards
Elk Antler Outfitters
Richard Ashburn
Elk Mountain Outfitters
Myron J. Wakkuri
Elk Ridge Outfitters
Terry Reach
Even Toe Outfitters
Phil Gonzales
*Fair Chase Outfitters/River S
Enterprises
Mike & Debbie Schwiebert*
Far Horizons Trophy Hunts
Raymond Hall
Five Star Expeditions, Inc.
Ed Beattie
Floyd Ranch Hunts
Herb Kretschman
Flying H Ranch
Phil Bates
Flying S Outfitters
Kathleen M. Steele
Flying U Ranch
Ralph Foster
Flying X Ranch
Earl (Sonny) Malley
Full Circle Outfitters
Buck Braten
Gary Fales Outfitting
Gary Fales
Gene Saltz Big Game Outfitting
Gene Saltz
General Outfitter
Ronald O. Titterington
Gilroy Outfitting
Paul Gilroy
Grand Slam Outfitters
Mark Condict
*Grand & Sierra Outfitters
Glen Knotwell*
Granite Creek Outfitters
J.H. King
Granstorm Outfitters
Swede Granstorm
Grant Ranch Outfitters
Richard Grant
Grassy Lake Outfitters
Dan Blair
Great Rocky Mountain Outfitters
Robert Smith
Green River Guest Ranch Outfitters
Phillip Reints Jr.
Green River Outfitters
Bill Webb
*Greer Outfitters
Randy & Lora Greer*
Greys River Outfitters
Ken Clark
Grizzly Outfitters
Cole Benton

Grizzly Ranch
Frank & Rick Felts
Haderlie Outfitters
David Haderlie
Half Moon Lake Guest Ranch
Frank Deede
Hart Brothers Partnership
William Hart
Hayden & Sons Ranch
Troy Hayden
Heart Six Ranch
Terry Linn
Hejde, Chester F.
Hell Hole Outfitters
Lamont Merritt
Hensley Trophy Outfitter
Rob Hensley
*Hidden Basin Outfitters
Phillip & George Engler*
Hidden Creek Outfitters
Bill Perry
Hidden Valley Ranch
Duaine & Sheila Hagen
High Island Ranch
Frank Robbins
High Mountain Outfitters
Robert Deroche
High Plains Outfitters
Mervin Griswold
High Plains Pronghorns
Fazilath (Tim) Qureshi
Highland Meadow Outfitters
Mark Thompson
Hiland Outfitters
Don Bennett
Holland Ranch Outfitters
Jeffrey Holland
Hook, George F.
Horse Creek Land Co.
Kenneth Neal
Hunton Creek Outfitters
Clark Noble
Indian Creek Outfitters
Bruce Moyer
Indian Summer Outfitters
Steve Robertson
J & B Outfitters
Jim Fritz
Jack Creek Outfitters
Jackson Hole Area Outfitters
Maury Jones
Jackson Hole Mountain Guides
Andy Carson
Jackson Peak Outfitters
Charlie Petersen Jr.
Jenkins Hunting Camp
Larry Jenkins
Jensen Hunting Camp
Keith Jensen
Jiggs Pack & Guide Service
Jiggs Black
*John Henry Lee Outfitters
John Lee*
Johnson Outfitting
L. Dean Johnson
Johnson's A Bar One Ranch
Clyde Johnson
Jones Outfitters
Patrick Jones
J.T. Tinney Outfitting
James T. Tinney
Kalus, Joe
K Bar Outfitting
John Buxton II
*K Bar Z Guest Ranch &
Outfitters–Dave Segall &
Dawna Barnett*
Kedesh Guest Ranch
Charles Lander
Kym Taylor Outfitting
Kym L. Taylor
Lander Llama Company
Scott Woodruff
Laramie Range Outfitters
John Bisbing
Larry Stetter, General Outfitter
Larry Stetter
Larsen, Peter
Lazy BJ Outfitters
Bill Woodworth
Lazy TX Outfitting
Clayton Voss
*Lightning Creek Ranch
Jim & Dawna Werner*
Linn Brothers Outfitting
Eugene Linn
Little Bighorn Outfitters
Tim Moyes
Little Sunlight Outfitters
Don J. Vitto

Llano Outfitters
John F. Savini
Lone Wolf Outfitters
Bambi Schumacher
M & M Outfitters
Mark K. Teel
Magic Mountains Outfitters
S. R. Dayton
Majo Ranch
Grant Stambaugh
Mankin Wildlife
James R. Mankin
McNell & Sons
Merrill McNell
Medicine Bow Outfitters
Harold Embree
Mike Smith Outfitters
Michael Smith
Mill Iron Ranch
Chancy Wheeldon
Milliron 2 Outfitting
Billy Sinclair
Mooncrest Outfitters
Robert Model
Mott, Joseph F.
M.F.Hunting
Larry Feuz
Nelson Outfitting
David & Dennis Nelson
North Fork Outfitters
Jim VanNorman
North Laramie Outfitting & Guide
Allen L. Cook
North Rim Outfitters
Roy Gamblin
Northern Wyoming Outfitters
George K. Warner
NX Bar Ranch
Brian MacCarty
Old Glendevey Ranch
Garth W. Peterson
Open Creek Outfitting
John Billings
Outfitters Unlimited
Todd Jones
Outwest Safari Unlimited
Gene Carrico
*P Cross Bar Ranch
Marion & Mary Scott*
Paintrock Outfitters
William F. Craft
Papoose Peak Outfitters
Louis Cary
Paradise Ranch Co.
James Anderson
Pass Creek Outfitters
Richard Miller
Pat Garrett Outfitter
Pat Garret
Pathfinder Outfitters & Guides
Greg Burgess
Pennoyer Outfitting
George Pennoyer
Petersen Outfitting
Greg Petersen
Pilgrim Creek Hunting Camp
John Watsabaugh
Pine Creek Outfitters
Earl Wright
Piney Creek Outfitters
Ron Reece
Platt's Guides & Outfitters
Ronald Platt
Porter, John A.
Powder Horn Outfitters
Darwin Powers
Powder River Breaks Outfitters
Glenn Sorenson
Powder River Outfitters
John Francis
Preemption Creek Hunts
Ralph Abell
Press Stephens Outfitter
Press Stephens
Pronghorn Adventures
Greg Salisbury
Pumpkin Buttes Outfitters
Bill Bruce Hines
Rafter B Outfitters
Larry Brannian
Rand Creek Outfitters
Ron McCloud
Randy's Outdoor Adventures
Randy Edmunds
Ranger Creek Ranch
Claude A. Powell
Raven Creek Outfitters
Kent Drake
Red Cloud Outfitting
Brett L. Sorenson
Red Desert Adventures

Vic Dana
Red Valley Outfitters
Mike Wolcott
Rendezvous Outfitters
Bruce Blanthorn
Reynolds, Jeff
Ridgemaster Outfitting
Charles Cureton
Rim Rock Hunts
Lee Miller
Rimrock Hunts
Dan Artery
Rimrock Ranch
Glenn Fales
RNR Rainbows N Racks
Raymond Stroup
Roberts, Stephen
Rocking L-H
Larry J. Henry
Rocky Butte Outfitters
Ed G. Schaffer
Rocky Top Lion Outfitters
Scott Q. Schroer
Romios Outfitters
Pete Romios
Ron Dube's Wilderness Adv.
Ron Dube
Ronell Skinner Guide & Outfitters
Ronell Skinner
Rough Country Outfitters & Guides
James D. Schell
R.E. Evans Grizzly Creek Outfitters
Richard Evans
S N S Outfitters & Guide Service
SY Gilliland
Sagebrush Outfitters
Don Hockett
Sand Creek Outfitters
Jim P. Collins
Saratoga Safaris
Tim Barkhurst
Savage Run Outfitters
James F. Talbott
Schmalz Outfitting
Don Schmalz
Schutte, Thomas E.
Seven J Outfitters
Jeffery L. Smith
Sheep Creek Outfitters
Johnny Campbell
Sheep Mesa Outfitters
Ronald Good
Sheep Mountain Outfitters
Tim Haberberger
Shirley Mountain Outfitters
Steve Steinle
Shoal Creek Outfitters
Scott Millward
Shoshone Outfitters
Keith Dahlem
Simons Hunting Camp
Frank Simons
Skinner Brothers
Robert Skinner
Sleeping Indian Outfitters
Paul Crittenden
Snake River Outfitters
Thomas Grieve
Snyder Outfitting
Stanley Snyder
Southern Wyoming Outfitters
Dale Pribyl
Southfork Double Diamond X Ranch
Dale W. Sims
Spearhead Ranch
Frank N. Moore
Spear-O-Wigwam Ranch
James Niner
Spotted Horse Ranch
Dick Bess
Squaw Creek Ranch & Outfitters
Gail Zimmerman
Star Valley Outfitters
Reed S. Clark
Steve Sheaffer Outfitters
Steve & Connie Sheaffer
Suda Outfitters
Wayne Suda
Sully Outfitters
Sully Simons
Sunrise Outfitters
Mike Heins
Sweetwater Gap Ranch
Robert Wilmetti
Sweetwater Outfitters
Ray A. Dennis
*Swift Creek Outfitters
B.J. & Vicki Hill*
Swift Creek Outfitters
Therese Metherell
T Lazy T Outfitters

Tom Toolson
Table Mountain Outfitters
  Dale Critchfield
Talbott, James R.
Tally-Ho Outfitters
  Allan Perry
Taylor, Ridge W.
Taylor Outfitters
  Tory Taylor
Taylor Ranch & Outfitting
  Glenn B. Taylor
Temple Creek Outfitter
  James Porter
Teton Crest Outfitters
  Phil Major
Teton Wilderness Outfitting
  Nate C. Vance
The Head Hunters
  Don C. Malli
The Last Resort
  Dru Roberts
The Trophy Connection
  Julia Dube
Thompson Outfitters
  Dick Thompson
Thunder Ridge Outfitters
  Ron Morrison
Timberline Outfitters
  Craig P. Oceanak
Top Two Ocean Pass
  John Winter
Tracker, Packer & Guide Outfitting
  Gary Dean Talbott
Trails West Outfitters
  Robert Sundeen
Trefren Outfitters
  Tim & Sharon Trefren
Triangle C Ranch
Cameron W. Garnick
Triangle X Ranch
  Donald Turner
Triple Creek Hunts
  Jim Freeburn
Triple Three Outfitters
  J. Craig Smith
Trophy Chasers Outdoor Adv.
  Mark Lantz
Trophy Connection
Trophy Outfitters
  Dwight N. Heater
Turpin Meadow Ranch
  Stan Castagno
Twin Pine Ranch
Larry & Peg Gerke
Two Ocean Pass Outfitting
  John R. Winter
UL Ranch Outfitters
  Jerry R. Palm
Ullery Outfitters
  Brad Ullery
V Bar F Cattle Co.
  Neal R. Schuman
Wade's Piney Creek Outfitting
  Bobbi Wade
Wayne Graves Outfitters
  Wayne Graves
Western Wyoming Outfitters
  Jerry Thune
Western Wyoming Trophy
Hunts–Levi & Irv Lozier
Whiskey Mountain Outfitters
  Gari Epp
Whitetail Creek Outfitters
  Raymond M. Hulse
Wild Game Outfitters
  Paul Strausner
Wildcat Outfitters
  Pat Phillipps
Wilderness Trails
  Galloway M. Clover
Wind River Mountain Outfitters
  Fritz Meyer
Wind River Mt. Lion Outfitters
  James D. Rice
Wind River Outfitters
  Kim Merchant
Wind Walker Outfitters
  Rick Garrison
Windy Peak Outfitters
  Darin Geringer
Wocicki, Gene
Wolf Lake Outfitters
  Mike Nystrom
Wolf Mountain Outfitters
  Guy Azevedo
Wolverine Creek Outfitters
  Warren Fleming
Wycon Safari
  Wynn Condict
Wyoming Big Horn Sheep Hunts
  Stanley Siggins

Wyoming Country Outfitters
  Kevin McNiven
Wyoming Dark Timber Adv.
  Dave Parrish
Wyoming Professional Hunters
  Jay Lesser
Wyoming Trophy Hunts
  Kenneth Metzler
Wyoming Trophy Outfitters
  Randy & Sharon Brown
Wyoming Wilderness Outfitters
  Jake Kay Clark
Wyoming Wildlife Outfitters
  Bob & Rob Marosok
Wyoming's Choice
  Dick Vandeveer
Yellowstone Outfitters
  Gary Caskey
Yellowstone Outfitters
  Lynn & Marcene Madsen
ZN Outfitters
  George Williams

MEXICO
Acosta Trailer Ranch
  Sr. Carlos Cesar Acosta Garcia
Alcampo Hunting Adventures
  Lic. Javier Artee Valenzuela
Arrow Five Outfitters
Jim Schafsma
Baja Cfa. Bird's Paradise
  Sr. Rafael Valle Vitela
Big Gama Outfitters
  Ing. Carlos Gonzalez Hermosillo
Campillo Brothers Outfitters &
  Guides   Roberto F.
  Campillo
Coues Hunt
  Ing. Manuel R. Garcia Puebla
Gabino's Yaqui Valley Hunting
  Sr. Francisco Javier Ruiz Zubia
Hacienda Cazadores
  Sr. Polo Acosta Garcia
Hotel del Rio
  Lic. Martin Ernesto Bouvet Arvizu
La Cabana Hunting Resort
  Sra. Luz Alicia Molina Zavalza
Mex-Bass, SA.
  Arq. Miguel Puig Davison
Moteles El Rancho, SA. de CV.
  Sr. Gustavo Adolfo Cuevas
  Garibay
Muy Grande Outfitters
  Lic.Sergio Estrella Sau
Reserva Cinegetica "Fuente Clara"
Solimar Hunting Safaris
  Ernesto Zaragoza
Sonora Adventure
  Ing. Jorge Camou Leon
Sonora Outfitters
  Sr. Alberto Noriega Diaz
Sonora Outfitters
  Sr. Leon Hoeffer Ramirez
Yaqui Hunting Club
  Sr. David Artee Valenzuela

ALBERTA
Alberta Bighorns
  RW Bobby Turner
Alberta Bowhunting Adventures
  Ted Hansen
Alberta Bush Adventures
  Richard Deslauriers
Alberta Native Guide Service
  Ken Steinhauer
Alberta Rocky Mtn. Trail Adv.
  K&M Robinson–L&M Nielson
Alberta Trophy Hunters &
  Outfitters–Richard Page
Alberta Whitetail Connection
  Don Tsyschuk
Alberta Wilderness Guide Serv.
  David Bzawy & Terry Birkholz
All-Terrain Guide & Outfitting
  Ronald Bell
Alstott Outfitting
  Edwin Alstott
AMERI-CANA Expeditions
  Pat Frederick
Anchor D Guiding & Outfitting
  Dewy & Jan Matthews
Andrew Lake Lodge & Camp
  Glen Wettlaufer
Athabasca River Outfitters
  Bryan Radke & Bruce Wierenga
Baird, Darrell
Bar JJ Outfitting

Jim & Connie Kelts
Barrier Mountain Outfitters
  A. H. Johnson
BBD Guiding & Outfitting
  Dave Moore
Bearpaw Outfitting
  Scott Taylor
Beaverhill Outfitters
  Brent Reil
Big Rack Adventures
Blair & Kathy Trout
Big Smoky Outfitting
  Gary Kruger
Blue Bronna Outfitting
  Glenn Brown
Blue Ridge Outfitters
  Wynder & Billl Barrus Dee
Boss Guiding Services
  Bob Byers
Brewster Mountain Packtrain
Broadhead Outfitters
  Kent Butterfield
Buck 'n Bears Outfitters
  Wendell Mann
Buckbrush Outfitters
  Rod Hunter
Buffalo Lake Outfitters
  Brad Steinhoff
Canadian Hunting Co.
  Dean Yardley
Cheemo Lodge
  Ed Granger
Chester Sands Outfitting
  Chester Sands
Chimney Creek Outfitter
  Miles & Joanne Stern
Chinchaga River Hunts
  Dennis Potter
Classic Outfitters
  Jim Hole Jr.'s
Cook & Sands Ranch
  Bill Sand & Sons
Cougar Outfitters
  John Cassidy & Mark Tannas
Cree Lake Lodge
  Vern & Gerri Biller
Cypress Expeditions
  Lyle Czember
D & S Guiding
  Robert Dean Cumming
DeBolt Guiding & Outfitting
  Hugh Alexander
Del Bredeson Guiding & Outfitting
  Del Bredeson
Diamond And-A-Half Outfitters
  Bill Sinclair
Diamond Jim & Sons Mtn. Rides
  Jim Colosimo
Diamond Outfitters
  Byron Tofteland
Don Ayers Outfitters
  Don Ayers
Double Diamond Outfitters
  Gordon Burton
Double Diamond Wilderness
  Trails–John & Jeramy Hatala
Double H Outfitters
  Herb & Heather Bailey
Elk Island Outfitters
  Bernd Light
Eric's Wilderness
  Eric Twardzilk
Excell Outfitters
  Al Schulz
Folding Mountain Outfitters
  Dale Drinkall
Frank Kuhnen
George Kelly Outfitters
  George Kelly
Glacier Peak Adventures
  Nancy Koopman
Goffitt River Outfitters
  Rod E. Roth
Golden Bear Outfitting
  Eldon Hoff
Great North Outfitters
  Neil Wunderlich
Great White Holdings
  Lloyd McMahon
Grist Haven Lodge
  Tony M. Kòssey
Grizzly Trail Guiding & Outfitting
  Leo Schmaus
Grosso Outfitting
  Clayton & Hilda Grosso
Guinn Outfitters
  Rick & Denise Guinn
Gundahoo River Outfitters
  Art Thompson
Hallett, Nayda

Happy Hunters Guiding & Outfitting
  Willi Kratzmann
Hebert's Guide Service
Joe & Doreen Hebert
Homeplace Ranch
  Mac Makenny
Jack Franklin Outfitting
JH Trail Rides
  Del Whitford
Jim Fisher Guiding & Outfitting
  im Fisher
Jordy McAuley Outfitting
  Jordy McAuley
J.W. & Edith Nagy Outfitting
  J.W. & Edith Nagy
K Country Outfitting
  Keith Koebisch
Kevin Rolfe Outfitters
  Kevin Rolfe
Kostynuk Outfitting
  Sam Kostynuk
Lazy H Trail
  Richard & Connie Blair
Lee, Roger A.
Leonard Outfitting
  Bazil Leonard
Lloyd Lake Lodge
  Richard & Mary Jean Pliska
Lost Guide Outfitters
  Gary Bracken
M & M Ranch
  Neil & Becky Maclaine
Magnun Outfitters
  Roy Thompson
McKenzie Brothers Outfitting
  Bruce & Linda McKenzie
McKenzie's Trails West
  Ron McKenzie
McMillan River Outfitters
  Dave Coleman
Mike Zelman & Son's Outfitter
  Service–Mike Zelman
North Alberta Outfitters
  Troy A. Foster
North Alberta Ventures
  Dollard Dallaire
North River Outfitting
  Ron Nemetchek
Northeast Alberta Wilderness
  Outfitters–Charles Graves
Northern Adventures
  Pat Frederick
N.W.T. Outfitters, Ltd.
Darrell & Duane Nelson
Outlaws Guiding & Outfitting
  Frank Raymond
Packsaddle Adventures
  Larry Chapman
Palmer, Irvin
Pawistik Lodge
  Scott Jeffrey
Percival Trophy Hunts
  Doug Percival
Plihal Guiding & Outffiting
  Gene Plihal
Poplar Ridge Outfitters
  Harvey McNalley
Porcupine Creek Outfitters
  Brent Sinclair
Rams Head Outfitters
  Stan Simpson
Ranch Country Outfitters
  Perry McCormick
Raven Outfitters
  Wayne Whitherspoon
Ray Cross & Sons Outfitting
  Ray W. Cross
Redstone Trophy Hunts
  David & Carol Dutchik
Ridge Country Outfitters
  Bill Morton
Rocking Star Trail Rides
  Willie Kadatz
Ron Loucks Outfitting
  Ron Loucks
Ryk Visscher Bowhunting
  Adventures–Ryk Visscher
Saddle Peak Trail Rides
  Dave Richards
Sands & Miller Outfitting
  Don Miller & Charlie Sands
Saracen Head Outfitter
  Ed Regnier
Sheep Creek Outfitters
  Frank Simpson
Sherwood Guides & Outfitters
  Lois or Pete McMann
Silver Fox Outfitters
  Eric Rauhanen
Silver Sage Outfitters
  Billy Franklin

Silvertip Outfitters
  Eric Grinnell
Skyline Trail Rides
  Dave Flato
Smith & Overguard Outfitting
  Jim Smith & Steve Overguard
South Paw Outfitters
  Rene & Kelly Semple
South Ram Outfitters
  Lorne & Sharmane Hindbo
Stafford, Robert
Stricker Outfitting, Ltd.
Charlie Stricker
Sunset Guiding & Outfitting
  Duane Papke
Sven-Erik Jansson Associates
  Sven-Erik Jansson
Tall Timbers Outfitting
  David Sharp
Tamarack Hunting Enterprises
  Justin Henry
Team Whitetail Outfitting
  Darcy Zelman
Timberline Tours
  Paul Peyto
Tom Scott Outfitting
Tom Scott
Tonquin Valley Pack Trips
  Wald Olson
Trails Unlimited
  Hank Peterson
Triple S Outfitters
  Stuart & Ruby Sinclair-Smith
Trophy Quest Outfitters
  Dean Regehr
Trophy Stalkers
  Doug Olson
Tsayta Lake Lodge
  Graham Perry
Twilight Guiding & Outfitting
  Marcel Morin
Ukrainetz Guided Hunts
  Mike Ukrainetz
Upper-Edge Outfitters
  Rick Borysiuk
Vic Forchuk & Sons Outfitting &
  Guides–Vic Forchuk
Warner Guiding & Outfitting
  Ron Warner
West Coast Safaris
  Rod Hunter
Western Adventures
  Glenn & Leslie Huber
Western Guiding Services
Greg, Dave & Betty Molloy
Whispering Hill Trophy Hunters
  & Outfitters–Jay Stewart
Whispering Pine Outfitters
  Gordon & Lynn Utri
Whitetail Safaris
  Paul Glen Carlson
Wild Rose Whitetails
Wilderness Ranch
  Dick Hansen
Willow Lane Ranch
  Keith & Leanne Lane
Willsie, Glen
Wind Valley Guiding & Outfitting
  Ken Fraser
Wolf-Creek Outfitters
  Robert Irvine
Wolverman Wilderness Outfitters
  Walchuk & Degenhardt & Slage

BRITISH COLUMBIA

Albert Cooper Guide & Outfitters
  Albert Cooper
Alpine Ridge Guiding & Outfitting
  Allan Strauss
Andy Hagberg Guiding
  Andy Hagberg
Ashe, William
Ashnola Guide & Outfitter
  Clarence Schneider
A/Z Outfitters Ltd.
Bill DuBois
Baldy Mountain Outfitters
  Harry Leuenberger
Bear Lake Guides & Outfitters
  Gerald Pattison
Bear Paw Guide and Outfitters
  Dennis & Irene Smith
Beaverfoot Lodge
  Don Wolfenden
Bell, Denys
Betemps, George
Big Nine Outfitters
  Barry Tompkins
Blaine R. Southwick Outfitting

Blaine Southwick
Blaney, Norman
Bookmyer, Peter L.
Boot, Shawn
Bougie Mtn. Besa River Outfitting
  Paul Gillis
Bowron River Guiding
  Jack Pichette
Bracewell's Alpine Wilderness
  Adventures–Gerry Bracewell
Bracewell, Kevan
Bradford & Co. Guide Services
  Myles & Sherry Bradford
Buchholtz, Daryl
Burghardt, Werner
Burr, David L.
Cahoose, Andy
Cahoose, Danny
Campsall Outfitters
  Hank Campsall
Canadian Adveuntre Safaris
  Odd Aasland
Cariboo Mountain Outfitters
Bradley Bowden
Cariboo West Outfitters
  Gary & Peggy Zorn
Carry, Raymond J.
Cassier Stone Outfitters
  Dan Stobbe
Chilcotin River Guide Outfitter
  William Mulvahill
Chingee, Harry
Christina Falls Outfitters
  Darwin Watson
Christy, Thomas
Churn Creek Outfitters
  Eric Mikkelson
Coast Mountain Holidays
  Roma Richburg
Coldwell, Ray
Collingwood Bros. Guides &
  Outfitters–Ray & Reg Collingwood
Columbia River Outfitters
  Richard Hark
Connors, Keith B.
Cooke, Terry E.
Copper River Ranch
  Ben Ridennoure
Coyote Creek
  Edward Cretney
Cushman, Timothy
Cutts, Robert J.
Dalziel, Rush
Davidson, Charlie
Davis, Douglas A.
Desjarlais, Marvin
Diamond M Outfitting
  Terry Spriggs
Dick Blewett Outfitting
  Dick Blewett
Double Eagle Guides & Outfitters
  Stewart Berg
Drinkall, Glen R.
Eagle Crest Guide Outfittters
  George Pedneault
Eagle River Guide Outfitting
  Eric Havard
East Kootenay Outfitters
  Joe Juozaitis
Elkins, Lawrence
Elk Valley Bighorn Outfitters
  Bob Fontana
Elliott, Gordon M.
Ellis, Leonard
Emmelkamp, Ron
Ernst, Walter
Ethier, Dale
Eureka Peak Lodge Outfitters
  Stuart Maitland
Faessler, Charlie
Fahselt, Richard
Farr, Scott
Fawnie Mtn. Outfitters & Moose
Lake   Lodge–John
Blackwell
Findlay Creek Outfitters
  Eric Godlien
Finlay River Outfitters
  Rick McLean
Fournier Bros. Outfitting
  Greg Fournier
Frank, Terry
Frontier Hunting
  Doug Davis
Gana River Outfitters
  Bill MacKenzie
Gemstar Outfitting
  Brian Schuck
Geraci, Gerald
Giesbrechm, Lawrence
Glacier Peak Adventures
  Gary Koopman
Granby Guides & Outfitters
  Barry Brandow
Grinder, Floyd
Grizzly Basin Outfitters
  Wilfrid Boardman
Grizzly Lake Outfitters
  Ron Fitch
Grizzly Outfitters
  Phil Gillis

Grove, Norman
Grundmann, Peter W.
Gunn, Dennis
G.F. Moore Enterprises
  Gordon F. Moore
G.O.A.B.C.
Hale, Dennis
Hallett Lake Outfitters
  Allen Ray
Hamilton, Jack E.
Heaton, Sr., William
Hicks, Frank
Hochsteiner, Albin
Hodson Guiding Services
  D. Hodson
Horseshoe Creek Outfitters
  Ray Jackson
Hussinger, Rolf
Icha & Illgatcho Mountain Outfitters
  Roger Williams
Indian River Ranch Guides &
  Outfitters–Jamie Schumacher
Inzana Outfitters
  Terry Stocks
Irvine, Mark
Isnardy, Amedee G.
Itcha Mountain Outfitters
  B.H. Fraser
Jimmie, Robert
Joseph, Alfred
Kawdy Outfitters
  Stan Lancaster
Kazchek Lake
  Harm Wernicke
Kettle, John R.
Kettle River Guides & Outfitters
  Melvin Kilback
Kiniskan Outfitters
  Bruce Creyke
Klukas Lake Ranch
  Glen Kilgour
Krebs, Juergen
Kyllo Brothers
  Ken Kyllo
Lady Ester Ranch Big Game
  Outfitters–John Nielsen
Lakes District Hunting Lodge
  Hans-Joerg Hartl
Lamoureux Outfitters
  Martin Lamoureux
Larry Erickson's Alpine Outfitters
  Larry Erickson
Layton Bryson Outfitting & Trail
  Riding–Layton Bryson
Leake, Herb
Lehman Creek Outfitters
  Dave Altherr
Letcher, Donald F.
Liard River Outfitters
  Mike Belfour
Loney, Larry
Lougheed, David
Louie, Wayne
Love Bros. & Lee Ltd.
Ron Fleming
Lower Kootenay Guide Outfitters
  Joe Pierre
Mackenzie Mountain Outfitters
  Stan Stevens
Madley, Alan
Maitland, Stuart G.
Marcer, Gary & Terry
Matarozzo, James
McCowan's Sporting Adventures
  Harry McCowan
McKay Bros. Guides & Outfitters
  Bernard & Patrick McKay
Middle River Hunting & Fishing
  Martin Grainger
Meldrum, Arthur
Methot, Frank
Milligan, Robert
Mohr, Steven J.
Monashee Outfitting
  Volker Scherm
Monroe Cattle Co.
  Mike Monroe
Moore, Gary Lynn
Moose Valley Outfitters
Ronald Steffey
Mooseskin Johnny Lake Outfitters
  Don McIntyre
Morice River Outfitting
  John Shepert
Muncho Lake Outfitters
  Arnold Henhapl
Muskwa Safaris
  Garry & Sandra Vince
Mussfeld, Eberhard
M. Mulvahill Hunting
  Mike Mulvahill
M.C. Outfitting
  Chuck Christensen
Nahanni Butte Outfitters
  Greg Williams
Nanika Guiding
  Jim Tourand
Nass Headwaters Guiding &
  Outfitting–Ken Belford
Nichol, Tom
Nicol, Shelly

Nicola Outfitters
  Dan Stobbe
Nisutlin Bay Outfitters
  Philip Smith
North Coast Adventures
  Wayne Price
Northern Woodsman Outfitting
  Les Allen
Northwest Big Game Outfitters
  Jack Goodwin
Northwest Ranching & Outfitting
  Heidi Gutfrucht
Norwest Guiding & Outfitting
  Jeff Beckley
Obst, Harro
Okanagan Outfitters
  Marc & Marcella Hubbard
Olson, Fred
Omineca Guide & Outfitters
  Herb Badey
One Eye Outfit
  Mike McDonough
Ottertail River Outfitting
  Alan & Mary Young
Oysmueller, Karl
Paley, Robert G.
Paley, Wallace J.
Palliser River Guides & Outfitters
  Cody Tegart
Palliser River Outfitters
  Gordon Burns
Parrot Mountain Outfitter
  Miles Fuller
Peace Country Wilderness
  Adventures–Horst Mindermann
Peaceful Valley Wilderness
  Outfitters–Len Pickering
Peden, Mrs. Barbara
Peisl, Fred
Petal, Tony
Pine River Ventures
  Dale & Andy Copeland
Pink Mountain Outfitters
  Klaur Knocke
Pitka Mountain Outfitters
  Colonel R. Anderson
Powell, Grant
Price, Ronald
Purcell Wilderness Guiding &
  Outfitting–Gary E. Hansen
Quesnel Lake Wilderness
  Ken Davis
Rainbow Mountain Outfitting
  David Dorsey
Ram Creek Outfitters
  Steven Leuenberger
Reinhart, John
Reynolds, Thomas
Roberts, Allan B.
Rocky Mountain Adventures
  Gordon Jeck
Rocky Mountain High Outfitter
  & Guides–Barry Scott
Rocky Mountain Lodge
  Henry Fercho
Rocky Mountain Outfitters
  Carmen Dempsey
Ross Peck Outfitters
  Ross Peck
Sage Creek Outfitters
  Darrel Winser
Salmon River Outfitters
  Dwayne Nikkels
Saugstad, Randy
Schmideder, Karl
Schneider, Michael
Schuk Outfitting
  Doug Schuk
Schwartz, Arnold
Scoop Lake Outfitters
  Darwin Cary
Searls, Max & Viola
Selkirk Big Game Outfitters
  Phil Desmazes
Sentinel Mountain Ent.
  Dave Drolet & Roy Pattison
Shesley River Outfitters
  Rudy Day
Shockey, James E.
Sikanni River Outfitters
  Doug Percival
Silent Mountain Outfitters
  Dieter Bohrmann
Sill, Frank
Smith, Don
Smith, Steve
Smoke Mountain Guiding
  John Mould
Solmonson, Richard
Sorensen, Victor
Sorensen, William
Spruce Lake Outfitting
  Bryan Buchanan
Squinas, Mack
Stein River Outfitters
  Leo & Doris Ouellet
Steiner Bros. Guide & Outfitting
  Ray Steiner
Stelkia Ranch
  Aaron Stelkia
Stone Mountain Safaris

Dave & Ellie Wiens
Stuart-Trembleur Outfitters
  William Stanton
Sugar Valley Outfitters
  Bernie Jaeger
Sulin, Larry
Suskeena Lodge
  Floyd Boyd
Swift, Brian
Sylvester, Jack
Tahltan Outfitters
  Fletcher Day
Taku Safari
  Guy Anttila
Tatlatui Wilderness
  Bob Henderson
Tetsa River Outfitters
  Cliff Andrews
Thunder Mountain Outfitters
  Larry Bartlett
Timothy, Tommy
Toby Creek Guides & Outfitters
  Lyle Barsby
Toby Creek Outfitters
  Lloyd Harvey
Trembling Pines Outfitter
  Roy Mulvahill
Trophy West Guide Outfitters
  Donald Rose
Tsuniah Lake Lodge
  Eric Brebner
Tsylos Park Lodge & Adventures
  Lloyd McLean
Tukii Lodge
  Dave Hooper
Turnagain River Outfitters
  Eugene Egeler
Tweedsmuir Park Guides &
  Outfitters–Bob Nielsen
Uncha Mountain Outfitters
  Stefan Muehlmeyer
Upper Stikine River Adventures
  Ltd.   Jerry Geraci
Vantine, James
Vaseux Creek Outfitters
  Jim Wiens
Voll, Randy
Waloszek, Rudolf
Wayne Mueller Guide & Outfitters
  Wayne Mueller
Webb Outfitting
  Fred A. Webb
West Coast Outfitting
  Bob Welsh
West Kettle Outfitters
  Peter Grosch
Whatshan Guides & Outfitters
  Ken Robins
Wiebe, Wayne N.
Williams, Boyce J.
Williams, Theodore L.
Wistaria Guiding
  Gary Blackwell
Wolverine Mountain Outfitters
  Tim Chushman
Yohetta Wilderness Adventures
  Goetz Schuerholz
Zimmer, William C.
Zorn, Gary & Margaret
Zorn, Wayne

LABRADOR
Double Mer Fishing Camps Ltd.
  Howard Michelin
Drover's Labrador Adventures
  Alonzo Drover
Hunt River Camps
  Clyde House
Labrador Hunting Safari
  Robert & Stella Kelly
Labrador Salmon Lodge
Michikamau Outfitting
Northern Lights Fishing Lodge
  Yves Ste. Marie
True North Outfitting Co.
  Winston White
Wabush Outfitting Ltd.
  Bruce Woolfrey

MANITOBA
580 Outfitters
  Ron Girardin
Agassiz Taxidermy & Outfitting
  Rick Liske
Aksarnerk Adventures
  Randy & Donna Lee Bean
Anderson's Outfitting Service
  Oscar Anderson
Angell's Resort
Artemis Outfitting & Guiding
  Service   Hans Muenchow
Asmundson Outfitting Services
  Ed Asmundson

Atikaki Wilderness Camp
  Bob Jackson
Barron Land Outfitters
  Joe Barron
Barta's Outfitting Service
  Stan Barta
Barwick's Sportshop
  Bert Barwick
Bator Boy Outfitting
  Geraldine & Michael Bator
Bear Camp Outfitting
  Garry Nemetchek
Bear Creek Outfitters
  Dieter Boehner
Bear Guiding Service
  Kim & Roxanne Molyneaux
Bear Valley Outfitters
  Chris Switzer
Big Bear Outfitting
  Teddy Balcaen
Big Bear Paw Outfitters
  John Jebsen
Big Game Outfitter
  John Reimer
Big Netley Outfitters
  George Walker
Big Northern Lodge & Outfitters
  John Eisner
Big Rock Hunting & Fishing Lodge
  Gus Borkofsky
Big Trophy Outfitters
  John Hatley
Birch Lake Outfitters
  Glen Heroux
Birch Point Outfitters
  Erik Thienpondt
Bird River Outfitters
  Ron Alexander
Bissett Outfitters
  Byron Grapentine
Blind Creek Outfitters
  Walter & Diane Dmyterko
Bloodvein River Outfitters
  Nick Arseniuk
Boggy Creek Outfitting
  Maxwell Nemerchek
Bows & Bullets
  Pat Bergson
Breken Guided Trophy Hunts
  Ken & Brenda Maxymowich
Buck Stop Outfitting
  Gary M. Kochan
Bull Moose Outfitters
  Albert & Terri De Lichte
Bushman's Paradise
  Robert John Rath
Call of the Wild Outfitters
  Nick Gorda
Canadian Wilderness Outfitters
  Jack Smith
Caribou Country Adventures
  Stan B. Suess
Carpenter's Clearwater Lodge &
  Out-   fitters–Jim Lorden
  or Doug Sangster
Childs Lake Lodge & Outfitters
  Brian & Joan Forbes
D & O Soloway Outfitters Service
  Orville & Debbie Soloway
Darrell's Outfitting
  Darrell Dushanek
Davis Point Lodge & Outfitting
  Dr. Peter Kalden
Dawson Bay Outfitters
  Ken Klyne
Desjardins Outfitter
  Alexis J. Desjardins
Double M Guiding & Outfitting
  Mike Romaniuk
Duck Mountain Outfitters
  Leslie E. Nelson
Dudman Farms
  Barry Dudman
D. W. Outfitting
  Daryl R. Woodbeck
E&D Outfitters
  Ed & Diana Balan
Eden Eagle Outfitters
  Gerald & Elaine Leforte
Einarsson's Guide Service
  Helgi Einarsson
Elk Ranch Outfitters
  David Channon or Roger Whittington
Flin Flon Outfitters
Fox River Outfitters
  Randy Naismith
Grandview Outfitting
  Thomas Ainsworth
Great North Lodge

Glen Hoodle
Hal Valley Outfitters
  Lorne Huhtala
Hanson's Bear Creek Outfitters
  Lloyd Hanson
Hazel Creek Outfitters
  Kurt Witt
Head Water Ranch
  Bill McLeod
High Mountain Outfitters
  Dean Sandulak
Hillbilly Outfitters
  Keith Tucker
I & R Outfitters
  A. H. Knowles
Indian Trail Outfitters
  Bob Cherepak
J & D Jumbo Outfitters
  Jim Hoard
Johnson Road Outfitters
  Jim Wilson
J. R.'s Outfitting
  John W. Rudyk
Kerosene Creek Outfitters
  Alan or Karen Lanny
Kettle Hills Outfitters
  Victor Gervais
King Buck Safaris
  Larry Leschyshyn
Krec's Hunting & Fishing
  Kris Snydal
K. C.'s Outfitting
  Ken C. Holme
K. D. McKay Outfitting
  Kenneth D. McKay
K. S. B. Outfitters & Guiding Service
  Kenneth S. Biglow
Lamaga's Guiding & Outfitting
  Myron Lamaga
Lonely Lake Outfitting
  Ken Spence
Magson's Camp Outfitting Services
  Al & Mary Magson
Manfred Racine's Guiding &
  Outfitting   Svce.–Manfred
  Racine
Manitoba Buck Masters
  William Friesen & Gary Langan
Manitoba North Outfitters
  Mel Podaima
Manitoba Outfitters
  Tim Hastings & Dave Malko
Mantagao Outfitters
  Buddy or Marlene Chudy
Marlin Marv's Guiding
  Marvin Anderson
Marshall Quelch Outfitter
  Marshall Quelch
Maurice's Sportsman Outfitters
  Maurice or Sandra Thibert
Megabucks Outfitting
  David Olson & Darren Cook
Meridian Outfitters
  Terrence & Robert Truthwaite
Michie's Ranch & Lodge Outfitting
  David Michie
Mink Creek Outfitters
  Mike Dudar
Monkman Outfitting
  Bob Monkman
Mr. Walleye Taxidermy & Outfitter
  Robert R. Check
Murray, David
Nelson River Outfitters
  Bill Cordell
North of 54 Outfitters
  Glen & Kelly Whitbread
Northern Bear Adventure
  William Bruce Simms
Northern Manitoba Outfitters
  Jack & Georgia Clarkson
Opaskwayak Guiding & Outfitting
  Thomas Cook & Chris Constant
Otter Creek Outfitters
  Lynn & Lee Nolden
Outdoors Unlimited
  Glen J. Gulay
Outland Outfitting
  Jerry & Geraldine Cook
Pacey Lake Outfitters
  John & Audrey Ewasiuk
Parkland Outfitters
  Georg Voelkel
Parkside Outfitting Service
  Boris Chuey
Peace Garden Outfitting
  Gary Canada
Peter Wiibe Outfitting Service
  Peter Wiebe
Pine Lake Outfitters
  Al Pinder

Pioneer Outfitters
  David or Charlene Doan
Pistol Lake Outfitters
  Joseph Cormier
Porcupine Mountain Outfitters
  Ed Racine
Pukisimoon Outfitters
  Fred Hobbs
Rainbow Outfitters
  Tery Leochko
Red River Adventures & Outfitters
  Kim Meger
Rice Creek Outfitters
  Earl Schenk
Riding Outfitting Service
  Ron & Helen Sweetman
Rolly Outfitters
  Ron & Kelly Shykitka
Rupertsland Guiding & Outfitting
  Services–Werner Batke
R-K Outfitters
  Ron Dare & Ken Warkentin
Sandy River Outfitters
  Harry Walker
Sarah Lake Outfitters
  Mr. Senchuk
Serene Lake Outfitters
  Ingi & Cindy Bjornson
Silence of the North
  H. Kirtzinger & M. Schlosser
Silver Bear Creek Outfitters
  Bruce Crossley
Skownan Black Bear Outfitting
  Services–Ruth & Thomas Pfister
Smi's Outfitters
  David Semeniuk
Souris Valley Outfitters
  Dale McBurney
South Side Outfitters
  Rudy & Marion Usick
Spence's Mantario Outfitters
  Steve Spence
Spruce Grove Outfitting
  George Bullock
Spruce Ridge Outfitters
  Jermey & Dr. Helen Metner Ross
Stag Lake Outpost Camp
  Keith Ripplinger
Stoney Ridge Outfitters
  Leo MacCumber
Stu McKay Outfitters
  Stu & Dianna McKay
Sturgeon Bay Outfitting Service
  Leonard & Terry Stagg
Summerberry Outfitting Services
  Peter & Doug McAree
Superior Outfitters
  Walter Kolodka
Sutherland & Sutherland
  A. J. Sutherland
T & A Johnston Outfitting
  T. Johnston
T & J Outfitters
  J.R. Zilinsky
Tan Lake Outfitters
  Jim Knowles
Ted Jowett Outfitting Service
  Ted Jowett
Tee Pee Outfitters
  Donna Hohle
Tent Town Outfitters
  M. Mahlberg
Terry Neely Outfitters
  Terry Neely
Terry's Taxidermy & Guiding
  Terry Ledoux
Timberline Outfitters
  Derald Wlasichuk
Tonapah Lodge & Outfitters
  Frank Murnick
Trapper Don's Lodge & Outfitting
  Don & Lynn McCrea
Trapper Mike's Outfitting
  Service–Mike Snihor
Turtle Mountain Outfitting
  Don & Lynn Smith
Vickers Lake Outfitter
  Martin McLaughlin
Wallace McLaughlin Outfitting
  Wallace McLaughlin
Wallace Outfitters
  Kevin Allen
Waterhen Band Outfitting
  Chief Harvey
Waterhen First Nations Outfitting
  Melferd Carcheway
Wellman Lake Lodge & Outfitters
  Linda & Alvin Wiebe
Whitetail Outfitters
  Darlene & Justin Giasson
Wild River Outfitting

Harold Westdal
Wilderness Bear Guides
  Art & Braig Henry
Wilderness Gardens Outfitters
  Fred Salter
Wilderness Outfitters
  Larry Gogal
Woodlands Outfitting
  Clement Saulnier

NEW BRUNSWICK
Adair's Outfitting
  Larry D. Adair
Betts Kelly Lodge
  Keith Betts
Black Bear Lodge
  Gilbert Pelletier
Black's Hunting & Fishing Camps
  Juanita Black
Burntland Brook Lodge
  Joan & Barrie Duffield
Canoose Camps
  Thomas Mosher or Faith Winters
Chickadee Lodge
  Vaughan Schriver
Craig's Sporting Camps
  Dale & Brian Craig
Crouchers Outfitters
Dave Winchester's Sporting
Camps
  Dave Winchester
Deerville Camps Ltd.
  W. Alton Morrison
Dorrington Hill Outfitters
  Shaun & Joy Collicott
Dyer's Hunting & Fishing Camps
  Lawrence A. Dyer
Fundy Lodge
  Sid & Lynette Weinman
Fundy Outfitters
  Malcolm Rossiter
Governor's Table Camp
  Hugh B. Smith
Guimac Camps
  Ralph Orser
Harrison's Long Lake Sporting
  Camps–Steve & Vicki Harrison
Henderson's Hunting Camps, Ltd.
  Robert & Glenna Henderson
Juniper Lodge & Cottages
  Frank & Eileen MacDonald
Kelly's Sporting Lodge, Ltd.
  Carmen Kelly & Lorne McDonald
Little Bald Peak Lodge, Ltd.
  Al King
Long Meadow Cabins
  Darren Johnston
Malarkey Cabin Guiding Service
  Ray Dillon
May's Brooks Camp
  Wilson H. Briggs
Miramichi Four Season Outfitters, Inc.
  Thomas J. MacLean
Miramichi Gray Rapids Lodge, Inc.
  Guy A. Smith
Miramichi Inn
  Andre Godin
Mountain View Hunting & Fishing
  Camps–Colin Hudnut
Nepisiguit River Camps
  Kenneth Gray
Nerepis Lodge
  Reginald Fredericks
North Lake Guiding Service
  Mrs. Edmond Fredericks
North View Hunting & Fishing
Lodge   Wayne DeLeavey
Northern Lights Lodge
  Dan Henry
O'Donnells Cottages on the
  Miramichi–Valerie O'Donnell
Palfrey Lake Lodge
  Mrs. Larry G. Day
Parsons Hunting & Fishing Lodge
  Lloyd & June Parsons
Perrin's Hunting & Fishing
  Blake Perrin
Pond's Chalet Resort
  Keith Pond
Riverside Lodge
  Kenneth Hayes
Rousselle's Camp
  Gilles Rousselle
Silver Maple Lodge
  Bernard M. Duffy
Slipp Brothers, Ltd.
  Ronald & Duane Slipp
Spring Brook Camps

Eugene Oneill
Stoddard Hunting & Fishing Camp
  Clinton Norrad
Tamarack Lodge
  John S. Davidson
Tobique & Serpentine Camps, Ltd.
  Donald McAskill
Victor Hunting Camp
  Victor Copp
Wauklehegan Outfitter
  Ronald J. Painter
Welovet Lodge
  Douglas Chase
White Birch Lodge
  Andy Boss & Volker Strasser
White Pine Lodge
  Paul & Barb Leahey
Wilson's Sporting Camps, Ltd.
  Keith Wilson

NEWFOUNDLAND
Adies Lake Hunting Lodge
  Don & Rod Stowe
Adventure Lodge, Inc.
  Gerry Pritchett
Adventure North, Ltd.
  Bill Murphy
Amalijek Lodge
  Melvin Jeddore
Angus Wentzell's Hunting
  Angus Wentzell
Beaver Lodge Ltd.
  Wayne Thomas
Big River Camps, Inc.
  R. W. Skinner
Blue Mountain Outfitters
  Carol & Adrian Payne
Brophy & Sons
Burnt Pond Outfitters
  Daniel Ryan
Cal's Hunting & Fishing
  Calvin White
Caribou Pond Outfitting
  Baxter Slade
Caribou Valley Outfitters
  Donald & Yvonne Bonia
Central Newfoundland Outfitters
  Bev & Gord Robinson Reg
Clarenville Aviation Ltd.
  Neil Pelley
Conne River Outfitters
Cow Head Outfitters
  Eileen Hynes
Cross Pond Lodge
  Neil Lucas
Deer Pond Camps Ltd.
  Gregory Lucas
Dhoon Lodge
  George Pike
Downey's Cabins
  Raymond Downey
Eagle Mountain Lodge
Gander River Tours
  Terry Cusack or Dan Stiles
Goose Bay Outfitters
  Peter Paor
Grandy's River Hunting Camp
  Charles Gillam
Grey River Lodge
  Tony Tuck & Dennis Taverner
Hammond Outfitters
  Leo Hammond
Heatherton Lodge
  Ed & Al Skinner
Hideaway Lodge
  Robert Folkes
Hilliard's Cabins
  John T. Hilliard
Hilliard's Hunting Lodge
  Clifford Hilliard
Ida Patey & Sons
Eric & Ida Patey
Iron Bound Outfitters
  Derreck Payne
Island View Cabins
  Leonard J. Ryan
James P. Gillam Outfitting
  James P. Gillam
Labrador Sportsfish Ltd.
  Vince & Jim Burton
Lake Douglas
  Alberta Mitchell
Little Harbour Deep Lodge
  Cyril Pelley
Log Cabin Lodge
  George Pike

Long Range Mountain Hunting
  Sharon Biggin
Long Range Outfitters
  G.J. Pumphrey
Mayflower Outfitters
  Ross Pilgrim
Migules Mountain Outfitters
  Dave Toms
Mitchell's Pond Hunting Lodge
  Don MacInnis
Moosehead Lodge
  Reginald White
Moosehill Cabins Ltd.
  Michael & Margaret Gillam
Mountain Top Cabin
  Wilfred Ryan
Mt. Peyton Outfitters
  Don Tremblett
Newfoundland Adventure Ltd.
  Todd Wiseman
Newfoundland & Labrador Hunting
  Ltd.–Roland Reid
Northwoods Ventures Outfitting
  Cyril Smith
Ocean Side Country Lodge
  Chris Rowsell
Owl's Nest Lodge Inc.
  Ron Parsons
O'Quinn's Outfitters
  Vincent O'Quinn
Parson's Pond & Triple K Outfitters
  Roger Keough
Peddle's Outfitting Ltd.
  Joseph Peddle
Perry's Hunting Camp
  Gerald Perry
Pine Ridge Lodge & Wilderness
  Tours–David & Wayne Holloway
Portland Creek Outfitters Ltd.
Leonard Payne & Aster Caines
Ray's Hunting & Fishing Lodge
  Raymond & Daphne Broughton
RiverRun Outfitting & Tours Ltd
  Horace Lane
Rocky Ridge Lodge
  Denis Taverner & Tony Tuck
Sam's Hunting & Fishing
Camps–Sam Caines
Saunder's Camps
  Calvin Saunders
Snowshoe Lake Hunting & Fishing
  Inc.–John & Ron Hicks
Sou'wester Outfitting
  Dean & Bonnie Wheeler
Stag Hill Hunting Camps
  Stewart House
Stag Hill Outfitters
  Sam Kettle
Steel Montain Lodge
  Ben Alexander
Thorburn Aviation Ltd.
  Gene Ploughman
Tri-T Camps
  Tony Kennedy
Tuckamore Wilderness Ldoge
  Barb Genge
Twin Lakes Outfitters
  Don Pelley
Twin Valley Outfitters
  Eric & Kathy Cranford
Victoria Outfitters
  Dave Evans
Viking Trail Outfitters
  Wallace Maynard
West Woods Outfitters
  Neil Sweetapple & Neil MacArthur
Wilderness Horizons
  Howard Hewitt & Lester Goobie
Wilderness Outfitters
  Gene Mercer
Woodland Lodge Ltd.
  Kevin Decker

NOVA SCOTIA
Adams, George M.
Adams, Keith
Andrews, Ian R.
Atwood, Frederick
Barnes, Donald L.
Barnes, Robert B.
Bartlett, Dave
Beaver, Aubrey
Beaver Lake Outfitters
  Garnet Purdy
Boudreau, Robert G.
Breen, Donald J.
Brown, Brian W.
Bryson, William
Burke, Earl

Burke, J. Louis
Burke, Paul E.
Burke, Robert
Butler, Richard H.
Cahill, Daniel
Caldi, Leonardo
Cameron, Carl
Campbell, Duncan A.
Campbell, Fred M.
Campbell, James & Donald
Chiasson, Joseph
Clark, Lionel
Clarke, Gordon
Cole, Greg A.
Comeau, Anthony
Conway, Alexander J.
Cook, Arthur Joseph
Cook, Frederick J.
Cook, George E.
Copeland, William H.
Corbett, Gary N.
Corcoran, Randy
Cosman, Bernard E.
Cotton, Gordon J.
Cotton, Wally K.
Cottreau, Victor
Croft, John F.
Croft, Richard M.
Cross, Wallace Rex
Crouse, Allen Bradford
Crouse, Dwight
Crouse, L Willard
Dagley, David Bruce
Dalton, Brian G.
Dawson, John D.
Day, Richard W.
Demeter, George B.
DeMille, Garnet
DesJardins, Cyril
Dexter, John Warren
Dexter, Noel
Dexter, Warren C.
DeYoung, Francis J.
Dillman, John W.
Dillman, Ray O.
Dunlop, John H.
Durling, Robert E.
Ells, Kevin
Elworthy, William L.
Ernst, Welton B.
Fahey, Alonza E.
Ferguson, Ross
Ferris, Brent
Fillion, Joe
Findlay, Kevin J.
Finigan, Alex J.
Fleming, Blair
Foley, Thomas
Forsyth, Larry S.
Fraser, Larry
Freeman Jr., Harry
Freeman, Harry Charles
Furey, Ferman
Furlong, Joseph
Galley, Gary
Galley, Jack
Gaudet, Louis J.
George, Daniel R.
Gillis, Everett D.
Gloade, William T.
Gosset, Selby
Graham, Gerald M.
Grandy, David
Grantham, Ronald T.
Graves, Bruce
Green, Vincent
Greenwood, Frederick M.
Hache, Gilles
Hadley, Shawn P.
Haldeman, Ronald W.
Hardy, Gerald W.
Harris, Wayne B.
Hart, John F.
Harvey, Gerald F.
Harvey, Morris F.
Hatt, Tony L.
Hemming, Timothy
Henderson, Kevin D.
Hickox, George
Higgins, I. Wayne
Hingley, Newton A.

Hogan, Peter
Holmes, Allen B.
Hunt, Lloyd
Hutchison, Thomas
Huyghue, George
Ingraham, Gerald S.
Jennex, Elmer Wayne
Jerram, James S.
Johnstone, David A.
Jones, C. Gerald
Joudrey, Terry & Wade
Juteau, Bill
Kaegudeck Lake
Kajdas, Tadevsz B.
Kelly, Joseph A.
Kennedy, Brian & David
Kennedy, James A.
Kennedy, Ken B.
Kennedy, Todd
Kennedy Sr., Tom
Kulanek, Daniel
Landry, Alexander L.
Landry, Fred
Latwaitis, A. David
LeBlanc, Adrian J.
Le Blanc, Eugene
LeBlanc, Michael & Patrick
LeBlanc, Nivard
Leese, J. David
LePage, Ronald Raoul
Leslie, Geofrey H.
Lewis, David G.
Lovitt, William S.
Lowe, Basil W.
Lowe, Ricky
Lutz, Stephen V.
Lynds, Dennis D.
Lynds, Owen W.
Lynds, Russell L.
MacAskill, Tom
MacCalder, Ean D.
MacCormack, William L.
MacCulloch, Brian
MacDonald, Donald J.
MacDonald, Hugh R.
MacDonald, Paul A.
MacDonald, Thomas E.
MacDonnell, Sean
MacFarlane, Ray
MacIntosh, Gordon
MacIntosh, Thomas A.
MacKay, David
MacKay, Jack L.
MacLean, Donald George
MacLean, Duncan J.
MacLean, Osborne P.
MacLeod, Morris A.
MacLeod, Stewart M.
MacPherson, Royce A.
MacPherson, Stewart
Maillet, Kenneth
Mailman, Scott
Mansfield, George S.
Martin, John T.
Mason, Brian & Mary
Matthews, Gerald A.
Mattinson, Donald C.
McKinnon, Richard
McMasters, Hugh E.
McNeil, Eric V.
McWhinnie, Irving & Madeline
Meekins, George W.
Mellish, Barry J.
Mouzar, Robert G.
Muise, Larry C.
Mundle, Brian
Munro, C. Perry
Murphy, Blair & James K.
Murrin, Eric
Naugler, Michael Bruce
Nemeth, Alex S.
Newcap Inc.
Nickerson, Cleve A.
Osmond, Eugene
O'Brien, Mike
Palmer, Milton L.
Parsons, Gary
Patterson, William R.
Paul, Lance
Peach, Donald George
Peck, Watson A.
Peddle, Darren

Pencer, Edward L.
Petrie, George J.
Pittman, John D.
Porteous, Richard
Pottier, Raymond V.
Powers, Joseph F.
Purdy, Brian T.
Rafuse, Harris R.
Rankin, Bill
Roach, Joseph W.
Roach, Ron
Robarts, James
Robarts, Thomas B.
Ross, Bryden
Ross, David & Gregory
Roy, Michael
Rudderham, Earl
Schumacher, John
Seney, Ronald S.
Shaw, Daniel
Sims, James
Slauenwhite, Ben
Slauenwhite, Clarence E.
Smith, David L.
Smith, Glendon W.
Smith, Kevin C.
Snyder, Guy F.
Spencer, Earle F.
Sprague, Phillip
Steeves, A. Leslie
Stewart, Hugh
Stewart, Russell
Stewart, Ruthven
Stewart, Tony A.
Sturdy, Gordon A.
Sutherland, Sandy
Swim, Jon Garth
Tait, Donald
Terrio, Terence M.
Thompson, J. Forbes
Thornhill, Randy
Timmons, David E.
Timmons, Leo E.
Timmons, Ralph E.
Todd, James F.
Tooker, John B.
Tovey, Jerome B.
Veinot, Susan
Vitiello, Tom
Walker, Donald J.
Walker, Gary R.
Walsh, Thomas P.
Wamboldt, Paul D.
Wanless, Gary
Warner, Donald
Weir, Bruce M.
Wheaton, Bruce
White, John
Whitty, Leonard
Whynot, James E.D.
Whynot, Victor
Wicks, William M.
Wile, Rhonddah Alvin
Wilson, John H.
Wood, Robert J.
Young, Paul K.

NORTHWEST TERRITORIES
Adventure Northwest
  Bill Tait
Arctic Red River Outfitters
  Kelly Hougen
Arctic Safaris
  Barry Taylor
Arviat HTO
  President George Kuksuk
Aurora Caribou Camp
  Greg Robertson
Baker Lake HTA
Banks Island Big Game Hunts
  Sachs Harbour HTC
Beaufort Outfitting & Guiding
  Services–Tuktoyaktuk HTC
Cadieux's Caribou Pass Outfitters
  Don Cadieux
Coppermine HTA
Deh Cho Wilderness Tours
  Digaa Enterprises
Ekaluktutiak (HTA)
Gjoa Haven Tours
  Paul Iqualluq
Mayukalik HTA
Paulatuk HTC

Qutsiktukmiut Outfitting
  President David Akeeagok
Rabesca's Resources, Camp Ekwo
  Moise & Joyce Rabesca
Rendezvous Lake Outpost Camp
  Billy Jacobson
Taloyoak HTA
The "J" Group/Peterson's Point
  Lake Camp–The Petersons
True North Safaris
  Gary Jaeb
Ulukhaktomiut HTC
Umingmaktok HTA
  Jack Kaniak

ONTARIO
Agimac River Outfitters
  Harold St. Cyr
Agnew Lake Lodge Ltd.
  Mitchell & Catherine Turcott
Air Ivanhoe Ltd.
  George & Jeanne Theriault
Air Kenda
  Roy & June Bennett
Air-Dale Flying Service Ltd.
Alconsen Fly-In Outpost Camps
  Alex & Helene Bosse
Andy Lake Resort
  Marc & Judy Bechard
Angus Lake Lodge
  Elizabeth & George Tamchina
Antler's Kingfisher Lodge
  Doug & Sandra Antler
Ara Lake Camp Ltd.
  Dick & Shirley Fayle
Argyle Lake Lodge
  Chuck & Joan Fernley
Barr Woods Resort
  Burrows Family
Bear Paw Lodge
Becca's Haven
  Phyllis & Rick Flewelling
Berglund's Outposts
  Wayne & Carol Berglund
Big Eagle Lodge
  The Christisons
Big North Lodge
  Alex & Pat Rheault
Black Bear Outpost Camps
  Mary & Walter Fleming
Blake's Wilderness Outpost
  John & Marie Blake
Blue Fox Camp
  Dr. Paul R. Morgan
Brooks Cottages
  Chris & Christine Brooks
Brown's Clearwater West Lodge
  Outposts–Barry Brown
Brunswick Lake Lodge
  Marcel Dumais
Bullock's Gowganda Lake Camp
  Dave & Mary Bullock
Camp Can-USA
  Nelson & Brenda Leudke
Camp Des Grands Bois
Camp Hiawatha
  Lloyd Lindner
Camp Memewin
Camp Michi-Wawa
  Ken & Luanne Brezenski
Camp Narrow Lodge
  Tom Pearson
Camp Quetico
  Marshall & Karen Manns
Camp Richfield
  The Kmetzs
Camp Sag-A-Me-Sing
  Davide & Barbara Weber
Canada North Outfitting, Inc.
Canoe Canada Outfitters & Outpost
  Cabins–Bud Dickson & Jim Clark
Caribou Falls Lodge
  Ed Pries & Donna Daman
Chalet St-Hubert Enr.
Chalets Du Huard/Chalets Scarf
  Ron & Mary Waye
Cianci's Holiday North Lodge
  Frank & Lucy Cianci
Clear Lake Cottages
  Daniel & Deanne Cudmore
Cochrane Air Services Limited
  Jerry & Verena Krahenbuhl
Come By Chance Resort Ltd.
Coppen's Resort Limited
  Syd Coppen & Ed Plichta

Delay River Outfitters
  Craig Bogie
Docks Inn Resort
  The Warkentins
Donnelly's Minnitaki Lodge
  Fran & Lil Donnelly
Duncan Lake Camp
  Ed & Faye Barnstaple
Dunlop Lake Lodge
  Don & Pat Mackay
Eagle Lake Lodge
  Orrie & Paula Colegrove
Edgewater Park Lodge
  Tom Thornborrow & Bob Harris
Elk Cabins
  Rene Pelissier & Serge Marin
Elliot Lake Aviation Ltd. Fishland
  Camps–Bruno Rapp
English River Motel
  Ron & Fran Syncox
Ernie's Cottages & Campground
  Ernie Martel
Esnagi Lodge
  Donna & Wally Leigh
First Island Cottages
  Roly & Rhea Primeau
Fisherman's Cove
  The Denzlers
Five Mile Lake Lodge
  Frank & Carol Yuhas
Flame Lake Lodge
  Gary & Karen Pedersen
Fox Lake Lodge
  Vickie & Dave Ormerod
Frontier Lodge
  John & Betty Middleton
Gardiner Outfitters & Air Service
  Ron & Shirley Barron
Gawley's Little Beaver Lodge &
  Outpost–Doug & Brad & Doug Sr.
Gogama Lodge & Outfitters
  Madge & Dick Harlock
Golden Eagle Camp
  Donna & Roy Enair
Goose Bay Camp
  A. Langford
Gosenda Lodge Ltd.
  Richard & Evelyn Glazier
Grant Outfitters
  Ted & Linda Grant
Gravel Lakes Cabins
  Sven & Shirley Lindfors
Green Island Lodge
  Bob & Angie Korzinski
Green Wilderness Camp
  Rita & Walter Wawryszyn
Gurney-By-The-Sea
  Roger & Linda Ferguson
Hache's Bear Camp Ltd.
  Camille & Marlene Hache
Hackl's Kashabowie River Resort
  Joe & Pat Hackl
Hanson's Wilderness Lodges
  Ltd.–The Hansons
Happy Day Lodge
  Ken & Ruth Weber
Hart's Pine Falls Lodge
  The Harts
Hearst Air Service
  George & Michael Veilleux
Hillsport Wilderness Hunting
Camps   Mark & Karen
  Stephenson
Holinshead Lake Resort & Outposts
  Mitch Hagen
Horseshoe Island Camp
  Don & Marjorie Hueston
Horwood Lake Lodge
  Cindy & Barry Edwards
Huron Air & Outfitters Inc.
  Donna & Ernie Nicholl
H&C Family Lodge
  Henri & Carole Savoie
Ignace Outposts Ltd.
  Brad & Karen Greaves
Indiaonta Resort
  Herb & Vi Humphreys
Island Lake Camp
  Gord & Ellie Mitchell
Ivanhoe Resort
  Russell & Shirley Litt
Jackfish Lake Motel Efficiency
  Cottages–Jack & Shirley Richards
James Bay Adventures
  Arthur Taillon
John Theriault Air Ltd.
  John Theriault
Kamp Kinniwabi
  Bill & Barb Beckham
Kanipahow Kamps Ltd.

Kap Outfitters
  Ron & Lise Marchand
Kenda Wilderness Lodge
  The Bennetts
Kennisis Lake Lodge
  Adelheid & Dan Buhl
Kenogaming Lodge
  Karen Radlowsky
Ket-Chun-Eny Lodge
  The St. Germain's
Kinogami Lodge
  Robert & Marilyn Plourde
Labelle's Birch Point Camp
  Dale & Linda Labelle
Lac Seul's Scout Lake Resort
  The Schreiners
Lake Herridge Lodge
  Pat & Mike Thomas
Lake Obabika Lodge
  The Herburger FAmily
Land O'Lakes Lodge
  Christine & Robin Burke
Lindbergh's Air Service
  Brian Simms
Lochlomond Camp
  Larry & Deb Hadenko
Log Chateau Lodge
  Geoff & Jenny Pinckston
Long Point Airways
  The Wilsons
Long Point Lodge
  The Bowens
Lookout River Outfitters
  Bruce & Margaret Hyer
Loon Lodge
  Moskwa Family
Lukinto Lake Lodge
  Bob & Faye Harkness
Mache-Kino Fly-In Lodge
  Denis & Val Ladouceur
Maiden Bay Camp
  Joan & Bill Hubbard
Marsh Bay Resort
  Jim & Debbie O'Brien
Marten River Lodge
  Scott Marlatt
Martin's Camp
  Bing & Dainne Hoddinott
Matabitchual Lodge
  Dieter & Marlis Maurer
Mattice Lake Outfitters Ltd.
  Don & Annette Elliot
Megisan Lake Lodge
  George & Brenda Nixon
Memquisit Lodge Inc.
  Jeanne Trivett
Missinaibi Outfitters
  Owen & Denyse Dorpela
Moose Horn Lodge
  Roxann Lynn
Moosewa Outpost
  Ivor & Brenda Horncastle
Morin's All Seasons Resort Ltd.
  The Morins
Motel Bienvenue
  Ray & Pauline Dubreuil
Mountain Home Lodge
  Peter & Beryl Nicholson
Naiscoot Lodge
  The Lutscher
Nakina Outpost Camps & Air
Service   Don & Millie
Bourdignon
Normandy Lodge
  Klaus & Wilma Brauer
North Country Lodge
  Dale & Doreen Leutschaft
Northern Lights Resort
  Hermann & Lise Stroeher
Northwinds/Pine Grove
  Rod & Gail Munford
Okimot Lodge
  Wayne & Rona Currie
Oskondaga River Outfitters
  Allan & Mary Wark
Outdoor Hunting & Safari
  Greg Binions
Owl's Nest Lodge
  Betty Ann & Wayne Hawthorn
O-Pee-Chee Lake Lodge
  The Woitallas
O'Sullivan's Rainbow
  Al & Donna Reid
Pavillon Du Lac Ogascanan Enr.
Pine Acres Resort & Outfitters
  Rene & Joyce Lavoie
Pioneer Lodge/Dog Lake
  Mike & Claude Gratton
Polar Bear Camp & Fly-In Outfitter
  Billy Konopelky
Polar Star Lodge

Norah & Ross Finch
Pourvoirie Pommeroy Inc.
Pourvoirie Rodfam Inc.
Pourvoyeurs De La Riviere Delay
Inc.
Pourvoyeurs De La Riviere Ottawa
Inc.
Pozniak's Lodge
  Robert & Cecile Fielding
Rainbow Point Lodge
  Bob & Gale Extence
Red Cedar Lake Camp
  Bob St-Cyr & Denis Sauve
Red Pine Lodge
  Garry & Cathy Litt
Redden's Camp Ltd.
  Lorne & Pat Redden
Riverlake Cottages & Campground
  Ed & Helen Larson
Riverland Camp & Outfitters
  Jay & Maryann McRae
Rob's Canadian Wilderness
  Resort–Rob & Sandy Brodhagen
Royal Windsor Lodge
  Art & Olga Jalkanen
R.A.M. Outfitters
  The Despres
Sac Bay Lodge Camp
  Fred & Heidi Wittwer
Sandy Point Camp
  Bill & Penny Higgins
Savanne River Resort & Camp-
  ground–Davide & Patricia Coates
Shining Tree Tourist Camp
  Bob & Sue Evans
Shooting Star Camp
  Shane & Betty Looby
Silver Poplar Grove Camps
  Bill & Gail Paul
Slippery Winds Wilderness Lodge
  Doug & Georgie Knipe
Snug Haven Resort
  Donna & Brian Graziotto
Sportsman's Paradise
  Nancy Ferring
Spruce Shilling Camp
  Chris & Verva Gaebel
Stanley's West Arm Resort
  Marvin & Carol Wisneski
Stanton Airways
  John & Helen Stanton
Stewart Lake Airways Ltd.
  William & Lynn Krolyk
Stillwater Trailer Park
  Bill & Gina Barnes
Sudbury Aviation Ltd/No.Trails
Out-   post Camps–
Marg. Watson-Hyland
Tata-Chika-Pika Lodge
  The Neils
Ted McLeod's Sunset Country
Outfit-   ters Inc.–Ted
McLeod & Lana Hurd
Temegami Shores Inn & Resort
  The Bickells
Territoire De L'Original
Thousand Lakes Resort
  George & Jenny Brown
Tornado's Canadian Resorts Inc.
Rogerson's Lodges
Totem Lodge
  The Browns
Totomenai Lodge
  Frank & Susan Charbonneau
Trail's End Lodge
  The Williams
Vista Lake Outfitters
  Dennis & Evelyn Mousseau
Walser's McGregor Bay Camp
  Mary & Gary Walser
Walsten Outpost Camps
  Neil & Kevin Walsten
Walton's Kay Vee Lodge
  The Waltons
Waterfalls Lodge
  Bob & Marilou Rogers
White Pine Lodge
  Joseph & Mary Ellen Schaut
White River Air/Mar Mac Lodge
  Don MacLachlan
Whitefish Lodge
  John & Lorna Chiupka
Wilderness North
Wolseley Lodge
  Nicole Jenner
Woodhouse Camp
  The Woodhouses
Woods Whiskey-Jack Lodge
  Terry & Lorna Wood
Wright Point Resort
  Joe & Carrie Whitmell

Young Lake Lodge
  Steve & Debbie Vincent
Young's Wilderness Camp
  Perry & Carol Anniuk

PRINCE EDWARD ISLAND
MacLeod, Malcolm & Margie
Birch Grove Outfitters
Flyway Outfitters
Hunters Chance
  David Montgomery
Leisure Services Inc.
  Jim Duggan

QUEBEC
2428-6114 Quebec Inc.
  "Auberge Le 22"
9007-6605 Quebec Inc.
9010-5347 Quebec Inc. "Aigle
  Vollant"
9013-6896 Quebec Inc.
9029-7789 Quebec Inc. "Pourv.
  Lac Hirondelle"
Air Aventure Cote-Nord Enr.
Air Bellevue Inc.
Air Melancon Inc.
Air Mont-Laurier (1985) Inc.
Air Nord-Ouest Inc.
Anima-Nipissing Adventures
  Nancy & Wayne Lapp & Family
Artic Adventures
Ashuanipi Hunting Outfitters
  Francis Rioux
Association Cerf-Pro Enr.
Assoc. Amis De La Foret Du Lac
  Anais Inc.
Assoc. De C & P De Havre St
  Pierre
Auberge De La Gatineau Enr.
Auberge De La Griffe D'Ours Inc.
Auberge Riviére Georges
Inc.–Pierre Paquet
Auberge de la Riviere Noire
Auberge Des Bles
Auberge Des Pins Enr.
Auberge Du Bouleau Blanc
Auberge Du Lac Bowman
Auberge Du Lac Joncas Inc.
Auberge Du Lac Matchi-Manitou Inc.
Auberge Du Lac Parent Enr.
Auberge Du Lac Victoria (1988) Inc.
  Auberge Du Serpent
Auberge Et Pourvoirie Du Lievre Enr.
Auberge La Barriere (1985) Inc.
  Auberge Parker
Auberge Wedge Hills Inc.
Aux Berges Des 11 Rapides
  "2961-2215 Quebec Inc."
Aventure Caribou Adventure
Aventures Nipissi Inc.
Aventures Roch Roy Inc.
Bar Bonnet Rouge Enr.
Base Plein Air Cockanagog Inc.
Buckeye Camp
B. M. May & Sons
Cabine Dulong
Cabines Du Lac Watson
  Cain Jr., Johnny
Camp Bertrand G. L. Poisson Blanc
Camp Bitobi Enr.
Camp Corbeau
Camp De C & P Du Lac Portage
Camp De L'Oie Blanche
Camp Des 3 Saisons Inc.
Camp Des Rivieres Jumelles Ltee.
Camp Eloigne Du Lac Saseginaga
Camp Et Coucoushee
Camp Grassy Narrows
Camp Kipawa Enr.
Camp McKenzie
Camp Puunik Limitee
Camp Ratte
Camp Sylvestre
Camping & Camps Gillies Enr.
Camps Baskatong M. L. Enr.
Camps Eloignes Du lac Achepabenca
Camps Ronoda Enr.
Canada Loisirs

Cargair Ltee.
  Oliver Prudhomme
Cecaurel Inc.
Centre Du Pourvoyeur
  Mastigouche Ltee.
Centre Expedition Plein Air
  Laurentien
Chalet De La Baie Arc-En-Ciel Enr.
Chalet De La Tortue
Chalet De L'Epinette Enr.
Chalet Feuille D'Erable
Chalet Miwapanee Enr.
Chalets Alisich
Chalets Baie Des Plongeurs
Chalets Barrage Des Cedres
Chalets Belle-Vue Enr.
Chalets Campion Lodge Inc.
Chalets Diane Enr.
Chalets Gouin Chasse & Peche Inc.
Chalets Jean-Paul
Chalets Laurenzo Valiquette
Chalets McGillivray Lake
Chalets Peasler
Chalets Vallee Des Cedres
  Charbonneau Andre
Chez Rainville Enr.
Club Basque Enr.
Club Brunet Lac Baskatong Enr.
Club C & P Des Sept Patriotes Inc.
Club Cesar (1993) Inc.
Club Chambeaux Inc.
Club Chasse & Peche Le Refuge Enr.
Club Chevreuil Blanc Val Des Bois
  Inc.
Club Claire Enr.
Club Colonial Inc.
Club Commercial Raoul Lavoie Enr.
Club C&P Epinette Rouge Homano
  Inc.
Club De C & P Lac Fontaine Inc.
Club De C & P Montagnais (1980)
  Inc.
Club De C & P Shamrock Inc.
Club De C & P Ste-Anne De Portneuf
Club De C & P Stramond Inc.
Club De C & P Tadoussac Inc.
Club De C & P Tuktu Enr.
Club De C & P Wapoos Sibi Inc.
Club De Chasse & De Peche B.B.
  Enr.
Club De Chasse & De Peche Rudy
  Inc.
Club De Chasse & Peche De Ripon
  Inc.
Club De Peche Du Lac Justone Inc.
Club Des Hauteurs De
  Charlevoix Inc.
Club Des Trois Castors Inc.
Club Du Lac Des Baies Inc.
Club Du Lac Des Perches Inc.
Club Du Lac Pierre Inc.
Club Du Pont Flottant De Travers
Club Duplessis C & P Enr.
Club Fontaine Inc.
Club Haltaparche
Club Hosanna Enr.
Club Kergus Enr.
Club Lac Bernier Enr.
Club Lac Brule Enr.
Club Lacs Sables, Paradis, Saguenay
  Inc.
Club Le Rochu Inc.
Club L'Oasis De Marc Enr.
Club Margaret Inc.
Club Marmette Enr.
Club Notawissi Inc.
Club Oswego (1987) Inc.
Club Parades Sauvege Inc.
Club Pine Grove
Club Piscatosin
Club Pointe Des Pins Enr.
Club Quoquochi Enr.
Club Rossignol Enr.
Comite D'Amenagement Lacs
  St-Alban Inc.
Courville Vincent
Denis Camp Inc.
Domaine A L'Aube Du Lac Enr.
Domaine Batchelder Inc.
Domaine C & P Gaudias Foster Inc.
Domaine Claudette & Real
Domaine De La Baie Au Sable
Domaine De La Manic
Domaine De L'Ours Enr.
Domaine Des Deux-Ours

Domaine Des Sportifs D'Oskelaneo
Domaine Du Bois Rond Enr.
Domaine Du Canyon Inc.
Domaine Du Chevreuil
Domaine Du Lac Charette Enr.
Domaine Du Lac Des Coeurs Inc.
Domaine Du Lac Dionne Inc.
Domaine Du Lac Ha! Ha!
Domaine Du Lac Malloon Enr.
Domaine Du Lac Sauniat Inc.
Domaine Forsythe Inc.
Domaine Gaston Constantineau
   Enr.
Domaine La Sorbiere (1991) Inc.
Domaine Lac Castor Blanc Enr.
Domaine Larry Boismenu Enr.
Domaine Lounan Inc.
Domaine Mont St-Michel Inc.
Domaine Preissac
Domaine Sportif Du Lac Loup
Domaine Vanier Enr.
Draper, Winnifred
Dufresne, Raymond
Forestiere Des Trois Couronnes Inc.
George River Lodge, Inc.
Pierre and JeanPaquet
Gestion Jean-Claude Parent Ltee.
Gravelle, Dana
Hoffer, Ingrid E.
H/Motel & Pourvoirie Du Lac
   Frontiere
Jack Hume Adventures Inc.
   Jack Hume
Jean-Guy St-Aubin
Jessup, Edward Joseph
Kan-A-Mouche
Kenauk, La Seigneurie De
   Montebello
Koroc Ilkalu Lodge Inc.
La Baronnie De Kamouraska
La Domaine Poutrincourt Inc.
La Hutte Du Castor Enr.
L'Allier, Yves
La Loge Des Baies Ltee
La Pointe Du Paradis
La Pourvoirie Baie Johan-Beetz Inc.
La Pourvoirie Domaine Lac
   Betchie Ltee.
La Pourvoirie Du Barrage Gouin Enr.
La Pourvoirie Du Cerf-Sau Inc.
La Pourvoirie Du Col Vert Inc.
La Pourvoirie Du Kakuskanus Inc.
La Pourvoirie Du Lac Cranson Inc.
La Pourvoirie Du Lac Demi-Lune
   Enr.
La Pourvoirie Du Lac Husky Enr.
La Pourvoirie Du Lac Matonipi Inc.
La Pourvoirie Du Lac Repos Enr.
La Pourvoirie Fort Chimo Inc.
La Pourvoirie Le Goeland Enr.
La Pourvoirie Magpie Inc.
La Pourvoirie Menjo Inc.
La Pourvoirie Vital Inc.
La Reserve Boismenu Enr.
La Seigneurie Du Triton (R.F.G.V.Q.)
La Soc. Commandite Reserve
   Beauchene
Labrador 2BG Adventure Inc.
Mr. F. Denis Boisvert
Le Centre De Services Ikkaruq
Le Chateau Gouin Enr.
Le Club 2000 Enr.
Le Club de C & P Lac O'Sullivan Inc.
Le Club Explo-Sylva Inc.
Le Club Jumeaux Enr.
Le Club Kapitachouan
Le Domaine Du Lac Bryson
Le Domaine Hazelwood Enr.
Le Domaine Le Pic Bois Inc.
Le Domaine Oregnac Inc.
Le Domaine Pipmuacan Inc.
Le Domaine Shannon Inc.
Le Fer a Cheval Enr.
Le Gite Phare Pointe Des Monts Enr.
Le Pourvoyeur Tawanipi Enr.
Le Vacancier Enr.
Le Vent de la Savane Inc.
Les Camps C & P Nordiques
Les Camps C & P Nord
   Frontiere Inc.
Les Camps Trio Inc.
Les Camps Wolf Enr.
Les Entreprises Du Lac Lucault Inc.
Les Entreprises Du Lac Perdu Inc.

Les Entreprises Lac Villebon Enr.
Les Entreprises S. Annanack Inc.
Les Expeditions Manicouagan Ltee.
Les Fermes Recreatives Brennan
Les Fournisseurs du Nord Inc.
Les Gerances De La Horde
   Sauvage Inc.
Les Guides de La Vallee Dumoine
Les Pourvoiries D'Anticosti Inc.
Les Pourvoyeurs De La Galette Enr.
Les Pourvoyeurs Du Lac Holt Inc.
Les Quatres Chenes
Lynus Langevin Pourvoyeur Enr.
L'Auberge en Bois-Rond Manic 5 Inc.
L'Auberge Kempt Inc.
L'Auberge Riviere Aguanus Inc.
Mabec Ltee.
Martin, Marcel
May, May
Mongrain Carl "Camp Alwaki
Lodge"
Motel Sur Le Lac Inc.
Municipalite De Kiamika
Natashquan Safari Inc.
Oasis Du Gouin Inc.
Obatogamau Eenou Lodge Enr.
Paradis C & P Du Lac Jim
Pavillon Arc-En-Ciel Enr.
Pavillon Basilieres Enr.
Pavillon Baskatong Enr.
Pavillon Boreal (1988) Inc.
Pavillon C & P De Pontiac Inc.
Pavillon Cabonga Inc.
Pavillon De La Baleine Inc.
Pavillon de L'Esturgeon Enr.
Pavillon De L'Orignal
Pavillon De L'Ours Noir Enr.
Pavillon Deer Horn Lodge
Pavillon Des Deux Lunes
Pavillon Des Pins Gris Enr.
Pavillon Dore Enr.
Pavillon Du Cerf Enr.
Pavillon Du Lac Berthelot Inc.
Pavillon Du Lac Gueguen Inc.
Pavillon Eastview Enr.
Pavillon Kipawa Inc.
Pavillon La Verendrye
Pavillon Moosehead Enr.
Pavillon Paul Caron Enr.
Pavillon Pin Blanc Letang
Pavillon Pointe Au Bouleau Enr.
Pavillon Richer Inc.
Pavillon Wapus Inc.
Pavillon Whitefish (1989) Inc.
Place Du Lac Enr.
Poirvoirie Mike's Outfitters
Porvoirie Yajo Enr.
Pourvoirie 4 Saisons Enr.
Pourvoirie Achimac Enr.
Pourvoirie Aime Beauregard
   "Kazabazua"
Pourvoirie Andre Beauvais Inc.
Pourvoirie Anthony Outfitter Enr.
Pourvoirie Archer Inc.
Pourvoirie Au Pays De Real Masse
   Inc.
Pourvoirie Aya-Pe-Wa Inc.
Pourvoirie Baie Des Cypres Enr.
Pourvoirie Baroux Inc.
Pourvoirie Beaulieu Enr.
Pourvoirie Beausejour Enr.
Pourvoirie Bernard Dube Enr.
Pourvoirie Bertrand Richard
Pourvoirie Boismenu Enr.
Pourvoirie Boreal 51
Pourvoirie Bout Du Monde
Pourvoirie Camachigama
Pourvoirie Ca-Mord Inc.
Pourvoirie Chalifoux Inc.
Pourvoirie Clauparo Inc.
Pourvoirie Clova Ltee.
Pourvoirie Club Fontbrune Ltee.
Pourvoirie Coin Lavigne B. & R. Enr.
Pourvoirie Constantineau Enr.
Pourvoirie Daaquam "Qoapec Inc"
Pourvoirie Damville Inc.
Pourvoirie De La Baie Du Sud Inc.
Pourvoirie De La Baie D'Ungava
Pourvoirie De La Comporte
Pourvoirie De La Gaspesie
Pourvoirie De La Riviere Aux Lacs
Pourvoirie De La Riviere Coucou Inc.
Pourvoirie De La Seigneurie Du
   Lac Metis Inc.

Pourvoirie De La Truite Rouge
Pourvoirie De L'Estrie Enr.
Pourvoirie De L'ours Brun (1984) Inc.
Pourvoirie De Messines Enr.
   (2955-7444 Quebec Inc.)
Pourvoirie Denis Morin
Pourvoirie Des 100 Lacs Nord Inc.
Pourvoirie Des 100 Lacs Sud Inc.
Pourvoirie Des Grands Ducs Enr.
Pourvoirie Des Lacs A Jimmy Enr.
Pourvoirie Des Lacs Robidoux Enr.
Pourvoirie Des Laurentides Ltee.
Pourvoirie Domaine Bazinet Inc.
Pourvoirie Domaine du Trappeur
   Inc.
Pourvoirie Domina Gravelle
Pourvoirie Doolittle
Pourvoirie Du Balbuzard Sauvage
   Inc.
Pourvoirie Du Bras D'Olaf Inc.
Pourvoirie Du Club Bataram Inc.
Pourvoirie Du Club Chateauguay
   Inc.
Pourvoirie Du Domaine Du Lac
   Edouard Enr.
Pourvoirie Du Haut-Richelieu Inc.
Pourvoirie Du Lac Allard Inc.
Pourvoirie Du Lac Beauregard Inc.
Pourvoirie Du Lac Berneuil Enr.
Pourvoirie Du Lac Croche Enr.
Pourvoirie Du Lac Croche Inc.
Pourvoirie Du Lac Cypras
Pourvoirie Du Lac Dix Milles
Pourvoirie Du Lac Forant
Pourvoirie Du Lac Genevieve
Pourvoirie Du Lac Laflamme Inc.
Pourvoirie Du Lac Moreau Inc.
Pourvoirie Du Lac Oscar Inc.
Pourvoirie Du Lac Paimpont Enr.
Pourvoirie Du Lac Rond
Pourvoirie Du Lac Tourigny-Tessier
Pourvoirie Du Magnan Enr.
Pourvoirie Du Massif Des Torngats
   Inc.
Pourvoirie Du Nord-Est Enr.
Pourvoirie Du Reservoir Gouin
Pourvoirie Du Triangle De
   Bellechasse
Pourvoirie Fluviale 4 Saisons
Pourvoirie G.R.B. Region 10
Pourvoirie H/Motel Restigouche
Pourvoirie Jodoin Enr.
Pourvoirie Jos Malo Enr.
Pourvoirie J.B. Scott Inc.
Pourvoirie J.-Emile Goyette Enr.
Pourvoirie Kanasuta Enr.
Pourvoirie Kanawata Inc.
Pourvoirie La Jeannoise Inc.
Pourvoirie La Rocheuse
Pourvoirie La Tourette (1986) Inc.
Pourvoirie Lac a L'Ours Inc.
Pourvoirie Lac Degelis Inc.
Pourvoirie Lac Des Dix Milles
Pourvoirie Lac Des Iles
Pourvoirie Lac du Cerf Enr.
Pourvoirie Lac Duhamel Inc.
Pourvoirie Lac Faillon
Pourvoirie Lac Georges Enr.
Pourvoirie Lac Goeland &
   Macaisagi Enr.
Pourvoirie Lac La Truite Inc.
Pourvoirie Lac Marie
Pourvoirie Lac Maude
Pourvoirie Lac Maxime Enr.
Pourvoirie Lac Suzie Inc.
Pourvoirie Lacs Roger Et Faucille
   Inc.
Pourvoirie Le Chanail Du Nord Inc.
Pourvoirie Le Chasseur Inc.
Pourvoirie Le Grand Lac Du Nord
Pourvoirie Les As De Parent (1987)
Pourvoirie Les Quatre Outardes
Pourvoirie L'Appel Du Hibou Inc.
Pourvoirie L'Aventure Inc.
Pourvoirie L'O-Oie-Sis Enr.
Pourvoirie Manicouagan Inc.
Pourvoirie Manoir Sur Le Lac Enr.
Pourvoirie Martin Enr.
Pourvoirie Mekoos Enr.
Pourvoirie Mer Bleue
Pourvoirie Michel St-Louis Enr.
Pourvoirie Mirage (9006-2530
   Quebec Inc.)
Pourvoirie Moisie-Nipissis Inc.

Pourvoirie Moko "Rozon, Benoit"
Pourvoirie Monet Inc.
Pourvoirie Morin
Pourvoirie M.L. Enr.
Pourvoirie Nadeau Outfitter
Pourvoirie Nemiskau Enr.
Pourvoirie Niko Enr.
Pourvoirie Normandin
Pourvoirie Obaska Enr.
Pourvoirie Oskelaneo Lodge Enr.
Pourvoirie Page
Pourvoirie Pelletier
Pourvoirie Pignon Rouge (1984) Inc.
Pourvoirie Pip-Camp Enr.
Pourvoirie Poulin De Courval
   (1984) Inc.
Pourvoirie Quebec Nature Inc.
Pourvoirie Rejean Patoine Enr.
Pourvoirie Riviere La Galette Inc.
Pourvoirie Riviere St-Roch
Pourvoirie Roger Fortier Inc.
Pourvoirie R.Y.M.M. Inc.
Pourvoirie Safari Inc.
Pourvoirie Sammy Tukkiapik
Pourvoirie So-Nord Inc.
Pourvoirie St-Zenon Enr.
Pourvoirie Triple R Inc.
Pourvoirie Vaillancourt Enr.
Pourvoirie Waban-Aki Inc.
Pourvoirie Wapishish Inc.
Pourvoirie Windigo
Pourvoirie Yo-Ri Enr.
Pourvoiries Kipawa (1991) Inc.
Pourvoyeur En C & P St-Damien Inc.
Pourvoyeur Fern
Pourvoyeur Lac Lareau Enr.
Pourvoyeur Le Portage Enr.
Pourvoyeur Panama 82 Enr.
Pourvoyeurs Laurentides &
   L'Ungava
Pourvoy' Air Ltee
Pourv. Domaine Touristique La
   Tuque
Pourv. Du Lac Matchi-Manitou Enr.
Pourv. Sassaguinaga (L'Appel Du
   Nord)
Pourv. Seigneurie Du Lac Lacroix
   Inc.
Pour. Du Lac Miquelon Ltee
Relais 22 Milles Inc.
Relais Chez Black Enr.
Relais Gabriel Inc.
Roy Touriste Accomodation Enr.
R. Lehoux Et L. Lecours
Safari Anticosti Inc.
Safari Caribou du Nouveau
   Québec–Roch St.Laurent
Safari Norkik Inc.
   Henry Poupart
Sentinelle Du Nord Inc.
   Sepaq Anticosti
Service Aerien Drummond Enr.
Service De Guide Ronald Henri
Service De Pourvoyeur Trudeau
   Ltee.
Simdar Inc.
Soc. De Developpement Des
   Naskapis
Soc. Dev. Tour. Riviere-Eternite Inc.
Sport G.R.P. Ltee.
Tamarac Air Service Ltee.
Territoire De P & C Poirier Inc.
Tommy Cain & Sons Outfitter Ltee.
Trudel, Georges
Tumik (Les Aventures Silak Inc.)
Ungava Adventures
   Sammy Cantafio
Villa Basque Enr.
West Point Lodge

YUKON TERRITORIES

Arctic Red River Outfitters, Ltd.
   Kelly & Heather Hougen
Babala Stone Sheep Outfitters
   Ltd.–Jim Babala
Blackstone Safaris
   Lee Bolster
Bonnet Plume Outfitters
   Charlie Stricker
Cassiar Mountain Outfitters
   Kirby Funnell
Ceaser Lake Outfitters
   Terry Wilkinson
David Young Outfitters Ltd

Devilhole Outfitters
Dickson Outfitters Ltd.
 David Dickson
Dolhan, Edward G.
Jensen, Pete
Kluane Outfitters Ltd.
 Ross Elliott
Koser Outfitters
 Pete Koser
Kusawa Outfitters
 Klaas Heynen
MacMillan River Outfitters
 Dave Coleman
Nahanni-NWT Safaris
 Rick Furniss
Peter Jensen Guide & Outfitter
 Pete Jensen
Rogue River Outfitters
 Cliff Hanna
Ruby Range
 Keith & Debbie Carreau
Stan Reynolds Outfitting, Ltd.
 Stan Reynolds
Teslin Outfitters
 Doug Smarch
Teslin Outfitters
 Terry Wilkinson
Trophy Stone Safaris Ltd.
 Curt Thompson
Widrig Outfitters Ltd.
 Chris Widrig
Yukon Hunting & Guiding Ltd.
 Rod Hardie
Yukon Outfitters' Association
 Stan Reynolds
Yukon Outfitting

SASKATCHEWAN
24 North Outfitters
 Phil Chalifour
A & E Outfitters
Aerial Adventures
 Barry & Lana Prall
All-Terrain Outfitters
 Marlon Parasiuk
All-The-Way-Holloway Outfitters
Antonichuk Outfitters
 Willard Antonichuk
Athabasca Camps
 Cliff Blackmur
A.R.M. Outfitters
Bait Master Hunting Camps
 Brain E. Hoffart
Barrier Beach Resort
 Scott O'Bertos
Barrier Chaparral Lodge
 George & Kasandra O'Bertos
Bay Resort
Bear Claw Outfitters
Bear Creek Outfitters
Beyond La Ronge Lodge
 Andy & Beatrice Fecke
Big Eddy Camp
 Solomon Carriere
Big Foot Outfitters
Big Island Cove Resort
Big Sandy Resort
 Calvin & Annie Wingert
Black Bear Island Lake Lodge
 Earl Mockellky
Bloomfield's Ballantyne Bay Resort
George & Fran Bloomfield
Bronson Lake Outfitters
Buck & Bear Wilderness
 Adventures
Buckskin Joe Outfitting
Bucks, Bulls, and Bears
Camp Kinisoo Ltd
 Christopher and Sheila Brown
Campeau Guiding & Outfitting
 Alvin J. Campeau
Can-Am Outfitters Ltd.
 Chris or Cindy Shea
Careen Lake Lodge
 Jack & Eileen O'Brien
Caribou Creek Lodge Ltd.
 Dwight & Bev Whitley
Carriere's Camp
 Freda & John V. Carriere
Carrot Lake Outfitters
Charlie Brown's Outfitting & Guiding
 Service
Churchill River Wilderness Camps
 Klaas & Norman Knot
Circle Lakes Angus
Clarke Lake Lodge/Clearwater Adv.
Copeau Creek Outfitters
 David Osecki

Cracking River Guides
 Al Fiddler
Craig's Place—Outfitters
 Dorothy & Craig Osborne
Cree River Lodge
Crystal Lodge
 John Midgett
Cumberland House Outfitters Ltd.
Cup Lake Fishing Camp
 Lindsay & Barry Brucks
CutArm Outfitters
Dahl Creek Outfitting
Darsana Lodge
 Carl & Marg Boychuk
Deception Lake Lodge
Delaronde Resort
Deschambault Lake Resort
 Twylla Newton
Dore Lake Lodge
 Alex & Vicky Shukin
Elusive Saskatchewan Whitetail
 Outfitter–Harvey McDonald
Ena Lake Lodge
 A. Shane MacKinnon
Flotten Lake Resort
 Abram & Paula Rempel
Foster Lake Lodge
 Trent Brunanski
G W Outfitting
 Garry Walters
Gary Simon Outfitting/Thunder
 Rapids Lodge
Ghost Ranch Outfitting
 Paul Chartrand
Glen Hill's Sask River Hunting
 Camps   Glen Hill
Goose Creek Outfitters
 John Zwack
Green Lake Lodge
 Karen & Bob Henderson
Greenwater & Marean Lake
 Outfitting
Hawkrock Outfitters
John Fonos Outfitting
Johnson River Camp
Johnson's Resort
Katche Kamp Outfitters
 Bill & Jeanne Blackmon
Kee Kamps Ltd
 Dean Orosz or Barry Elton
Keeley Lake Lodge
 Gary & Gloria Callihoo
Kevin Tourand Outfitting
Kutawag Lake Outfitter
Lamplighter Lodge
 Roy & Cynthia Petrowicz
Little Bear Lake Resort
Lone Spruce Outfitters
 Steven & Nancy Butler
Lucky Lake Outfitters
 Willard Ylioja
M & M Outfitters
 Moe Morley
M & N Resort
 Wayne Chepil
Mann Lake Outfitters
 Larry K Stoudt
Martineau River Outfitters
Martin's Cabins
Medinski's Outfitting Services
 Larry Medynski
Mel-Sask Outfitters
Mercer Outfitting
 Ken & Pat Auckland
Michel Lodge
 Wayne & Kathy Berumen
Ministikwan Lodge
Minor Bay Camps
 Gerald & Paulette Howard
Minowukaw Lodge and Joe's Cabins
Mistatim Outfitting
Moen's Riverside Lodge
Moose Horn Lodge
 Marvin Peterson
Moose Range Lodge
Mystic Magic Wilderness Lodge
Nagle Lake Outfitters
Newmart Fishing Resort
 Humen & Mauthe
Niska Hunting & Fishing Camp
Norseman Outfitters
 D. Rutherford & A. Kjerstad
Northern Cross Resort Ltd.
 Jeff Jesske & Co.
Northern Echo Lodge
 Jim or Carol Eberle
Northern Lights Lodge Ltd.
 Ted & Diana Ohlsen
Northern Nights

Bruce & Brian Basken
Northern Reflection Lodge
 Eddy Jones
Northern Sask Wilderness Hunts
 Keith Heisler
Oliver Lake Wilderness Camp
 Michel Dube
ON TARGET Guiding &
 Outfitting–Dan Dunn
Otter Creek Outfitters
Overflow River Outfitters
 Gerald Melnychuk
Overland Cross Country Lodge
 Wayne & Diane Elliott
Paull River Wilderness Camp
 Wayne Galloway
Pickerel Bay Cabins
 Ray or Gail Twedt
Pickerel Point General Store
 Cliff & Susan Maruk
Pierceland Outfitters
Pine Cove Resort
Pipe Stone Guiding
Prairie Outfitters
 Potter & Westin & Slabik
Prairieland Outfitters
 Don Anderson
Preferred Habitat Management
R P Outfitters
R & R Wilderness Lodge
 R. Jenson & R. Reylonds
Rabbit Creek Outfitters
 Allan Folden
Rainbow Lodge
Riel Bosse Outfitting & Guiding
Riverside Service & Cabins
 Ron Anderson
Russell's Churchill River Camps
 Jim Russell
Sask Can Outfitters
 Bonace Korchinski
Schmidt's Outdoor Expeditions
Scott Lake Lodge
 Ken & Suzanne Gangler
Selwyn Lake Lodge
 Gord/Mary Daigneault-Wallace
Shadd Lake Cabins
 Nancy McKay
Silver Tip Outfitting
 Garry & Zay Devienne
Skull Lodge
Slim's Cabins
South Bay Cabins & Services
 Percy Depper
Springwater Outfitters
Spruceville Outfitters
 Brian Washburn
Squaw Creek Outfitters
T & D Amisk Cabins
The New Canoe West Resort
 Harold Breault
Thistlethwaite Outfitting
Thompson Lake Lodge/Triple Lake
 Camps–Mike Chursinoff
Thunderbird Camps
Thunderhill Outfitter
Timberline Outfitting
 Bernard or Harvey Nokinsky
Tobin Lake Resort
 Connie Anklovitch
Toby's Trophy Treks
 Toby Coleman
Tower Lodge
Trails End Outfitters
 Roile Morris
Twin Bay Resort Ltd.
 Ken & Naomie Selb
W J Wilderness Camp
 James Custer
Whiskey Jack Camp
White Fox Hotel Outfitting
 Robert Shatula
White Gull River Outfitters
 Tom McLane
White Swan Lake Resort
 Gerry Wenschlag
Whitetails Only
 David Fountain
Wild Man Outfitters/Poplar
 Point Resort
Wild Thing Outfitters
 Tim Fehr
Wild Wings Outfitters
Wilson's Lodge

YUKON TERRITORIES
Arctic Red River Outfitters, Ltd.
 Kelly & Heather Hougen
Babala Stone Sheep Outfitters

Ltd.–Jim Babala
Blackstone Safaris
 Lee Bolster
Bonnet Plume Outfitters
Charlie Stricker
Cassiar Mountain Outfitters
 Kirby Funnell
Ceaser Lake Outfitters
 Terry Wilkinson
David Young Outfitters Ltd
Devilhole Outfitters
Dickson Outfitters Ltd.
 David Dickson
Dolhan, Edward G.
Jensen, Pete
Kluane Outfitters Ltd.
 Ross Elliott
Koser Outfitters
 Pete Koser
Kusawa Outfitters
 Klaas Heynen
MacMillan River Outfitters
 Dave Coleman
Nahanni-NWT Safaris
 Rick Furniss
Peter Jensen Guide & Outfitter
 Pete Jensen
Rogue River Outfitters
 Cliff Hanna
Ruby Range
 Keith & Debbie Carreau
Stan Reynolds Outfitting, Ltd.
 Stan Reynolds
Teslin Outfitters
 Doug Smarch
Teslin Outfitters
 Terry Wilkinson
Trophy Stone Safaris Ltd.
 Curt Thompson
Widrig Outfitters Ltd.
 Chris Widrig
Yukon Hunting & Guiding Ltd.
 Rod Hardie
Yukon Outfitters' Association
 Stan Reynolds
Yukon Outfitting

Questionnaire

Name of Outfitter _______________________________   Specie(s) Hunted_______________

Weapon Used: ☐ Rifle
              ☐ Bow
              ☐ Muzzleloader
              ☐ Handgun

Name of Guide___________________________________Date of Hunt_____________

Location of Hunt_______________________________ ☐ Drop Camp   ☐ Fully Guided

1 Were you successful in your hunt?   5 ☐ Yes   0 ☐ No

2 If not successful, did you have the opportunity for a shot
   that you missed or decided not to take?   ☐ Yes   ☐ No

3 Did you observe a good number of animals, and did you
   have the time to make a selection?   ☐ Yes   ☐ No

	OUTSTANDING	EXCELLENT	Good	ACCEPTABLE	POOR/INFERIOR	UNACCEPTABLE
	5	4	3	2	1	0
4 Was the outfitter helpful with permits/tags/hunting regulations before, during, and after the hunt?	☐	☐	☐	☐	☐	☐
5 How helpful was the outfitter with travel arrangements (hotels, flight info, etc) realizing that he is not a travel agent?	☐	☐	☐	☐	☐	☐
6 Did the outfitter provide you with DETAILS that better prepared you for your hunt. (clothing, level of physical fitness, distances to be traveled, etc.)?	☐	☐	☐	☐	☐	☐
7 How do you rate TRANSPORTATION to camp and back to civilization(airplane, boat, horse, vehicle, hike, etc)?	☐	☐	☐	☐	☐	☐
8 How do you rate the CAMP FACILITIES?(cabin, tent, lodge)	☐	☐	☐	☐	☐	☐
9 How do you rate the COOKING?						
a. Quantity?	☐	☐	☐	☐	☐	☐
b. Quality of food?	☐	☐	☐	☐	☐	☐
c. Cleaniness of service?	☐	☐	☐	☐	☐	☐
10 How do you rate your GUIDES?						
a. Attitude	☐	☐	☐	☐	☐	☐
b. Knowledge of the area	☐	☐	☐	☐	☐	☐
c. Knowledge of the game	☐	☐	☐	☐	☐	☐
11 How was your animal dressed, packed & caped?	☐	☐	☐	☐	☐	☐
12 How do you rate the STAFF's ATTITUDE?	☐	☐	☐	☐	☐	☐
13 How do you rate the OUTFITTER OVERALL?	☐	☐	☐	☐	☐	☐

14 Is there any question you should have asked the outfitter
that would have improved your hunting experience?   5 ☐ Yes   0 ☐ No

Comment ____

____

15 Is there anything that the outfitter omitted to tell you that
would have improved your hunt?   0 ☐ Yes   5 ☐ No

Comment ____

____

16 Did you provide the outfitter with truthful statements
regarding your level of fitness and your expectations?   0 ☐ Yes   5 ☐ No

17 How would you describe the WEATHER CONDITIONS?   0 ☐ Good   3 ☐ Fair   5 ☐ Poor

18 How would you rate the HUNTING PRESSURE?   0 ☐ High   3 ☐ Average   5 ☐ Low

	YES	YES, with reservations	NO
	10	5	0
19 Would you use this outfitter again?	☐	☐	☐
20 Would you recommend this outfitter to other hunters?	☐	☐	☐

Final Comments: _______________________________________

____

____

____

____

____

____

____

____

____

____

____

____

Will you permit Picked-By-You to disclose the result of this questionnaire to the Outfitter
without mentioning your name?   ☐ Yes   ☐ No

Hunter's Name (Print)
____

Signature
____

Antelope

4 + 2 T Ranch
Arrowhead Outfitters
Beaver Creek Outfitters
Boulder Lake Lodge
Cecil Ralston Guide & Outfitters
Cow Creek Outfitters
Darby Mountain Outfitters
Double J Outfitters
Esper's Under Wild Skies
Garvey Bros. Outfitters
Grand & Sierra Outfitters
Greer Outfitters
Hidden Basin Outfitters
Hidden Hollow Hideaway
John Henry Lee Outfitters
K Bar Z Guest Ranch & Outfitters
Kibler Outfitting
Lightning Creek Ranch
Lone Tree Outfitting
Mitchell Outfitting
P Cross Bar Ranch
Phil's Bowhunting Adventures
Ponderosa Outfitters…
Pusch Ridge Outfitters
Ramshorn Outfitters
Red Desert Adventures
Rick Wemple Outfitting
River S Enterprises
S&W Outfitters
T Lazy T Outfitters
Timberline Outfitters
Triangle C Ranch
Twin Pine Ranch
Western Wyoming Trophy Hunts
Wild West Outfitters

Bears
Black Bear

Adams Alaskan Safaris
Arrow Five Outfitters
Arrowhead Outfitters
A/Z Outfitters Ltd.
Big Rack Adventures
Bill Slemp's Wild Alaska
Blind Creek Outfitters
Bonnet Plume Outfitters
Bristol Bay Outfitters
Brooks Range Adventures
Buckhorn Ranch Outfitters
Camp Michi Wawa

Cariboo Mountain Outfitters
Castle Creek Outfitters
Cecil Ralston Guide & Outfitters
Chip's Call of the Wild
Darby Mountain Outfitters
Denali Wilderness Outfitters
E&D Outfitters
Echo Canyon Guest Ranch &
  Outfitters
Elk Creek Outfitting
Esper's Under Wild Skies
EW Watson & Sons Outfitting
Flat Iron Outfitting
Garvey Bros. Outfitters
George River Lodge, Inc.
God's Country Guide Service
Grand & Sierra Outfitters
Hebert's Guide Service
Hidden Basin Outfitters
Hidden Hollow Hideaway
Horse Creek Outfitters
Ida Patey & Sons
Jack Hume Adventures Inc.
JM Bar Outfitters
John Henry Lee Outfitters
K Bar Z Guest Ranch & Outfitters
Kichatna Guide Service
Lake Country Lodge, Inc.
Lightning Creek Ranch
Lone Tree Outfitting
Love Bros. & Lee Ltd.
Moose Valley Outfitters
O'Rourke's Outdoor Adventures
Portland Creek Outfitters
Pusch Ridge Outfitters
Ramshorn Outfitters
Renshaw Outfitting, Inc.
Rick Wemple Outfitting
R.L. Sourbrine Out. & Sons
S&W Outfitters
Safari Caribou du Nouveau Québec
Sam's Hunting & Fishing Camps
San Juan Outfitting
Sheep River Hunting Camp
Stricker Outfitting, Ltd.
Swift Creek Outfitters
T. C. Lewis Lodge
T Lazy T Outfitters
Timberline Outfitters
Tom Scott Outfitting
White Tail Ranch/WTR Outfitters
Wild West Outfitters

Outfitters by Animal Species

Brown Bear

Adams Alaskan Safaris
Afognak Wilderness Lodge
Alaska Wilderness Trophy
Bill Slemp's Wild Alaska
Bristol Bay Outfitters
Brooks Range Adventures
Denali Wilderness Outfitters
Hebert's Guide Service
Kichatna Guide Service
Lake Country Lodge, Inc.
Sheep River Hunting Camp
T. C. Lewis Lodge

Grizzly Bear

A/Z Outfitters Ltd.
Bonnet Plume Outfitters
Kichatna Guide Service
Lake Country Lodge, Inc.
Love Bros. & Lee Ltd.
Moose Valley Outfitters
Renshaw Outfitting, Inc.

Bison

Beaver Creek Outfitters
Elk Creek Outfitting
Greer Outfitters
Kibler Outfitting
P Cross Bar Ranch
R.L. Sourbrine Out. & Sons

Bobcat

Chip's Call of the Wild
Mitchell Outfitting
O'Rourke's Outdoor Adventures

Caribou (**Barren Ground, Mountain, Québec-Labrador, Woodland**)

Alaska Wilderness Ventures
Bill Slemp's Wild Alaska
Bonnet Plume Outfitters
Bristol Bay Outfitters
Brooks Range Adventures
Denali Wilderness Outfitters
George River Lodge, Inc.
Ida Patey & Sons
Jack Hume Adventures Inc.
Kichatna Guide Service
Lake Country Lodge, Inc.
Love Bros. & Lee Ltd.
Moose Valley Outfitters

N.W.T. Outfitters Ltd.
Portland Creek Outfitters
Safari Caribou du Nouveau Québec
Sam's Hunting & Fishing Camp
T. C. Lewis Lodge

Cougar

Arrow Five Outfitters
A/Z Outfitters Ltd.
Beaver Creek Outfitters
Castle Creek Outfitters
Cecil Ralston Guide & Outfitters
Echo Canyon Guest Ranch & Outfitters
Elk Creek Outfitting
Flat Iron Outfitting
Garvey Bros. Outfitters
Grand & Sierra Outfitters
Hidden Hollow Hideaway
Horse Creek Outfitters
JM Bar Outfitters
K Bar Z Guest Ranch & Outfitters
Lightning Creek Ranch
Lone Tom Outfitting
Lone Tree Outfitting
Phil's Bowhunting Adventures
Pusch Ridge Outfitters
Rick Wemple Outfitting
R.L. Sourbrine Out. & Sons
Timberline Outfitters
Wild West Outfitters

Coyote

Chip's Call of the Wild
Garvey Bros. Outfitters
Lone Tree Outfitting
Mitchell Outfitting
O'Rourke's Outdoor Adventures
P Cross Bar Ranch
Stricker Outfitting, Ltd.

Deer
Blacktail Deer (Columbia)

Arrow Five Outfitters
River S Enterprises

Coues' Deer

Arrow Five Outfitters
Ponderosa Outfitters…
Pusch Ridge Outfitters
Timberline Outfitters

Outfitters by Animal Species

Mule Deer (Rocky Mountain and Desert)

4 + 2 T Ranch
Arrow Five Outfitters
Arrowhead Outfitters
A/Z Outfitters Ltd.
Beaver Creek Outfitters
Boulder Lake Lodge
Buckhorn Ranch Outfitters
Cariboo Mountain Outfitters
Castle Creek Outfitters
Cecil Ralston Guide & Outfitters
Chase Hill Outfitters
Cow Creek Outfitters
Darby Mountain Outfitters
Darwin Ranch
Double J Outfitters
Echo Canyon Guest Ranch & Outfitters
Elk Creek Outfitting
Esper's Under Wild Skies
EW Watson & Sons Outfitting
Flat Iron Outfitting
Garvey Bros. Outfitters
Grand & Sierra Outfitters
Greer Outfitters
Hebert's Guide Service
Hidden Basin Outfitters
Hidden Hollow Hideaway
Horse Creek Outfitters
JM Bar Outfitters
John Henry Lee Outfitters
K Bar Z Guest Ranch & Outfitters
Kibler Outfitting
Lakeview Resort & Outfitters
Lightning Creek Ranch
Lone Star Trail Outfitters
Lone Tree Outfitting
Mitchell Outfitting
N.W.T. Outfitters Ltd.
P Cross Bar Ranch
Phil's Bowhunting Adventures
Ponderosa Outfitters…
Pusch Ridge Outfitters
Ramshorn Outfitters
Red Desert Adventures
Rick Wemple Outfitting
River S Enterprises
R.L. Sourbrine Out. & Sons
S&W Outfitters
Samuelson Outfitters
San Juan Outfitting
Spadafora Ranch Lodge
Stricker Outfitting, Ltd.

Swift Creek Outfitters
T Lazy T Outfitters
Terrero General Store & Riding…
Timberline Outfitters
Tom Scott Outfitting
Triangle C Ranch
Twin Pine Ranch
Western Guiding Service
Western Wyoming Trophy Hunts
White Tail Ranch/WTR Outfitters
Wild West Outfitters

Sitka Blacktail Deer

Adams Alaskan Safaris
Afognak Wilderness Lodge
Brooks Range Adventures
Kichatna Guide Service

Whitetail Deer

Adobe Lodge
Beaver Creek Outfitters
Big Rack Adventures
Blind Creek Outfitters
Buckhorn Ranch Outfitters
Chase Hill Outfitters
Chip's Call of the Wild
Cow Creek Outfitters
Cutbirth Cattle Company, Ltd.
E&D Outfitters
Elk Creek Outfitting
Esper's Under Wild Skies
EW Watson & Sons Outfitting
Flat Iron Outfitting
God's Country Guide Service
Greer Outfitters
Hebert's Guide Service
Hidden Hollow Hideaway
JM Bar Outfitters
Lone Star Trail Outfitters
Lone Tree Outfitting
Mitchell Outfitting
P Cross Bar Ranch
Ramshorn Outfitters
Renshaw Outfitting, Inc.
Rick Wemple Outfitting
River S Enterprises
R.L. Sourbrine Out. & Sons
S&W Outfitters
Stricker Outfitting, Ltd.
Tom Scott Outfitting
Twin Pine Ranch
Western Guiding Service
White Tail Ranch/WTR Outfitters
Wild West Outfitters

Elk (Rocky Mountain and Roosevelt's)

4 + 2 T Ranch
Afognak Wilderness Lodge
Arrow Five Outfitters
Arrowhead Outfitters
A/Z Outfitters Ltd.
Beaver Creek Outfitters
Boulder Lake Lodge
Buckhorn Ranch Outfitters
Castle Creek Outfitters
Cecil Ralston Guide & Outfitters
Chase Hill Outfitters
Cow Creek Outfitters
Darby Mountain Outfitters
Darwin Ranch
Double J Outfitters
Echo Canyon Guest Ranch &
  Outfitters
Elk Creek Outfitting
Esper's Under Wild Skies
EW Watson & Sons Outfitting
Flat Iron Outfitting
Frazier Outfitting
Garvey Bros. Outfitters
Grand & Sierra Outfitters
Greer Outfitters
Hebert's Guide Service
Hidden Basin Outfitters
Hidden Hollow Hideaway
Horse Creek Outfitters
JM Bar Outfitters
John Henry Lee Outfitters
K Bar Z Guest Ranch & Outfitters
Kibler Outfitting
Lakeview Resort & Outfitters
Lightning Creek Ranch
Lone Tom Outfitting
Lone Tree Outfitting
Phil's Bowhunting Adventures
Ponderosa Outfitters…
Pusch Ridge Outfitters
Ramshorn Outfitters
Red Desert Adventures
Renshaw Outfitting, Inc.
Rick Wemple Outfitting
R.L. Sourbrine Out. & Sons
S&W Outfitters
Samuelson Outfitters
San Juan Outfitting
Spadafora Ranch Lodge
Swift Creek Outfitters
T Lazy T Outfitters
Terrero General Store & Riding …
Timberline Outfitters

Triangle C Ranch
Twin Pine Ranch
Western Wyoming Trophy Hunts
White Tail Ranch/WTR Outfitters
Wild West Outfitters

Javelina

Arrow Five Outfitters
Cecil Ralston Guide & Outfitters
Ponderosa Outfitters…
Pusch Ridge Outfitters
Timberline Outfitters

Moose (Alaska-Yukon, Canadian, Shiras)

Arrowhead Outfitters
A/Z Outfitters Ltd.
Beaver Creek Outfitters
Bill Slemp's Wild Alaska
Bonnet Plume Outfitters
Boulder Lake Lodge
Bristol Bay Outfitters
Brooks Range Adventures
Buckhorn Ranch Outfitters
Camp Michi Wawa
Cariboo Mountain Outfitters
Darby Mountain Outfitters
Darwin Ranch
Denali Wilderness Outfitters
Elk Creek Outfitting
Esper's Under Wild Skies
EW Watson & Sons Outfitting
Flat Iron Outfitting
God's Country Guide Service
Hebert's Guide Service
Hidden Basin Outfitters
Horse Creek Outfitters
Ida Patey & Sons
JM Bar Outfitters
John Henry Lee Outfitters
K Bar Z Guest Ranch & Outfitters
Kichatna Guide Service
Lake Country Lodge, Inc.
Love Bros. & Lee Ltd.
Moose Valley Outfitters
N.W.T. Outfitters Ltd.
Portland Creek Outfitters
Red Desert Adventures
Rick Wemple Outfitting
R.L. Sourbrine Out. & Sons
Sam's Hunting & Fishing Camps
Sheep River Hunting Camp
Stricker Outfitting, Ltd.

Swift Creek Outfitters
T. C. Lewis Lodge
T Lazy T Outfitters
Tom Scott Outfitting
Triangle C Ranch
Western Wyoming Trophy Hunts
White Tail Ranch/WTR Outfitters
Wild West Outfitters

Mountain Goat

A/Z Outfitters Ltd.
Buckhorn Ranch Outfitters
Castle Creek Outfitters
Denali Wilderness Outfitters
Esper's Under Wild Skies
JM Bar Outfitters
K Bar Z Guest Ranch & Outfitters
Kichatna Guide Service
Love Bros. & Lee Ltd.
Moose Valley Outfitters
Rick Wemple Outfitting
R.L. Sourbrine Out. & Sons
S&W Outfitters
Sheep River Hunting Camp
Stricker Outfitting, Ltd.
White Tail Ranch/WTR Outfitters

Sheep
Bighorn Sheep

Arrowhead Outfitters
Beaver Creek Outfitters
Castle Creek Outfitters
Cecil Ralston Guide & Outfitters
Chase Hill Outfitters
Cow Creek Outfitters
Darby Mountain Outfitters
Darwin Ranch
Elk Creek Outfitting
Esper's Under Wild Skies
Flat Iron Outfitting
Grand & Sierra Outfitters
Hidden Basin Outfitters
Horse Creek Outfitters
JM Bar Outfitters
John Henry Lee Outfitters
K Bar Z Guest Ranch & Outfitters
Rick Wemple Outfitting
R.L. Sourbrine Out. & Sons
San Juan Outfitting
T Lazy T Outfitters
Terrero General Store & Riding…
Timberline Outfitters
Triangle C Ranch
Western Wyoming Trophy Hunts

Dall's Sheep

Alaska Wilderness Ventures
Bonnet Plume Outfitters
Bristol Bay Outfitters
Brooks Range Adventures
Denali Wilderness Outfitters
Kichatna Guide Service
N.W.T. Outfitters, Ltd.
Sheep River Hunting Camp
T. C. Lewis Lodge

Desert Bighorn Sheep

Ponderosa Outfitters…
Pusch Ridge Outfitters
Timberline Outfitters

Stone's Sheep

Love Bros. & Lee, Ltd.

Wild Boar

Arrow Five Outfitters
River S Enterprises

Wolf

Adams Alaskan Safaris
Alaska Wilderness Ventures
A/Z Outfitters Ltd.
Bill Slemp's Wild Alaska
Bonnet Plume Outfitters
Bristol Bay Outfitters
Brooks Range Adventures
Cariboo Mountain Outfitters
Hebert's Guide Service
Kichatna Guide Service
Love Bros. & Lee Ltd.
Moose Valley Outfitters
N.W.T. Outfitters Ltd.
Stricker Outfitting, Ltd.
T. C. Lewis Lodge

Wolverine

Alaska Wilderness Ventures
Bonnet Plume Outfitters
Bristol Bay Outfitters
N.W.T. Outfitters Ltd.

Alphabetical Index by Company Name